# NOT IN VAIN

## BY GERALD GREEN

*Fiction*

KARPOV'S BRAIN

MURFY'S MEN

THE CHAINS

CACTUS PIE: TEN STORIES

THE HEALERS

HOLOCAUST

GIRL

AN AMERICAN PROPHET

THE HOSTAGE HEART

BLOCKBUSTER

FAKING IT

TOURIST

TO BROOKLYN WITH LOVE

THE LEGION OF NOBLE CHRISTIANS

THE HEARTLESS LIGHT

THE LOTUS EATERS

THE LAST ANGRY MAN

THE SWORD AND THE SUN

*Nonfiction*

MY SON THE JOCK

THE STONES OF ZION

THE ARTISTS OF TEREZIN

THE PORTOFINO PTA

HIS MAJESTY O'KEEFE
(with Lawrence Klingman)

# NOT IN VAIN

## BY GERALD GREEN

DONALD I. FINE

NEW YORK   1984

C.3

FOR AUDREY AND STANLEY KLEIN

*It takes two to speak the truth—one to speak, and another to hear.*
—Thoreau

### Helen Christopher

Fifth anniversary of the death of three student in a campus demonstration awakens old animosities and feelings between the police and the parents of the deceased students.

Today, going through some dusty boxes in Jack's closet, I found that awful stuffed alligator. Jack must have been ten when Dan and I bought it for him in Sarasota fifteen years ago.

One beady eye is missing. A foreleg hangs by a thread. But it can stand, balanced on its tail, a mud-brown orphan. It is a bit horrid. And sad. I had no idea it was here. The cardboard box was labeled "Museum." The alligator was the centerpiece of Jack's private museum—shells, rocks, a crumbling snakeskin, a creased chart of the constellations, a bird's nest, a butterfly collection.

I try not to cry any more. It's been five years. But these souvenirs of his short life are painful to contemplate. What saddens me most is that they remind me of all the temporary interests Jack had. He never seemed to stay long with anything.

"I'm going to be a scientist," Jack used to say. "I'm a rock-hound and a bird-watcher." The truth was he was never much of a student, particularly in science and math. Oh, he passed all his courses. But I suppose you'd have to call him a C-plus student. That's why he went to Joshua College. It seemed an undemanding place for a boy who wasn't particularly gifted.

The museum collection was followed by a musical interlude. There is a clarinet case in the closet (I can't bear to take it out), an old set of drums and a broken guitar. Jack tried them all, lost interest, phased them out. Dan says I should have thrown them away years ago.

*The clarinet.* We had a springer spaniel at the time, a liver-and-white bitch named Susie. When Mr. DeVito came for Jack's weekly clarinet lesson, Susie would sit under Jack's chair and sing along with my son's off-key tootling. Dan said she sounded better than the clarinet. Mr. DeVito finally had to ask that Susie be locked up during the lessons. She wasn't much at harmony.

It's strange how these memories of small failures and unfulfilled

9

ambitions stab at me so much more than the thought of his death.

In my mind's eye I see the scene so clearly that I am devastated by a sense of utter loss. Pudgy and solemn, Jack is blowing out his cheeks as he strives to coax notes from the clarinet. Mr. DeVito (he was a music teacher at Old Surrey High School) is patiently turning the pages. The spaniel is arching her soft throat and crooning. The light is soft, gray-yellow. It is late afternoon of a mild winter's day. I'm in the kitchen with Beth. We're preparing dinner, waiting for Dan to come home on the 6:42.

The scenes form old photographs in merciless detail. They are soft-edged, colors faded, but the setting is so real I feel I could walk into the living room and find Jack and Mr. DeVito and our dog. And then (I know this sounds crazy) I will walk into the brightly lit kitchen and see myself, fifteen years younger, reading from the *Good Housekeeping Cookbook* and asking Beth to peel onions and slice mushrooms for the *coq au vin*.

Dan found me in Jack's room today when he got home from work. He'd had his two martinis. He always takes the train preferred by bridge players and drinkers. Actually alcohol no longer relaxes him. It makes him cranky. He didn't approve of my rummaging through Jack's effects. The room is pretty much as Jack left it. Yale and Princeton banners (his grades were never good enough for him to apply), rock-music posters, wallpaper depicting a comical marching band in reds and blues. I papered the wall myself and did a rather good job. We were always looking for ways to save money. I enjoyed doing things like painting, fixing furniture, gardening.

Now that I'm past forty-five I find I'm less interested in household chores. Dan is earning more money since he was appointed vice-president for quality control. Our children are gone. One dead, one married. We can afford help. (Or is it that the house is both a blessing and a curse and I've lost interest in it?) I see Jack everywhere. I hear his footsteps, his breathy voice. I think about his friends, Andy and Woody and Dave. I keep hoping I'll wander into the basement some afternoon and see them slamming a puck into their homemade hockey goal, while Susie barks in frustration.

I was turning pages in Jack's high school yearbook when Dan entered.

"Listen to this," I said. " 'John Daniel Christopher. Joshua College.

Ambition—to play drums with the Stones even if I have to fake it. Favorite line—'Can anyone lend me the math homework?' ''

Dan came toward me and closed the blue-covered book. He kissed me. I could smell the fruity vermouth. Dr. Aaronson says we drink— our social class, that is—because we have nothing better to do most of the time. He says we drink the way a Ubangi stretches his lips or an Amazon Indian paints his body.

"Why?" Dan asked.

"Why what?"

"You're in here. I don't find you in here when Rosa cleans it. And when does she do that? Once a month? Every two months?"

"I come in from time to time. I think I'm inured to the loss. Am I crying?"

"No."

"Do I look terribly sad?"

"No. But I know you. It's all inside. And not doing you any good."

He sat on Jack's bed, loosened his tie and ran his hands through his thick gray hair. It was lush wavy hair, like Jack's. If genes ran true to form, Jack would have had the same good luck with his hair. I never fancied bald men.

"This room," Dan said. "It's wrong. The boy's dead. Maybe we should make a nursery out of it. Pinks and yellows. For when Beth comes to visit with Laurie."

"The baby doesn't seem to mind the banners and pictures."

"But I do. It's time to lay it to rest. Other people lose sons."

"Maybe you're right."

Dan got up. "I was thinking maybe we should sell the house. It's too big. I know you love the garden and the convenience of Old Surrey. But there are some terrific new condos closer to New York. Two bedrooms, that's all we need."

He kept talking, his tongue oiled by liquor, his face reddening, his speech slurred. Maybe, he was saying, we might try New York City. It's true we were both Connecticut people, and we enjoyed the best of both worlds in Old Surrey, and we had good friends, and the country club, and freedom from crime and city dirt . . .

"You could start teaching again," Dan was saying. "Tutoring isn't satisfying to you. There're private schools in New York that would be glad to hire an experienced teacher. We could look into it."

As he spoke I lost track of his words. I barely saw him. What did

I see? Jack sitting on the bed, hunched over the telephone soliciting clients for his lawn-mowing business. We let him use the power mower to trim neighbors' lawns. Dan and I spent more than one weekend helping him lug the gas-powered monster around in the trunk of our old Chevrolet. Jack always insisted he was strong enough to lift it in and out of the trunk. But he was too young to drive. Why do I find this memory so searing? More unfulfilled hopes, boyhood yearnings. Last week I found a tattered notebook at the bottom of a desk drawer. In it Jack had listed his weekly earnings from the lawn-mowing business. I read the entries—five dollars from Mr. Greenbaum, ten dollars from Mr. Morrow, eight dollars owed him by Mrs. Dennison . . .

A soft-edged, summery picture haunts me. Jack is pushing the mower up the steep lawn of the Morrow place, grimacing, waving in annoyance at me as I ride by and he struggles with the machine.

He was strong. Chunky and soft-looking, but strong. Not in an athlete's coordinated way. Jack was never good at sports, although they made him play football. He was powerful, but he moved slowly and he didn't like to get hit or hit others. "Stick" is the expression I believe they use. Jack did not like to "stick" . . .

"I don't want to leave Old Surrey," I said. "I have so many friends here. You like it, don't you?"

"Sure. It's just . . ."

"It's where Jack grew up. His town. His high school. His friends. I know it's hard for both of us."

"I've tried to put it behind me. It was the luck of the draw. I've said that a hundred times. He was a good kid who did some dumb things. And one very big dumb thing. Don't you think I live with the pain too?"

I got up from Jack's scarred desk. He'd scrawled on it in indelible ink, HOCKEY PLAYERS ARE GOOD SKATES. "Let's not revive that, Dan."

During dinner the phone rang. We'd gotten into the habit of eating in the den and watching the seven o'clock news. Meals were no longer inventive, the way they had been when the children were home. I used to love cooking—growing and drying my own herbs, saving leftover broths for soups and stews, using only fresh vegetables. Dan would joke that he sometimes craved a can of Campbell's pork and beans instead of my winey sauces and delicate salads. These days he got canned or frozen food more often than not. I felt guilty about it, but the balm provided by the drinks in the bar car seemed to blunt his appetite. He ate fast and sparingly.

In the old days when the children were at home we usually took the phone off the hook while we dined. Mealtime was special for us— free-wheeling talk, joking, a review of the day's events. Now Dan and I had little to say to one another. We let Tom Brokaw do our talking.

"I'll get it," Dan said. His voice was thickening.

"No, no. It's probably Beth. I don't want you getting upset again."

Our daughter, Elizabeth Christopher Hare, has a well-paying job as personnel manager for an electronics firm near Boston. She lives in Waltham and has a daughter Laurie, who is three. Her husband Peter is a graduate of Emerson College, a school specializing in communications. Peter describes himself as a freelance producer of documentary programs for educational television. Dan says that means he's unemployed.

"If's about that lunacy I *do* want to talk to her," Dan said. He got up but only to raise the volume on the TV.

Beth and Peter are ardent disciples of Adnana Lal Yogi, the guru of the Creative Light Movement. My daughter and my son-in-law are Guardians of the Truth.

In a harmless way they have been proselytizing relatives and friends for years about the wondrous benefits of meditating. It not only endows one with inner peace, a refreshed mind, utter goodness and charity but they say it also improves one's grades. When Jack was in high school Beth, already a devotee of Adnana Lal, lectured her brother on the marvelous things her faith could do for him. "It will make you an A student," she told him solemnly. "No more C's, Jackie." His response was that if CM was so great, and if Adnana Lal was only sixty-five years old, how come he looked *eighty?* Jack never learned to meditate. As a matter of fact, I did learn the technique and I do it for twenty minutes every morning. It's relaxing. But I'm afraid it can't cure the ills of the world. I can't imagine the starving inhabitants of a Saharan village using Creative Meditation to raise sorghum production.

Beth and Peter had recently been talking about opening a Creative Light center. They had asked Dan to lend them seed money. He not only refused, he went into one of his rare rages. "Jesus God," Dan said, "the last place in the world they need another of those religious fakes.

13

That's like opening another jewelry store on West Forty-seventh Street. Creeps, health food stores, alternative lifestyles, all the leftovers of the sixties. That's *Boston*. You two and your kid would be the only clients. I'd sooner lend you money to open an opium den."

Beth is determined. And so dedicated to Adnana Lal (it does seem rather late in the day for people to be worshipping him) that she will absorb insults from Dan and come back for more. That's the way of the true believer, I suppose.

But it was not Beth who called that May evening.

It was an old friend, Professor Tom Finnegan of the sociology department of Joshua College. I was glad I'd taken the call. Dan, although tolerant of Tom—I think it has to do more with Tom having been a marine officer than any of his academic attainments—nonetheless regards him as part and parcel of the events that led to Jack's death.

"Hey, Helen," I heard Tom say, "how goes it?"

"Much the same."

We chatted briefly. He expressed pleasure over Dan's promotion, made much of my trivial tutoring business, asked about Beth. Mercifully he didn't fill me in on his eight yeasty children, ranging in age from three to sixteen. I can never keep them apart. They're all redheaded, green-eyed and good-looking. Judy, Tom's wife, was as busy as ever, organizing a committee to save the wetlands.

Then he got to the point. In two weeks, he said, there was going to be a memorial observance on campus. Would I come?

Even before answering I knew what Dan's reaction would be. I'm sure Tom Finnegan also knew. Dan had dissociated himself from the events of five years ago. He had compartmentalized them, blocked them out, saw them as occurrences that had happened to someone else, mistakes of history. His son, whom he had loved too much and perhaps unwisely, had been the victim of a foolish *accident* . . .

"Well, I'm not sure, Tom. What will it be like?"

"Rallies, speakers, workshops. It won't be a weeping and wailing session. We'll pass resolutions, see where the last five years have taken us, issue a report. There'll be meetings with local officials, Washington people, faculty, students, police experts."

"Local police? Or state police?"

"Well, they've both been invited, but they haven't answered. They figure it'll be one more attempt to hang them. It should be interesting. On the anniversary we'll have an all-night vigil at the site. Corny, but it'll get attention. Candles, hymns, poetry readings."

"Is the college cooperating?"

"Sullenly. We got President Cudlipp to okay the event, but he won't make it an official college function. That's good enough for us. He won't make an address of welcome. Won't permit any picketing or rowdyism. And who can blame the poor guy? He remembers what happened five years ago. They almost skinned him."

"I see. And you want me . . . ?"

"To attend, Helen. To be a guest of honor."

"Oh, no, Tom. You know me. I won't sit on a dais. I can't make a speech. I hate being the center of attention. The notion that I've achieved fame because I'm the mother of one of the Joshua Three doesn't appeal to me. It never did."

Dan shouted from the den to the kitchen, where I was taking the call. "What's that all about? Some reporter? Tell him to get lost."

I ignored him. Tom Finnegan was not so easy to ignore.

"Doc and Rita Schless are coming. Doc is in charge of the parents' committee. Joe and Sally Terragni have promised me they're coming. And you know how bitter they've been. And all the kids who were wounded except the Pulsifer boy. He's in Alaska. Hey, remember Wilma?"

"Of course. The Overstreet girl. The one who was paralyzed."

"Amazing. She's in a wheelchair but she's engaged to get married. She'll be there. So will Hubie and Billy and Keith. Helen, it would mean a lot to us if you came. I promise you, no speeches, no press conferences. I'm extending this invitation to Dan too."

"That's kind of you, Tom, but you know how Dan feels."

"Yeah, but people change. Three years ago I couldn't get Joe Terragni to say a word to me. I was one of those commie teachers who'd gotten Lucy killed. Today Joe is one of my best friends."

I thought: And my Dan felt as strongly as Joe Terragni did. Dan had rejected his role as father of a martyr. He had tried to convince me that the best response to Jack's death was silence and distance.

"I'll give it some thought, Tom," I said. "I know how Dan feels. He wants to do his remembering privately."

"I respect him for that. But maybe he's gotten over his feelings of enmity toward me and the others. After all, Helen, it's been five years since he wrote that letter."

I wished Tom hadn't mentioned the letter. There are events in our past that live on to embarrass us and pain us long after the world assumes they're forgotten. I don't mean the death of a child. That is a tragedy so devastating that it becomes part of the fabric of one's life. One lives with it, builds around it, disguises it, perceives it in different ways. But there are other traumas, avoidable and unnecessary acts, that persist to drown us in waves of regret. They make us wish to have the past back, so that we might forestall our actions, undo what we so foolishly did.

Dan's letter . . .

> . . . *my son, you died not knowing that you had been used and betrayed by those who claimed to have better answers than their superiors. You died needlessly, spurred on by disturbers of the peace, cynical, manipulative people. The state policeman whose bullet ended your life, I wish I could tell you now, was not your enemy. Your enemy wore jeans, taught class, sat beside you at basketball games, drank beer with you, argued politics with you* . . .

"Helen? You still there?"

"Yes, Tom."

"Give it some thought. If Dan won't come, maybe you could come without him. Judy and I would be glad to put you up. No chance you'd be lonely in our pad."

I mumbled an insincere thanks. The Finnegans are a rambunctious, chaotic family—and their home is no place for a fastidious type like myself. One usually ends up sharing a room with a ten-year-old given to nocturnal teeth grinding, or disputing a dog for the rights to an armchair.

"Is it worth it, Tom?" I asked. "Stirring up old hatreds, all the memories?"

"If it's for a good purpose. I have a hunch the country is heading for a new round of beating up on the lower orders. The courts and the cops have already gotten the message. Why not remind them of what happens when law-and-order loonies have their way?"

"You seem to forget. Eighty percent of the people in the country supported the police. It was even generally agreed that my son and those two girls got what they deserved—"

"Things change. The Reverend Al Jensen, who is still one of our heavy hitters, says they took a poll last year and we're only down sixty-forty."

Small comfort. Maybe I'm getting fed up with all of it. Maybe I'm calloused. I mourn Jack. I always will. But the whole terrible affair, the days of senseless violence, the final horror—"People have forgotten the issues," I said. "Joshua College is just a name for a place where students were killed. No one seems to remember why or how."

"Well, we want to make sure it's remembered in the right way. We aren't going to holler at the police or the state officials. We just want to remember the thing and pray it won't ever happen again. Helen, I truly think you and Dan should be with us."

I told Tom I'd mull it over. I had no enthusiasm for his invitation. Yet it's hard for me to disappoint people, especially people I like. And I have the highest regard for Tom and Judy Finnegan. I said I'd call him in a week.

NBC was wrapping up the day's news when I got back to the den. Dan asked me, "What was that all about?"

I tried to minimize the call. "Some kind of memorial observance marking the fifth anniversary of the Joshua Massacre. Tom Finnegan was inviting us."

He waited till the news was over, then turned off the set. It meant he was concerned. Usually he switched to the MacNeil-Lehrer Report. I noticed that he was cradling a brandy snifter. He'd poured himself a drink during the commercials.

"Finnegan, huh?" he asked. "Old red-beard. The man in the green tweed jacket and the space shoes. Hasn't he brought enough misery into our lives?"

"I've never looked at it that way."

"He was one of the worst. All that garbage he taught. He and Harriet Blochman and a few others. How the hell they stayed on faculty after that happened, I'll never know. How they ever got their appointments in the first place beats me. Look, I'm no right-wing nut, so stop staring at me like that."

I told him I wasn't staring. It was just that we were far apart on these matters and it was pointless to argue any more. We'd had five years of it.

"Of course you won't go," Dan said.

"I'm not so sure."

"You'll be *used*. They'll trot out all the lefto regulars—lawyers, writers, actresses. Wallowing in our son's death to promote their pet causes. Send Finnegan a note and tell him it's out of the question. We've heard the last of the Joshua Massacre. We've done all the mourning we care to." He sounded more plaintive than angry.

"It isn't a question of mourning. Tom feels that we have to build on what happened—learn from it."

Dan finished his brandy, got up and turned the television on. "I don't want to hear about it. You'd be foolish to go."

The TV screen arranged itself into colors and forms. The bright green of a baseball stadium. Dark blue sky, yellow globes of night-lights. Players in blue uniforms, white uniforms.

And then I had another of those wrenching images of the past—so vivid that I felt my heart accelerate, almost heard the *thump-thump*. I saw Dan fifteen-odd years ago, sitting in that same creaky Boston rocker, with Jack in front of him cross-legged. And Beth stretched out on the floor. Beth liked baseball as much as my husband and my son did. In fact, she could hit a ball better than her brother.

I could recall the conversation. Jack had asked his father to teach him to bat. They were having Little League tryouts that week. Of course, Jack could never expect to make the real Little League, like Andy Hanson or Dave Gross, but they had this second-string league. The kids played without uniforms and everybody got a chance.

I knew what saddened me . . . It had never worked out for Jack. Like so much in his short life. He had never been good enough for even the second string. He flailed at the soft pitches Dan patiently threw him in our backyard, fumbled grounders, dropped fly balls. Dan bought him a handsome tan glove—I even remember it was a Brooks Robinson— but it didn't make an athlete of Jack. He spent two games on the bench and quit.

Why are these memories so painful? I wish I had happier thoughts about him. His kindness. His generosity. There were always friends in the house. His love of music. The shy girls he dated. But my mind keeps returning to all the frustrations he suffered. Still, he was always healthy, reasonably happy, surrounded by people who liked him . . .

Baseball bores me. But I found myself staring at the game. Dan was silent, falling into one of his half-sozzled states. More and more, he's like that at night. I'm tempted to ask him about that long-ago attempt to make a Little Leaguer of Jack, but I say nothing.

*He's not a natural athlete,* Dan used to say. *Big, but clumsy, and no ball sense, not competitive . . .*

At times like this I have the feeling that Dan's burden is greater than mine. His impatience with Jack, his constant disappointments in him . . . I think all that makes it harder for him to bear our son's death . . .

I feel that he was lying to himself when he wrote that letter that was printed in our weekly newspaper, the Surrey *Sentinel,* and was unfortunately picked up by the New York papers and the Associated Press. Oh, Dan regretted it. It drove him wild. He even accused me once of not having the foresight to stop him while he was trying to cope with his sorrow, his rage.

*Pathetic.* There is something almost profoundly pathetic about my husband. I don't think he ever truly matured; he never was able to plumb the depths of his feelings, to say loud and clear, *I love you,* to his children. (And not too often to me. Usually in the throes of sex. But not on the spur of the moment, tenderly and unexpectedly.) And yet I feel sorry for him. I sense his devastation. He couldn't weep at Jack's funeral. I did.

But for months after Jack was killed I could hear him, locked in the bathroom, or working in the basement, or looking for tools in the garage, wracked by convulsive, wet gulps of pain, torment, remorse. How awful for a man to lose a son; how much worse when he feels he was never quite the father he should have been . . .

It has been a nightmare for me. Much worse for Dan. My bruised heart goes out to him, but I can find no way to give him solace. He hoards his agony, hides it from me. Why?

## *August Karl Frankendorf*

To be candid, I have never really liked the club. That's how we all refer to the Joshua Country Club. The *club.* Everyone knows it means *us,* and not the Polish Falcons, or the Jewish club, Rolling Meadows, or the Ladies Garden Club of Flagg County.

I am not, as Dr. Johnson once said, "a very clubbable man." But the membership has been useful to me in my career, and being a lifelong bachelor, it was convenient to have a congenial place to take guests or to dine alone.

Golf never intrigued me. I gave it up some years ago after I underwent a prostate operation. (Entirely successful, but leaving me a bit weary.) My tennis was once more than adequate, but I got bored with the back-and-forth routine and I could not stomach the deadly seriousness of the men in my age bracket. Winning meant all to them; I preferred to play for the exercise.

But I'm here, a founding father, a sort of ornament. *The judge.* Old Judge Frankendorf. Judge Gus. Retired from the federal district court after long years of notable service. Formerly justice of the state supreme court, county judge, prosecutor, leading legal light. I have been a large frog in a small pond, Joshua hardly being a state capital, let alone a Chicago or a St. Louis. I took a road of my own choosing, made my own way, and I'm not sorry.

At age eighty-one I am fit and clear-minded, and I confess I enjoy my status as elder, sachem, community pillar. So here I sit on the veranda of the clubhouse this warm May dusk, sipping Lillet, trim in gray Brooks Brothers summer-weight suit, white button-down shirt, Harvard tie. (I went to its great law school but did my undergraduate work at the state university.)

Waiting for George Dempsey and Merritt Winnington—they were playing the back nine—I took out my copy of Art News and began to read an article on Correggio. Was he or was he not a mannerist? A lively debate was raging between two Renaissance scholars, and I had followed it avidly. Of course I have seen the Correggios in Parma, and in Rome and Florence, and admired their lushness, their erotic content, the subtleties of shading and form.

Forgive me for sounding like a snob. I daresay that apart from the art history teachers at Joshua College and the university, you will find no one in the state's southern tier who can become aroused by a controversy over mannerism. I take a bit of joshing for my love of the arts. Every other year I go to Europe to look at paintings and churches. I helped found the local chamber music society. I occasionally write reminiscing pieces—light and humorous—about early life in Joshua for the state newspapers . . .

Merritt Winnington kids me about my "eastern" mode of dress.

"Watch those button-down collars and striped ties, judge," Merritt will say. He has popping chlorine-green eyes, spiky orange hair and a face wider than it is high. He married Tess Everson—"the Duchess"—and she is one of *the* Eversons. Merritt is the richest lawyer in town and a potent force in state politics. He once almost got the town council to pass an ordinance prohibiting anyone with a degree from Harvard or Columbia from serving on the school board. I prevailed upon him to do otherwise.

Calm and at peace, I packed my Charatan pipe with golden Balkan Sobranie, enjoyed those first heavenly fragrant odors and signaled to Ernest, the maitre d'. I'm on an extremely intimate basis with the help at the club. Ernest has known me a long time. He is intelligent, resourceful, and has a wonderful family. Years ago I helped his cousin Roosevelt out of a scrape involving a loose woman, and Ernest has never forgotten.

Yes, I suspect I have always been a trifle—what shall I say?—exotic, effete, genteel for the Joshua community. There were malicious whispers about the reasons for my bachelorhood (all lies) and some sneers at my predilection for the arts. For some years, when I was practicing law, and affected Savile Row suits (purchased during my trips to Europe) and always carried a furled umbrella, I was known as "the Count," or behind my back as "Count No-Count."

It never truly bothered me. If I marched to my own drummer, the good people of Joshua came to respect my independence. Especially five years ago at the trial of the policemen. They all knew me as a fair, modest and community-minded fellow, even though my tastes did not run to Little League baseball, ice cream socials and 4–H contests. I did not turn up my nose at these rustic events. I merely let it be known that my interests lay elsewhere. Indeed, I suspect that my successful rise to the highest court in the state had something to do with my emphatic individualism. That and two other factors. I was a crackerjack lawyer and a respected lower court judge. I knew my law. Secondly, it helped to have the Eversons—Merritt Winnington's in-laws—on my side, even though their advocacy of my career was always unspoken, subtle and diplomatic. Mrs. Winnington—"the Duchess"—always depended on me as the extra man at fancy dinners. Once a year she invited me to speak to the university women on some cultural subject, such as Japanese prints or the mosaics of Ravenna.

I doubt that Byzantine mosaics much concerned Merritt Winnington. Frog-eyed, pie-faced and sweat-stained, he was trudging off the eighteenth green, accompanied by George Dempsey, the new young prosecutor. Now that I'm retired I can socialize with them as much as I desire to. My service on the federal bench never kept me from the company of lawyers and law enforcement officials, but I never, *never* discussed any case, offered any opinion, said anything of a tendentious or prejudicial nature. I keep my own counsel.

George Dempsey is slender, dark, hatchet-faced, and an altogether splendid prosecutor. He was too young to have been involved with the Joshua affair five years ago. I think he was fresh out of the state law school. Merritt, of course, knew the case better than anyone. Although I am still supposed to be impartial, I can't help chuckling inwardly at the way Merritt made a monkey of that horrid creature, that bearded, bald, bespectacled Washington hotshot, Walter Kalt, who prosecuted the state policemen. Merritt was a shrewd one. He had a water-diviner's knack for sniffing out the way a judge and a jury felt. (Not that I ever let him influence me. Evidence was all that concerned me; evidence and testimony.)

"Judge," Merritt said. "Howdy." He pressed a sweaty palm, enfolding my delicate hand in his freckled paw. George nodded and they both sat down. They smelled ripe, sun-rich. A bit rank, if you will. I realized we offered an instructive comparison—me, frail, white-haired, in my dark gray Ivy League suit and crimson tie; they in vivid yellow-and-green polyester, tanned, exuding the odor of honest exercise.

After ordering drinks—I had a second Lillet-on-the-rocks, an eccentricity the club members have come to expect of me—I showed them the letter. It was scrawled in pencil on a lined sheet torn from one of those ring-bound copy books. The message was succinct, undated and unsigned.

> *You'll get yours some day, you old faggot. You let those murderers off the hook.*

"Some sicko," Merritt said. "Not to worry, judge."

"Mind if I run it through the police lab?" asked George.

"Of course not. Please don't get the idea I'm worried. I just thought George should see it."

"So noted," the prosecutor said.

A fellow who had been drinking at the bar, Ed Kettleman, came over. He was a bit worse for his third bourbon. Wonderful fellow, Ed, chairman of the civic association. He could not be dissuaded from trying out his latest smutty story on us. He asked us, "What's the last thing to go through a grasshopper's mind when it hits the windshield?"

None of us had the remotest notion, so Ed said, "His asshole."

I cringed, but laughed. Neither George nor Merritt thought it especially funny, but they obliged Ed, who had a retarded twenty-two-year-old son, by laughing appreciatively. Kettleman wandered about the bar, trying the story on other members, with varying results.

"It's got to do with that memorial observance, or whatever they call it, this weekend," Winnington said. "All those soreheads. Can't they let the damn thing alone? They lost. We won. You ran a fair trial. What do they want, blood?"

I made a tent of my fingertips, touched my lips, said nothing.

"Merritt's right," George Dempsey added. "This remembrance business will bring a lot of freaks out of the woodwork. Not the parents, or the kids who were wounded. I can sympathize with them. I can understand how they feel. And Prexy Cudlipp tells me it will be dignified, restrained and nonviolent. After all, five years have passed. Hardly anybody even remembers how the rioting started."

"Outside agitators," Merritt Winnington said. "We proved it."

Of course they had proved nothing of the kind. Not a single communist, Weatherman, radical or other creature purporting to represent "the oppressed" ever surfaced. The three students who were killed, as I recall, were rather nonpolitical. The riot began as a protest against a raise in tuition, plus the usual spring high jinks. Yet the public perception of the event was that it was an outbreak of radical violence, a prelude to revolution. Nonsense. But of course this disparity in viewing the affair did not influence my handling of the case.

"I'd forget it, judge," Merritt said. "There'll be more of the same. The media will swallow all that martyr stuff. You may get a few obscene phone calls. Then it'll blow over. Nobody cares anymore except a few soreheads like Schless."

"Schless," I said. "The dentist. His daughter was killed."

I recalled him well. A heavily built, powerful-looking man, frowning, his rugged face both hurt and angry. And he was fearless. His daughter had been shot through the chest and died on the spot. Schless had told the press he would never forget and never forgive. He had sat through the trial, marched on picket lines, hounded the offices of senators and congressmen, petitioned the courts.

"The battling dentist, yes," George Dempsey said. "He's behind it."

"None of the locals?"

Merritt scowled. "The usual collection of bleeding hearts. The Reverend Alvord Jensen, who is a disgrace to the Methodists. Couple of faculty pinkos. Finnegan, Blochman. They even got poor old Father Schmidt, who's so confused he doesn't know if it's Easter or Groundhog Day, to give it his blessing."

"Well, then, I shouldn't be concerned," I said.

Ed Kettlemen had been "kibitzing" our discussion, and he wobbled by, scarlet-faced, purple-necked. "Reds, the whole crowd. I'd run 'em out of town, judge."

I chuckled. "Now, Ed, that isn't the way the system works. Peaceful protest is a hallowed tradition." I sounded like a Joshua College instructor.

Merritt only laughed. Ed got the idea he wasn't wanted. His father used to taunt me when we were in high school. Old Karl Kettleman, and Duncan Everson, the two toughest boys in the senior class, football stars, hell-raisers. To them, I was always "Four Eyes," "Spider Legs," "Sister Mary," and most disturbing, "Rag"—for disgusting reasons.

"Don't concern yourself over this, judge," Dempsey said. "If you want, I'll have Sheriff Conlan put a watch on your house. Or maybe you should go up to the lake for the weekend."

"I will not be driven from my hearth by threats."

"Attaboy, judge," Merritt said. "Anyone gets funny with you, we'll tar-and-feather 'em."

Kettleman returned. "You guys talking about the thing this weekend? Too bad they only shot three. They should have killed three hundred."

"*Four* hundred," said a slender man at the end of the bar—Betts, or Bettman, his name was. He was a new member.

None of us at the table said anything.

"Looting, starting fires, threatening to kill people," Kettleman's voice was rising. "They got what they asked for."

I cleared my throat. "Looting was never proven."

"That's right," Dempsey said. "One or two stores were broken into. They arrested three bikers from downstate. They confessed."

"It doesn't matter," Kettleman said. "Those college kids started it. They had to take their medicine. That's the way it is in America."

I was grateful for Dempsey's show of fairness. Grateful because I suddenly felt alien, out of place. Justice had been served. But the aftershocks, the fallout remained. The law is dry, factual, precise. What happens in the murky area surrounding any case is harder to define, not subject to precision and formulae. If a man really believes that three or four hundred students should have been killed, how does one respond? And does this kind of judgment, heedless of life and decency, influence and direct our reading of the law?

"Ed's bombed," Merritt said. "Pay no attention to him." He looked at George. "That true about the looting? I never knew that. We thought we had proof that students looted Karlinsky's jewelry store."

"Woffler got depositions from Karlinsky, but they were somehow lost. Later they found the hoods who stole some watches. They confessed. Acne and Mohawk haircuts. Abe Karlinsky didn't want to press charges. It wouldn't have affected the trial anyway. But it is possible Woffler's jury responded to the looting charges."

Bates Woffler, now deceased, was the local prosecutor who presented the Joshua affair to a state grand jury. Under Bates's careful direction —he was an excellent, resourceful lawyer—this jury refused to indict any of the troopers. Instead they indicted twelve students and six faculty members. What happened to that curious indictment is another story. None of that involved me.

My mind was trying to recall the train of events that led from the dismissal of these indictments, to the federal grand jury, to the indictments of the six policemen, and eventually the trial before my court. As I tried to sort out these memories, George and Merritt sprang the surprise on me.

"There's talk about a civil suit," Dempsey said.

"Really?" It was the first I had heard of it. "On what basis?"

"Who knows?" Winnington said. "It's that bastard Schless. He's got a team of smart-ass New York lawyers reviewing everything—police files, trial transcripts, grand jury testimony. They're even interviewing reporters, TV people and naturally the six kids who were wounded, anyone who was a witness."

"How do we know this?"

Dempsey gave a rambling answer. Something about his wife learning it at a bridge club from Reverend Al Jensen's wife Carol, who was not keen on Al's dedication to "the cause."

"But what can they hope to achieve?" I asked. "There is not the remotest chance of their winning. I'm not sure they can even bring a civil suit to court. The state will stand on sovereign immunity. It will refuse to be sued. That will include the police, anyone associated with them and, by inference, the college administration. It's ridiculous."

Winnington rotated his glass, letting the ice cubes clink and the bourbon dilute. "Schless's New York sharpshooters are going two ways. One, a shot at the Supreme Court to see if they can't get an okay to bring the suit against *individuals.* Not a new idea, but it hardly ever works. Or else they might try to get the state legislature to pass a special bill allowing them to enter a suit. Schless has hinted he's after megabucks. Forty million dollars in damages. The dentist is no piker."

Dempsey shook his head. "Mrs. Jensen may have had it wrong. Once Schless's lawyers study the evidence and the transcript, especially Judge Frankendorf's instructions to the jury, they'll realize it won't fly."

"I'm inclined to agree," Winnington said. "Hell, I defended those troopers and I'll do it again. They exercised the right of self-defense. One of the most honored traditions in Anglo-Saxon law. They were standing between society and the jungle. They drew the line in the sand, and those who crossed it with malicious intent, determined to burn, kill and maim, had to pay the price."

"Is it only Dr. Schless?" I asked. "Or are they all behind this?"

Dempsey said, "Schless is too smart to make this a one-man show. Where in heck he's getting the money to revive the case, I don't know."

Merritt actually snorted. "Rich pinkos. Liberal airheads. Ralph Nader's crowd. The usual collection of bleeding hearts. You'd think by now those people would realize it ain't their ballgame any more. Eighty percent of the country sided with the cops and against the students. And in this state it was more like ninety percent."

I said, "There was never any question that public opinion was overwhelmingly on our side."

"And you don't have a thing to worry about," Merritt said. "It won't ever come to trial. No jury in this state would ever find against our troopers."

"Schless is pretty cocky," Dempsey said. "He's supposed to have told Al Jensen that he's going to try to get you on the stand."

"Me?"

"Just like that Arab," Merritt growled. "He would have the nerve to try to subpoena a judge."

"It can't be done, can it, judge?" Dempsey asked.

What a notion! I mulled this over, trying to recall any law or precedent. Then I said, "I doubt that he can be prevented from *trying* to get me to testify. But no trial judge would ever allow it. He would toss it out of court in a minute. There is absolutely no basis for subjecting a retired judge to such treatment."

"Right," said Merritt. "You're untouchable, judge. And don't think the city and the state, the whole country, isn't grateful to you. Civil suit, my fat freckled behind."

I wish he hadn't resorted to vulgarity. But then his toughness is what serves him so well in court. People tend to fear Merritt's jellied green eyes, his flat pale face with its dime-sized freckles, the great crown of frizzy orange hair. An odd man. Humble origins. Very shrewd. Lucky enough to marry into Joshua's first family . . .

Frankly I liked young Dempsey better. He is a gentleman. Merritt's wealthy in-laws have done little to polish his rough edges. Wealth, but no style. And his father-in-law, Duncan Everson, used to call me "Sister Mary" and once yanked my pants down in the school basement and then he and some other football players rubbed Vaseline all over my . . .

Oh dear, why do I remember these things? Why do they still pain me after more than sixty years?

That night, thank goodness, the educational TV station broadcast a delightful program of dance from New York. I particularly enjoyed the *Don Quixote* by Strauss. Extremely well choreographed and performed. I relaxed in my silk kimono, had my Courvoisier nightcap, but did not sleep well.

## Colonel Gregory Offitt

Rummaging through our attic this morning in preparation for our upcoming trip to Arizona, I came across the gun.

God knows why I took it with me when I retired from the state police. It was perfectly legal for me to do so. The state regulations permitted a retiring officer to take one weapon of his choice. I'm no gun lover or gun collector. I've seen what they can do. Particularly in the wrong hands. But I rather like the sleek black HK–91.

It's a rapid-fire automatic rifle, popular with hunters, farmers, ranchers, target shooters and, of course, law enforcement officers. Very, very versatile. Handles beautifully, well-balanced.

I took a whole kit with me. The weapon itself, a .308-caliber fully automatic piece, finished in dull black, with a stout oak pistol grip and stock. I also have a bipod, sling, sight adjustment tool, muzzle cap, cleaning kit and two additional clips. The clip in the rifle contains a full set of rounds. Why, I don't know. I don't hunt, and I would never use a rapid-fire weapon like this on some deer or bear if I did.

It had been buried at the bottom of my old army footlocker, where I keep my fishing clothing and gear. I thought that in Arizona I might get a chance to try my luck with the rainbow trout. When I started unlayering my waders, multipocketed shirts, heavy socks, etc., I suddenly saw the black barrel of the HK–91, and I took it out. Held it a moment, feeling its heft, thinking about how many weapons I'd fired in my long career, how many I'd made "expert" with. And felt sort of sad. But only for a moment. As I handled the weapon, admiring its design, its performance, I was suddenly relieved, in fact elated, that it was nothing more than part of my past. Behind me. Not at all part of my peaceful retired life.

Marge surprised me in the attic as I was holding the HK–91, sighting it through the slatted air vent.

"Greg! What in the world?"

I lowered the rifle and turned, smiling. "Found this in with my fishing gear, Marge."

"I didn't even know you had it."

"Didn't want to alarm you." Marge is frail and worries a lot. Especially the past few years. We took plenty of nasty phone calls, threats, criticism. It's dying down now, but she's still nervous. And drinks a bit more than she should.

"I liked the design. I'll never use it."

"It's the same thing, the same gun, that, I mean . . . at Joshua . . ."

"Yes . . . of course, this wasn't one of the weapons. This was brand-new, coated in Cosmoline, wrapped in sealed tar paper. A gift from the state for my services."

As a career officer's wife, the wife of a man who later commanded a state police force, Marge wasn't unfamiliar with the sight of weapons. But she's a tender soul and easily upset. I put the rifle back—it had a wonderful feel—in the locker, covered it with my flannel shirts and waders and closed the O.D. lid.

"Do we need to keep it in the house?"

"Perfectly safe." Then I told a small fib. "I don't have any ammunition for it."

We walked downstairs together. It touched me that her step was unsteady. I am fit, healthy and look ten years younger than I am. Marge is the same age as I am, and looks five years older than her age.

"So long as it doesn't remind you . . ." Her voice trailed off as we entered the living room. "The same gun. Those poor students. You want to forget."

"It doesn't bother me."

She walked into the kitchen to make supper. She wore a plain gray cotton dress and gray scuffs. I have tried to get her to wear, well, decent shoes around the house—a matter of personal pride, I tell her, it didn't matter if only the two of us were at home—but she pays little attention. When we go out to play bridge or visit or to a movie, she does try to dress up a bit more. I can't get her to doll up. I wouldn't mind if she dyed her hair.

It's been like that since the so-called Joshua Massacre. She changed. I guess I have too. Not that I look on that event as a reflection on me in any way. And I fully appreciate the grief of the parents, the suffering of the wounded students.

My finding the unused rifle in the attic revived memories. Memories I'd really like to suppress. *The way they fell.* The power of that weapon, the way it could spit bullets with such rapidity. Accurate at long range, automatic, semiautomatic or single-shot, fired from the hip with the pistol grip or from the shoulder with the stock . . . Was it wrong to blast away at the mob with such a destructive machine?

But of course that was not the issue. My men were suffering, injured, threatened, cursed, confused. Two of them were hyperventilating. And the larger issues. Society under attack. Breakdown of order.

Marge is right. We have to put it all behind us, cease to think about might-have-beens.

On the porch I picked up the evening edition of the Joshua *Clarion-*

*Ledger.* Normally I turn to the sports pages first, then the editorials. But there was an item on the lower left corner that drew my attention:

### PLANS COMPLETE FOR "MASSACRE" MEMORIAL: FINNEGAN ANNOUNCES EVENTS FOR VIGIL

Professor Thomas Finnegan of the Joshua College Sociology Department disclosed today the agenda for this weekend's memorial observance to honor the three students killed five years ago during a campus riot.

"This will be a learning experience and an attempt to create understanding," Professor Finnegan said. "We hope to enlist the participation of parents, survivors, college officials, townspeople and law enforcement personnel."

Well, they would never enlist me. I'd said all I wanted to say on the alleged massacre. Why did these people persist in opening wounds? What would be gained by it? I was glad we were going to Arizona. I bore no malice to the Schlesses, the Terragnis or the Christophers. I could understand their pain. But I wasn't the person responsible for the deaths of their children.

I heard Marge's shuffling tread and I opened the paper. Didn't want to upset her. The less she read about it the better. So I settled into my rocking chair, lit my pipe and turned to the sports news. Marge rarely reads the newspaper. Says she's too busy. But apart from some gardening now and then, she doesn't do much of anything.

## Dr. David Schless

Called Helen Christopher today.

Dan answered the phone. Frosty reception. Polite cool, his tongue a bit thickened. The nightly bar train and a few postprandial libations. It seems he's well on his way to lushdom. Too bad. Not a bad guy. In spite of that schmucky letter he wrote. Making excuses for those armed hoodlums who plugged his own son. And killed my Andrea. And killed Lucy Terragni. And put Wilma Overstreet in a wheelchair.

While I waited for Dan to get Helen to the phone I remembered the time I'd told him he was a damn fool for writing the letter. Who needed it? "A Father Speaks Out." *Son, I loved you and I shall miss you . . . You died needlessly, spurred on by disturbers of the peace . . .*

We became reasonably good friends later. I think I know why. Dan Christopher liked the way I stood up to that gang of vigilantes outside the hospital in Joshua. Self-appointed guardians of the law. Pot-bellied bums with guns under their jackets, waiting for the commies to invade Joshua. Dan heard about it from Helen and the Terragnis. I'm no hero. But I'm six-three, weigh in at one ninety-five. I boxed heavyweight in the navy, played high school football. Those bums couldn't believe that a middle-aged dentist from Long Island wasn't afraid of them. But Dan understood. As I say, I feel sorry for the guy.

I don't look for fights. Too old for that. It drives Rita crazy when she sees that glint in my eye, my fists tighten. But I walked up to the honcho of this collection of gun-toting shitheads, introduced myself and invited him to drop his weapon and join me in the parking lot. He laughed, sneered, cackled. And declined. I'm told he was publicly shamed that night in the Hog's Breath Cafe. He was never the same man after he finessed a fistfight with a fifty-two-year old Hebe.

Yes, Dan Christopher respected me for that. He tolerates my calling his wife to keep her up on developments in our case. There's nothing in the world (as I repeatedly tell my beloved wife Rita) like the use of fists and force to impress on a certain variety of *goy* that Jews are good buddies. Forget all that piety, mysticism, morality, lamentation. That's what *goyim* expect from Jews. And they don't love them for it.

"Dave, how nice to hear from you," Helen said. Always the lady, low-keyed, mannerly. Too much so. I'll be darned if I ever saw her cry over Jack.

"How are you, Helen?"

"Managing."

"You can guess why I'm calling."

"The memorial observance, or whatever it is. Tom Finnegan called a few days ago."

"I assume you'll join us. Then maybe Dan'll come. I guess Finnegan told you the Terragnis will be there. And all the kids."

"Yes . . ."

A long pause. Rita and I like Helen. A fine woman, intelligent, pretty, nothing of the snob about her, never mind her Old Surrey background, that ultra-WASP Connecticut enclave where nothing bad ever happens. So she wears green golf skirts and favors Lilly Pulitzer frogs. Proves nothing. She's tolerant and bright. And she would have stuck by us through this mess if it hadn't been for her husband.

"You don't sound too excited about it," I said.

"I . . . I'm not sure I'll be able to join you. Dan doesn't like the idea. He says it won't mean anything, it'll be exploited by a lot of, well, dubious people."

"Yeah, like Father Schmidt and Reverend Jensen."

"Not them. You know—professional radicals."

"All those agitators from New York and Chicago who were supposed to have invaded the Joshua campus and started the riots? They never located one of them. If thinking that makes Dan happy, who am I to disabuse him?"

I told her about our progress on the civil suit. Brian Dooley, our lawyer, was preparing an appeal to the Supreme Court to see if we could get a ruling on our right to sue the police and others as individuals. We were also looking at ways to move via the state legislature.

"What if the court says we can sue?" she asked.

"Then we hit them in the pocketbook for as much as the law and reason allow. Brian says a figure of fifty million dollars in damages isn't out of line."

"I wonder if it's right. I mean, putting a price on our children's lives."

"It's the only recourse we have, Helen."

She thanked me and said she'd think about attending the memorial weekend. There was no way Dan would show up. She'd have to handle him carefully. I was tempted to say, get him drunk enough, pour him on the plane and keep him bombed. But I respected her too much, and, as I said, I sort of liked Christopher. Anyone who has to live under the curse of that crazy letter has a right to stay sozzled. Poor guy, I'm sure he feels the pain as much as I do.

Later Rita and I talked about the Christophers.

"Helen's too much of a lady," Rita said. "She believes people are decent, that if we all keep cool heads and observe the amenities of life —gifts, anniversaries, thank-you notes—all will be well."

"She can afford to. She's secure and happy in her suburban heaven. If Dan were black or Puerto Rican and they'd been raised in East Harlem she'd behave differently. But what the hell, I like her too."

Rita busied herself with her knitting. Ever since Andrea's death, she's gotten into this mania for working with her hands—needlepoint, knitting, embroidery, stitchery, the sort of stuff she was never really interested in. She's cut down on friends, doesn't give dinner parties, talks less on the phone. The agony is deep inside her. I guess using her hands is a way of dealing with it. She is one courageous woman. But I wish she'd let herself get angrier over the murder of our only child.

"Helen," Rita said softly. "Such a perfect life. The white frame house. Furniture that belonged to her grandparents. The corporate husband. Two well-behaved children. I guess she was the least likely mother in the world to have a son killed in a campus riot."

"I give her high marks," I said. "She was never angry at us for pushing the thing. Remember, it was the Terragnis, the blue collars, who were sore. At first. They changed, though. Joe Terragni was barred from the American Legion and kicked off the Metalworkers' Union Council after he signed our petition for a federal grand jury investigation. He deserves credit. It hasn't been easy for him."

Rita said, "Maybe we'll get justice some day." She pushed the eyeglasses up her nose, pursed her lips. Calm, self-contained. From reading too many English novels. Her grandparents came from the other side, maternals from Lithuania, like my parents, her father's family from Romania. But somehow, for all her dark brown hair, round brown eyes, large features and olive skin, she suggests a dignified British matron. It's the gentleness, the poise, the way she pours tea. Maybe she and Helen Christopher have more in common than she thinks.

"I want more than justice," I said.

My stomach was churning. The old fury building up in me. The urge to confront the killers of my child, to hurt them, shame them, force them to admit their crimes, to confess that they were lying, yellow, murderous bastards . . . "I want . . ." The words clotted in my throat.

"Please, Dave."

"I want them to suffer. The way Andrea did."

33

"That's impossible. You can't kill them. And you mustn't think about it so much."

"Liars. Out-in-the-open liars. Two hundred photographs proved they were lying. For all the world to see. And by the time the good Judge Frankendorf was through with us nobody believed the photographs existed. People said they were faked. How do you fix twenty-seven photographers and fake all the pictures they took?"

"You know what Alvord Jensen said . . . We lost because there was too much justice on our side—"

"The hell we did," I said. "We lost because that's what the country wanted. I remember those galoots outside the hospital. Grinning at us, holding up three fingers. And that chant they had—"

"Don't, Dave. No more."

I ignored her. In a sing-song, I said, *"Nine got shot, ain't that hot. Three got killed, ain't we thrilled . . ."*

Rita dropped the needles and held her hands to her ears.

Just before I was ready to climb into bed, Brian Dooley phoned. I sleep in the den and I took the call there. Not that Rita and I aren't affectionate. It's just that since the death of Andrea, I've become a night prowler. Around two I wake up no matter what time I've sacked in. I roam. I listen to all-night talk shows. I read. I eat an apple. Sometimes I just stare at the ceiling.

I try to imagine the moment of impact. When the soft-nosed .308-caliber bullet ripped into Andrea's heart. Did she feel pain? How long? Did she know anything in that last second of her nineteen years?

Rita sleeps soundly. She's been on tranquilizers prescribed by our family doctor. I can't disturb her sleep. It's about all the solace she has left.

Brian Dooley is young and excitable. He's working with a volunteer team—a lot of young people doing the preparatory work *pro bono publico.*

"Doc, we're making progress," Dooley said. He has a high sort of womanish voice.

"Sounds good."

"Keep this confidential. You can tell Rita but nobody else."

I laughed. Brian knows that I've developed a keen sense of public relations. I've gotten to know the network reporters and the AP and UPI people on a first-name basis. I've never thrown them any curves. They treated us decently.

"What's up?" I asked. "That old stuff about police agents starting it?"

"No, no. It's got to do with grand jury testimony."

"State or federal?"

"State."

Two grand juries had reviewed the Joshua case at length. The state jury found no reason to return indictments against the troopers. Instead, they indicted students and teachers! Lives and property were threatened. The police acted prudently and in accordance with riot-control procedures. They were under attack, in danger of losing their lives. So they fired and killed three students. End of state investigation.

It was the federal grand jury that resulted in the trial. Of course the trial never got us any justice. *Some trial.* Foxy Frankendorf hogtied the federal prosecutor, made a fool of him, threw out evidence and favored the cops so you'd think they were honorees at a testimonial dinner instead of defendants.

"What about the state grand jury?"

"We're not sure. There's scuttlebutt that Woffler knew things he never let into court—testimony, conversations with some of the principals."

"But someone would know it existed."

"They might, but Woffler and whoever talked to him—and a lot of people did—may have decided it wasn't relevant. That would have been the prosecutor's privilege, I guess."

"Isn't that obstruction of justice?" I asked.

"Maybe. Depends what the information was."

"Whose was it?"

"Offitt's. At least that's the rumor. There are supposed to be tapes, or notes somewhere."

I whistled. Colonel Gregory Offitt, USA, Retired, was the commandant of the state police. He'd been on campus the day of the shootings but not actually present when the guns went off.

"Why would anyone want to hide his testimony?" I asked. "The guy stuck up for his cops from the start. He never uttered a word that cast doubt on the troopers' version."

"We can't figure that out either. The whole thing could just be wishful thinking."

Strangely, for a man whose daughter had been murdered by the police, I'd formed a fairly decent opinion of Colonel Offitt. He was a retired army officer, straight-backed, lean, close-cropped salt-and-pepper hair, rimless specs. Low-keyed, short answers. He was a West Pointer. They're straight arrows. I'd checked him out during the trial and found he had a drawerful of medals, a distinguished combat record, and had advocated racially integrated units. And he'd been an effective witness for the defense.

Of course he didn't have to work too hard at helping get his troopers off the hook. Winnington was one hell of a defense lawyer and he had Frankendorf in his corner most of the time. You have to remember all these people knew each other. We were outsiders—the feds, the parents whose kids were killed, the wounded students. We'd caused too many problems and we were getting to be pains in the ass.

I asked Dooley, "Does this stuff mean anything? These so-called secret notes or tapes? Could be nothing but idle chatter. Woffler was quite a talker."

"We won't know until we find them."

"If they exist."

"It's speculation, no question. But we'll try to run it down."

"But what could have been said that wasn't said in court, or in front of the grand juries?"

"Who knows? But maybe it would help move the civil suit forward a step or two."

I reminded him of a law journal critique of the federal trial he'd sent me. Some panel of hotshot lawyers had found nothing wrong with Judge Frankendorf's conduct of the trial. And of course the government couldn't appeal the acquittal. That would have been double jeopardy. And there was no way the state would ever try the cops.

Dooley agreed, but said that it might be interesting if we could get Colonel Offitt on the stand again at a civil trial.

I shrugged. "He'll say what he always said. His cops were threatened. They fired in self-defense at a mob that was about to overrun them."

"Maybe. Anyway, we'll keep looking. My guess is Woffler probably got rid of anything dangerous. And he's dead and gone now."

"Well, good luck, Brian."


Rita was reading when I entered the bedroom. I was glad she had the big bed to herself. I know the torment in her heart. I know she has to handle it alone, get her nine hours of sleep, nurture her love for Andrea, enclose the pain. I have the feeling that my bull-in-the-china-shop manner sometimes intrudes on her mourning.

I told her about Dooley's information, the possibility that there was suppressed or destroyed testimony that could help us get a new trial.

She closed her book. "It won't help, David. The country wanted the death of our child. They got it. And they'll spend anything they have to, do anything they have to, to prove it was right."

I kissed her, picked up my bathrobe, slippers, a copy of Time and went to the den.

I've given up feeling sorry for myself. Hell, I stopped when I was a 180-pound linebacker in high school, getting my bell rung every Saturday by 220-pound linemen. *You do it, or you don't.* I couldn't help feeling that Andrea's death had left an unhealing wound in our lives. That's obvious, I suppose. What I mean is, it isn't the same between us. It can't be. The death of a child—it's senseless, cruel, rips a chunk out of your guts, your mind, your heart. Where do you turn? What do you do? See the chaplain?

Rita read a lot, worked for the right causes, helped me with office accounting. And me? I was getting more and more to hate staring into mouths of carious teeth, inhaling bad breath, inflicting pain, bawling out my hygienist.

If my life meant anything, it would have to focus on securing a degree of justice for my dead daughter, for Joe Terragni's girl, for the Christopher boy.

## Helen Christopher

My tennis was dreadful this morning. I ruined the game for Nita Waldorf, Susie Barrister and the new girl, Carrie DeMuth.

A few years ago I was rather good. An "A" player, number three or four in interclub matches, often getting to the semifinals at our club tournament. Once I invited Dan's cousin, a former teaching pro, to be my partner on member-guest day, and we won the championship against some awfully good competition. This, as you may know, is tennis country. Tennis, platform, racquetball, paddleball, squash—a lot of it is played here, and the players are top drawer. I always held my own.

But this morning I was awful. My partner, Nita, didn't help. She's a haughty Cuban woman, and she plays tennis six days a week—when she isn't getting massages or working out with Nautilus. She's muscular, slender and pretty in a kind of carved way. Wears her black hair drawn back tight, flashes a lot of dazzling white teeth when she hits a winner. And can bare those teeth at you if you make an error.

"Helen, please," Nita kept saying, "when I rush the net, come with me. And if I cross over, cover the other side."

Dan says I'm too acquiescent. I should have told her to stop badgering me. All of us have our bad days. We had a chance to salvage the third set in a tiebreaker after Carrie and Sue had beaten us 6–3, 6–3. But I choked on my last two serves. I double-faulted once, then hit a soft second serve that Sue slammed into Nita's face at the net. We were down three sets.

Nita kept shaking her head, muttering to herself in Spanish. She's a poor loser. I felt sorry for her husband. She'd be at him all night, furious over having lost.

We sat down for a drink under the striped green umbrellas on the redwood deck overlooking the court. Around us the trees were coming into leaf. Dogwoods bloomed and the lawns were glowing with daffodils, tulips and iris. For a moment I was awed by what a good life we led. The lovely club with its immaculate courts. The Connecticut woodlands embracing us. The limpid blue sky. And our perfect, happy town of Old Surrey. Many times Dan and I reflected on how lucky we were to live here. Charming houses, lavish gardens, stone fences, a sense of order, cleanliness, beauty. People in Old Surrey are polite, helpful, interested in one another. (It is untrue, incidentally, that Old Surrey is a restricted community. We have several Jewish residents, and some Jewish members at the Old Surrey Racquet Club. Debbie Lieberman's son Chuck is the best junior player we've ever turned out—ranked fifth in New England. One's religion or racial background is never a subject for conversation. No one cares. There are a few black families in town, and a healthy infusion of Italians, who have been here a long time and run most of the filling stations, delicatessens, liquor stores. They just do.)

Nita had regained some of her Latin charm, and we chatted about various things. My friends respect the tragedy in my life. They don't talk too much about their own children. This one's son entering Princeton, this one's daughter graduating from Emma Willard . . . they think it must hurt me to hear about the achievements. It doesn't. I don't begrudge them their happiness.

Carrie DeMuth, who is a bit ditsy, blurted out that she and her husband Neal were off to France for a month but that Neal was worried about the student riots there that we'd been seeing on television.

Sue Barrister said that these manifestations usually didn't bother tourists. The French police—she'd lived in Paris when her husband was with IBM—were tough and could be counted on to keep things under control.

"Good for them," Nita said. "They should shoot a few dozen. They want to rip up the streets and burn cars and break windows. If Batista had shot a few hundred we would never have Castro . . ."

There was an icy silence around the green table.

"Well . . ." Sue said. "That really isn't necessary. There are ways of handling riots . . ."

Nita would not be deterred. "Listen to me, darling. I know about these things. You start with a mob throwing rocks, you end up with communists. Oh, it's the thing today to criticize Batista and Somoza and Trujillo, but they had the right idea. The same thing will happen here unless we start giving it to some of these—"

Sue was kicking Nita, gently at first, then a bit harder.

"Oh, oh," Nita said. "I'm sorry, Helen. What *your* boy was involved in . . . that was different . . . college pranks, an accident . . ."

I kept silent.

Carrie DeMuth tried to change the subject. She started chattering about a new member, a woman from Australia, who was the best player at the club and would easily win the singles championship in the fall. The woman was practicing with our pro just below us, and it was clear that she was in a class by herself.

"Look at that two-handed backhand," Carrie said. "She hits it like a man."

Nita, relieved to have found another area of conversation, looked glumly from behind her designer glasses at the Australian woman. "She is very good."

I could see the anger on her face. It was as if her own cruel comments —the implication that my son deserved to be killed—had irritated her. And now her ranking on the tennis ladder was in jeopardy. Her world was threatened. No wonder she refused to look at me the rest of the morning.

Leaving the club in my battered green Volvo wagon—Dan says all anyone is allowed to drive in Old Surrey are Mercedes, BMW's and *maybe* Volvos—I was annoyed with myself for not talking back to Nita Waldorf. I should have said something about the trial. Or the faked evidence. The lies they all told. The photographers that proved that the police had invented a false version. But it's all become jumbled, confused in my head. An irritant, like a low-grade migraine. Perhaps Dan is right when he tells me to bury it.

I shopped at our local supermarket, Nussbaum's, stopped to buy postage stamps, and took a stroll down Trumbull Street, our "main drag." For some odd reason I felt a bit exposed in my tennis outfit and white cashmere. I have good legs, and as Dan says, "a fine round butt." I thought I drew a few stares. *Good God, I'm forty-seven!* A Latin-looking man in jeans outside of Eddie's Pizza whistled at me.

The revival of thoughts about Jack—things I may have done wrong, advice not given, love held back, assurances not granted—troubled me. In that frame of mind it somehow did not seem proper for me to be parading bare-legged in my Ellesse dress and Adidas shoes.

I stared at the books in the Surrey Book Shop window, saw nothing that inspired me and drove home.

The afternoon loomed ahead of me—too long, too lonely, too aimless. I wished I had a few more students. I'm an excellent teacher, I feel, but in a town like Old Surrey parents can send problem children to special schools.

After a lunch of endive salad and iced tea I thought of calling the Schlesses and talking about the forthcoming events at Joshua. But I don't know if I should go. At three o'clock, about the time when Jack would usually be coming home from high school with a thump of heavy feet, slamming of doors, the ecstatic barking of Susie, I felt faint and had to lie down.

# August Karl Frankendorf

A rather interesting magazine, one of those new conservative journals, wants me to write an article about the Joshua College case.

Immodestly I admit to being a rather good writer, with a flair for the *mot juste*. But I will turn them down.

The magazine is entitled Manifest Destiny. It is edited by a man named Arnold Shreck, who wrote me a polite letter. I believe I've seen him on television. He is an outspoken enemy of affirmative action, and favors an invasion of Cuba.

Mr. Shreck was clearly sympathetic to my position on the Joshua trial.

> Attempts to depict the dead and wounded of the Joshua College case as martyrs or freedom fighters distort the truth. A tragedy, to be sure. But *martyrs?* Rather misguided children who were manipulated by the Left and swept up, as part of a deliberate plot, into a maelstrom of violence. The real villains are these cynical political desperadoes who used the occasion of a campus spring riot to attempt to overthrow the established order. What astonishes me, Judge Frankendorf, is the way so many left-liberal writers view you as an enemy of freedom rather than its brave shield. Our magazine, small in circulation but potent in influence, would be honored, if in your retirement, you would disclose to us your innermost thoughts on the matter . . .

I carefully composed a measured response to Mr. Shreck, thanking him for his appreciative remarks but stressing that I refused to make any public statement on the Joshua College matter.

With a touch of gentle humor, I told him that when I stepped down from the court I traded in my penal code book for a full set of Mozart's symphonies in stereo. Nowadays, I told him, I preferred Raphael to Blackstone . . .

After I had sealed and stamped the letter I wondered if perhaps his invitation to me had been too quickly spurned. There were things I wanted to make clear, facts about my career that were not well known, that the media had ignored in their attacks on my handling of the trial. It would have been gratifying, for example, to remind people, via Manifest Destiny (curious name), that I had a lot in common with William O. Douglas, although I never much cared for the man.

Like Douglas I felt that the First Amendment to the Constitution threw off "penumbras and emanations" that came down on the side of the poor, the oppressed, the voiceless of society. To put it another way, I felt, as did another great jurist, that the proper attitude for a judge should be that "those less favored in life would be more favored under law."

Yes, I do believe that. My record in race cases, labor matters, voting rights, the right to a fair trial reveals all that. I acted no differently in presiding over the trial of the six accused policemen. *Their* rights had to be respected also. Talk about penumbras! Surely the First Amendment must speak to the need for the body politic to defend itself against murderous mobs.

I put on Mozart's *Jupiter* Symphony and relaxed as its noble strains filled my living room. Then I turned the lights down low and reread Shreck's letter. Interesting fellow. He said he intended to come out to Joshua for the memorial and to write several syndicated columns on the event, exposing it as a left-wing attempt to besmirch the country. Agreeable chap, but I made my mind up not to talk to him.

Relaxing with my cognac, tired but never bored—oh, how Mozart inspirits and uplifts me—I opened the other letter that had come with the late mail.

It was from Trooper Dennis Boyle, one of the defendants who had appeared before me. He was a handsome, long-jawed young officer with a shock of dark red hair. It was utterly impossible (even though the federal government tried) to ever depict this man as a wanton killer. He simply did not fit the mold. His letter to me, a rather rambling one, said in part:

> I am considering applying to law school, as a part-time student. As you know, I'm a graduate of Joshua College. The state would permit me to continue working and would even pay for part of my tuition. Would you, Judge Frankendorf, be willing to write a letter

of reference for me? Needless to say, you are one of the most respected judges in the state. It would mean a great deal to me.

The truth is that my fellow troopers and I live under a cloud. I can't explain it. The majority of people in the state and the country approved of our actions. It was a tragic thing, but as the trial showed we were innocent. Every one of us—even Sgt. Adam Kazinski, who likes to put up a tough front—feels badly about what happened five years ago and would like nothing more than to see it laid to rest. We did not revel in what we did. We wish we could call back those bullets. I know Wallace Markland and Kevin Case and even old Kaz certainly feel that way. Have been out of touch with Francis Hofheimer and Louis Trippi, but I'll bet they are as sorry as I am. (They both resigned from the force some years ago, personal problems, and are living out of state, one in Florida, the other in the Southwest.)

I feel that devoting myself to the study of law may help resolve questions in my mind as to what happened and why. Do I make sense? Needless to say I would be honored, Judge Frankendorf, if you would write me a "To Whom It May Concern" testifying to my fitness and character.

I barely knew the man. The youngest of the defendants. He wasn't married. Of course he never got to the witness stand. I made sure of that. I saw which way the prosecution was going with the dubious photographs, the concocted evidence, the films and tapes and so on. As if these mere recordings of events were the actual truth.

I wonder if it would be ethical or proper for me to write the letter for him. I'll think about it. In any case, it was good to know that none of the men was permanently scarred by his ordeal. And equally good to know that they all felt badly about the entire event. As I certainly do.

Perhaps I should have gone to the lake for the weekend. The social diversions here in town are not enticing. I'm not one for poker or bridge, or dirty jokes or heavy drinking. I get invited out a great deal (by the best families) but I'm afraid they regard me as something of a snobby old dandy.

Suddenly I had a recollection of one of the mothers accosting me outside the court the day the jury returned its verdict of innocent. Who was it? Mrs. Schless, the dentist's wife? Or was it that stout woman, Mrs. Terragni? It certainly wasn't the Christopher boy's mother. My recollection is she only appeared for two days. An eminently refined and pretty woman.

Yes, it was the Terragni woman. How could I make clear to her that I bore her no ill will? That I regretted the death of their children? I almost wept when I saw the Overstreet girl confined to a wheelchair.

My clerk and I were about to enter my car when Mrs. Terragni approached.

It was a wintry day. The sky a hazed black-gray. The air charged with a cold mist. Joshua is foothill country, and fogs and mists collect here in the winter months. It can be as cold as Minnesota but without the snow.

And here was this woman—dark, plain, in a navy blue coat and a fur hat. Her husband (his name was Joseph and he was a metalworker in Flagg City) was trying to hold her back.

"Judge Frankendorf," she said. Her voice shook.

"Yes?"

"Maybe it will happen to your child some day. I hope not. But if it does, you'll know how it feels."

I wanted to tell her that I grieved for her daughter, that I bore no malice to anyone, that I conducted the trial in the fairest manner possible. (I could have added, I had no children). My clerk hustled me into my car before I could respond.

I wonder, does the sick mind that sent me that threatening obscene note understand the depth of my sorrow for Mrs. Terragni? *What's Hecuba to him, or he to Hecuba, / That he should weep for her?* Hamlet asks, reflecting on an actor's feigned agony. Oh, but I can tell you, those dead children are something to *me*. I could not, would not, dare explain it to Mrs. Terragni, or Mrs. Christopher, or Mrs. Schless. But they are very real to me, even dear to me. Yes.

From my screened porch—it's warm, and I have decided on a second cognac to help me sleep—I can hear a gardener working at dusk in the Holmes's estate next to my modest bungalow. It's the Kazinski boy, a sturdy lad, the son of Sgt. Adam Kazinski, one of the so-called Six. Nice lad. A back like a side of beef—pink, muscled, bland. I have nothing in common with him or his father. I daresay they would sneer at my love of ballet. But he waves to me. He *knows*. I am the *judge*.

*Kazinski.* "Old Sarge," the others called him. So many miles separate me from this world of male toughness, beery camaraderie. *Faggot. Spider Legs. Sister Mary, throws like a girl . . .*

Kazinski was the one who claimed he had found a handgun on the

44

corpse of the Christopher boy. (This was long before the case came before me, thank goodness.) He produced a Beretta 950, a 22-caliber weapon. It was rusty, twenty years old, and had a part missing. Kazinski said he saw Jack Christopher aiming the gun at him. Ergo, he had no choice but to defend himself.

Prosecutor Kalt tried to make much of this at the trial. Why had Sergeant Kazinski waited so long to produce the weapon? Why had no one else seen it? Kazinski said he took it from Christopher's right hand as the boy lay dead in front of a spreading yew. You have, of course, seen the photograph. The boy is crumpled, hands on his abdomen, as if felled by a tummy ache . . . except for the foot-wide trail of blood from his body, staining the pavement, melding into the dark earth.

As I look at young Kazinski laying down pine bark—goodness, he is a huge youth, blond as a Norse god—I think of his father. A bit of a brute. The other troopers all impressed me as reasonable men trapped in an impossible situation. But Adam Kazinski did not seem to understand anything. He changed his story about the handgun three times. Under what I decided was abusive questioning by that smarty-pants Kalt, he admitted he had perjured himself, lied, invented the story. The gun was what the police call a throw-down. Kazinski had found the weapon in a police bin.

It seemed to me, listening to the conflicting testimony, that the story of the gun on Jack Christopher's body had become so twisted, inflammatory and pointless that it no longer bore on the trial. So I barred any further testimony on it and instructed the jurors to disregard it. That seemed a fair decision to me.

You see, the issue was not whether Kazinski had lied about the gun or invented a story. Or whether the mob was twenty feet or three hundred feet from the troopers. It was a much larger issue. I did not need Merritt Winnington to tell me what my correct duty was.

No, my dear friend, I have no guilt. Like Othello, I have done much service for the state. And the state and the people appreciate it. Later, I dozed, listening to *Così fan tutti*. But I did not sleep well. Maybe I should go to my place on the lake.

Joe says no. I say yes. I think I'll win this one.

Joey says he's had enough of the whole mess and wants to forget about it. Me, I'm not as tough as he is. Or says he is. I admit it. I cry about an hour and a half every day. Usually when he's out of the house. I stare at the photograph of Lucy in her high school cap and gown. She was salutatorian at her high school graduation and was voted Most Popular Student. And she wasn't even a cheerleader or a beauty queen. It's just that everyone loved her. She ran the cleanup campaign, the newspaper collections, the toy drive for the orphanages, and was always the Catholic representative when they had an interfaith meeting.

Why should I lie? I have four other children, two wonderful boys and two sweet girls, but none of them are like Lucy. I'd guess that apart from my youngest, Bobby, none of them will go to college. But there was never any doubt about Lucy. From first grade she was a wonderful student. B-plus was an insult for her. A's or nothing, momma, she used to say. She loved working with children. When she was eight or nine she used to play school for hours—by herself.

She'd put boxes together for desks, sit behind a small table and run a class, except there were no students there. They had names, they took exams, they recited. (She played all the parts.) Her high school counselor, Mr. Shapiro, a wonderful man who encouraged her, knowing she came from a family of uneducated people, told me once there was no limit to what Lucy could attain in the field of nursing.

"Your daughter is an exceptional young lady, Mrs. Terragni," I can hear Mr. Shapiro saying. "She should be encouraged in every way to pursue her studies. I mean she should shoot for the best and think in terms of a graduate program."

Joshua College may not have been the best, but even with scholarship help we couldn't afford to send Lucy to Barnard or Vassar or the state university. Actually we might have managed if she'd gotten work and we had taken out a loan. But I think we were afraid of letting her too far out of our sight. We loved her so much we wanted to be able to see her every weekend.

Now she's gone. *Murdered.* And her name smeared and covered with filth. And the stories that got back to me . . . Bingo night at St.

Malachi's, I heard the women in the bathroom gossiping. *Lucy was pregnant. The Schless girl was covered with lice and sores.* Why? Why did they do this to our children?

Joe got kicked off the union council. Two of the other councilmen, Sal Malfitano and Vincent Garrity, members of the National Rifle Association, got furious with him when he said that the state police had lied. The next day Joe was off the council. And almost out of a job.

As for me, I don't get invited to poker parties much any more—*it's five years*—and a lot of so-called friends have stopped calling. When Bobby had his communion and we had a party for his friends, three couples wouldn't send their sons over. They didn't want them friendly with the Terragnis, those "reds" whose daughter "got what she deserved" at Joshua College. Yes, that's what they said.

You know that famous writer who came here and did the magazine article about the shootings? He couldn't believe what he heard. He had to go back and ask people, over and over. Leading citizens. Friends of ours. Lawyers, storekeepers, town officials. Some said three hundred, some five hundred. But they wanted a lot more students killed than just the three who died.

Well, we're going to Joshua, Joey and me. I mean it. I'm not afraid of any of them. And Joe, I have to say, got support from the union international this time. They even donated money to the defense fund. People do learn.

I remember how one day Joe and I ran into Bates Woffler, the state prosecutor. He was a thin man with a head of wavy brown hair, and he smiled a lot. He was considered a terrific lawyer. In fact, Joey had once helped him on a case—a shop steward who was shaking down apprentices. That was the kind of thing my Joey wouldn't tolerate. Woffler got a conviction, and Joey respected him, until that state grand jury business.

It was a Fourth of July picnic. Joe was pitching for the metalworkers' softball team. Mr. Woffler was umpiring. It was just after the state jury had indicted students and teachers, instead of the cops.

"Dammit, Bates," Joey said, "why'd they do it? You guys would indict the dead if you could. Why not my daughter? Or the Overstreet girl, who's in a wheelchair?"

Woffler ruffled his mop of hair. "Joe, that isn't fair. I know you've been hurt, but the law's the law."

Bates Woffler, as you've heard, is dead, keeled over with a heart attack last year, so maybe I shouldn't talk ill of the dead. He seemed to reflect what people wanted . . . seemed as if the whole country hated our kids. Actually felt they *deserved* to die. My God . . .

And those indictments that Woffler got from the state grand jury! Well, there was one judge who had the guts to do something. He said they were so outrageous, so at odds with the facts that he ordered all the copies shredded, then the strips of paper burned and the ashes buried! That was Judge Herman Althouse. He reviewed the case and called Bates's indictments "a stench in the nose of justice." He also said the wrong people were indicted.

It didn't seem to faze Bates Woffler. He told people Althouse was a left-wing liberal and didn't know right from wrong. But Judge Althouse's decision did get the case to a federal grand jury. Not that it did any good. The trial went to old Judge Frankendorf and we never really had a chance. I'm not sure it was *all* his doing that no one was punished. *Everyone* seemed to want it that way.

Let me tell you, it's no fun to feel the whole world, even your friends, don't care that your child is dead, and don't want the truth to ever come out of how she was killed.

## Helen Christopher

We had our blowup today. I knew it was coming. It's funny how trivial things can make up your mind for you.

I'm referring to the way Nita Waldorf behaved at tennis, the remarks she made about the need to shoot several hundred demonstrators. What is it that holds me back, that makes me bite my tongue?

My daughter Beth claims it's because I've let Dan "walk all over me." Beth's answer to all my problems is to meditate more. Adnana Lal would have an answer even for my shyness. Chant, sit cross-legged, think cool thoughts, repeat a *mantra*. I've tried it. The trouble is all sorts of extraneous notions clutter my mind and I find I'm more upset than before I started.

"Dad has dominated you so long, you've lost your identity," Beth says. "Even when you were getting your master's degree, when your kids were in high school and you were running yourself ragged traveling to New Haven three days a week cramming, writing papers, student-teaching, you catered to him."

"Your father was always under pressure—"

"Nuts. He drank too much. That paper-shuffling job of his. Asskissing his boss all day."

"It sent you to college, Beth. It would have sent Jack. It provides us with this ten-room house, three cars, vacations."

Beth shook her head. She's a tall, big-boned blonde girl, built like her father, not me. Not pretty, but attractive in an original way. "Everything *he* wanted. Tell me, mom, has he ever really done anything *you* want—like take you to a museum or a month in a villa in Italy, or buy an opera subscription?"

"You make me sound like a culture snob."

Beth also said I was "ten times smarter and more sensitive" than Dan, and that I had a right to develop my talents, follow my interests.

I often wonder what I'd do if I were single. Teach full-time again? Travel more? Go back to Yale for my doctorate? I admit, all these things cross my mind. After Jack died, everything was put aside. Dan needed me. I needed him. It's true. I do believe his suffering was worse than mine.

We seemed to draw closer, we tried to share more things. He appeared to listen to me more attentively, and I tried to show more interest in his work. (The problem was I knew that his job, despite the money and the so-called perks and the circumscribed power, irritated and sometimes shamed him.) What was incontestable, though, was that we had less sex. I would often see him looking at me longingly, with a misty glow in his gray eyes. Maybe we'd be dressing to go out, and I'd be in a lace-trimmed slip, sheer stockings, high heels. And the double strand of pearls with the emerald clasp that Dan's mother gave me. He'd stare at me as if he weren't sure I was his wife, as if wondering how at forty-three I could look so trim, attractive, my hair lustrous, my eyes bright. (Aided by a bit of cosmetic artifice, I confess.)

But nothing would happen. He'd pat my satiny rear end, peck at my neck and mutter, "Maybe later." But by bedtime, after an evening of hard drinking, arguments about golf and business, he would undress

49

quickly and be in bed before I was. Sometimes my body ached for him, craved his embraces. But all I got was a dutiful kiss. . . .

When I got home after that distressing morning of tennis, with Nita's barbs ringing in my head, I picked up the mail. Our mailbox rests rather forlornly on an old tree stump on Gunpowder Road. Dan got sick and tired of righting the pole over and over again. Cement, bolts, nails all failed to keep it safe from the depredations of boys, so Dan gave up and there it rests, an invitation to any teenager who wants to knock it over. "Kids who do that," Dan said, "should be strung up by the thumbs."

There was a letter from Dave Schless, still trying to persuade me to attend the fifth anniversary of the Joshua College Massacre. I am very fond of David and Rita. He's a courageous man, and the story of how he faced up to the vigilantes outside the hospital is one I'll never forget. I doubt that Dan or I would have done the same thing had we been there.

> . . . it won't be right without you. Believe me, Helen, you give us a touch of class. Me and Rita, we're old ADA members and civil libertarians. Obviously we're dangerous. The Terragnis are great. I love Joe and Sally and they'll make a real contribution. Amazing the way Joe's attitude has changed over the years. He used to be in favor of showing electrocutions on television to teach criminals a lesson. Now the guy is determined to find the cop who killed Lucy and punch him out. Not that it would help. But you and Dan, Helen, you're *America*. And you've got dignity, education, class, good manners. Who could possibly call you a radical commie agitator hippie?

I felt I was being patronized. David Schless does have this way of slotting people. Still and all, I was feeling an obligation to pay homage to my son. True, it would be walking into the enemy camp. The town detested the whole business, had refused to accept any memorial to the three dead—several statues had been rejected and whenever a plaque went up it was torn down—and I wondered if I needed any more confrontation in my life.

Dan came home while I was showering. I came out of the shower fragrant and powdered, in the satin peach robe he used to love to have me wear before we made love. *Pearls, robe and high-heeled shoes, that's all I ask,* he would say, *I'm a modest fetishist.*

His eyes glowed—from liquor and desire. He embraced me, kissed my neck and my ears and mouth, and this time we made love. It had been six weeks since he had touched me. It was gentle, relaxed.

"So good," I said. "Like when we were newlyweds."

"And before that."

He left the bedroom and returned, carrying a glass of bourbon in one hand and Dave Schless's letter in the other.

"I saw Dave's letter. The guy gets his jollies rubbing the scar."

I gathered the robe around me and sat up. I was quivering inside. "Maybe he's interested in justice."

"There ain't no justice."

"The country should be reminded of what happened."

"The country wants to forget it. So do I."

"I don't. Not that I want to rub the scar, as you say Dave and Rita are doing. But I want . . . I want . . ."

"What, Helen? *What?*"

"If there's going to be a civil trial, I want to contribute. I want to see that the people who killed Jack are made to pay."

Dan sat at the edge of the bed and stroked my thigh. "No wrinkles, no sag, no cellulite," he said. "Honey, I do survey courses in dames all the time. In the office, on the New Haven Railroad, on the street. Not one ever excites me the way you do. You look so great. You could be twenty-five years old. When you decide to leave me for a tennis pro, some kid in his twenties, at least give me warning."

"Maybe it's nature's way of hiding my sorrow. They say people who are severely ill, even dying, often get a healthy glow to their skin, their eyes are bright and alert—"

"Jesus Christ, don't talk that way." He ran his hand up and down my leg. "That's why I don't want you going to Joshua. Tell Schless *no.*"

All prim and proper now, with no desire to encourage his affectionate approaches, I sat up. Maybe it was cruel of me, because I felt he wanted to make love again. Before his drinking became a problem Dan was a strenuous yet considerate lover.

"Dan, I'm going."

"It won't help. You'll be miserable."

"Maybe. But I'll have the satisfaction of knowing I haven't deserted Jack."

"Wrong. Jack's dead. The kid paid the price for acting like a fool, for letting other people—"

"*Other* people, *other* people!" I was astonished by my anger. "At least give him the dignity of having made his own decisions!"

"He lost his dignity when he joined that mob."

His manner was more of a man who has been hurt than one who wanted to injure someone. He truly loved Jack. I think his disappointments in him as student and athlete and so forth made him love our son all the more. I believe that.

"Don't be angry with me if I go to Joshua. I owe it to his memory."

"I don't want you to. It may be over for us if you do."

I was not as stunned as I should have been. For all Dan's lethargy and indecision, he can often make these swift judgments.

"Over?"

"Well, it might make it harder for us to live together . . ."

"Over something like this? Dan, we each loved Jack in our own way. We wanted him to be happy. We shouldn't let the way we react to his death destroy us."

"Maybe I'm destroyed already." He sounded terrible . . . helpless as a lost child.

He left the bedroom. I lay there in the shade-darkened room listening to the chatter of the jays around the feeders and felt ice forming in my limbs. Fifteen minutes ago, making love, I'd been glowing. Now I was cold. I had to get under the covers.

Dan returned with another drink in his hand. He was wearing a gray silk *happi* coat that the secretaries had given him on his last birthday, his fifty-first. He sat on the beige boudoir chair, shook the glass slightly to let the cubes dissolve in the alcohol. The motions of a practiced drinker.

"I wonder if we can ever be honest with each other again," he said.

My voice struggled to make itself heard. "I . . . I'm beginning to wonder too."

Influenced by the bourbon, he began to talk in a meandering way—a neighbor's son in medical school at Columbia, a friend's son finishing at Amherst where he had played three sports, a boy we knew at the racquet club who had just landed a big job with IBM . . .

Invidious comparisons with the son he'd lost.

"Then maybe we've come to the end of the line, Helen. I didn't want it this way."

"I love you, Dan. It won't be easy."

He coughed. "I love you, too. But when the boy died, I think I lost some of my capacity for love."

"You never should have written that letter."

He set the glass down on the end table, buried his head in his hands and cried softly. I came to him and stroked his hair.

In the fading light with the birds chirping outside, a breeze rustling the lindens and red oaks, I had another of those shivery memories of Jack, the kind of evocation of the past that is so full of lost moments, treasured pictures. As if it were a photograph or a drawing, something I could stare at, marvel over, experience the sadness and the joy at the same time . . .

He was six or seven. A timid boy. I was glad he had an older sister rather than a brother. I always felt an older brother might have been mean to him. There was no aggressiveness in Jack, not a hint of cruelty or guile. Beth was good to him. It was a warm spring day, late May, with the temperature in the eighties. After dinner Jack had gone wandering around the lawn, looking for a lost rubber ball. To his delight, he had discovered a fledgling, fallen or pushed from the nest by the mother, sent into a world of predators to fend for itself. And it seemed to be hurt, flopping, making pitiful efforts to fly. It was, Dan said, a baby starling.

Jack picked up the injured bird and brought it into the house. I was in the bedroom putting up my hair and dabbing on makeup—Dan and I were going to the club for dinner—when I saw Jack standing in the doorway. He was wearing shorty pajamas—a loose pullover blouse and droopy shorts. Yellow seersucker. He was cupping the quivering bird in his pudgy fists, and the fledgling, seeming to understand it was in caring hands, had hooked its spidery feet to the yoke of his pajama shirt. It was making plaintive cheeps.

"Mommy," Jack said, "I found a little chickie. It was hurt."

There are moments when one's heart is so brimming with happiness, with the blessed awareness of common blood, that it makes one dizzy, transported from this hard earth to some other sphere of consciousness. (I think at that moment, as I look back, I knew what Beth and her husband mean by transcendental states of being.)

I patted the bird. I told Jack he'd done a kind thing in finding it, and that we'd go to the Old Surrey Nature Center and see if they would take it. We put it in a shoebox overnight, punching holes in the lid.

"Don't hurt it, mommy," Jack kept saying, "don't push the knife too deep."

The next day I drove Jack and his starling to the nature center. Well, life is full of unexpected defeats, even when one is six years old. They must hurt terribly at that age, when one sees the world as good and kind, and where unhappiness is a bruised knee or a lost kite.

The woman at the nature center, a white-haired, officious woman, told us that they made it a rule *not* to accept fledglings or injured birds. It would be a disservice to the "balance of nature," she explained.

"You see," she said, "the mother shoves them out. They have to fly or perish. It is nature's way of assuring that the strongest of the species survive. Therefore my advice to you is to return the bird to where you found it and let it take its chances."

I wanted to say, *It won't survive.* A cat or a jay would surely find it. But I merely nodded my head.

We drove home. Jack kept asking me why they couldn't take his chickie and make it all better—the way the doctor made him all better, or the way his daddy had gotten all better after his operation. *Or maybe we could keep it in a cage, mommy,* he kept saying.

It took some evasions on my part to keep him from bursting into tears. We let the bird loose in a thicket some distance from the house. The last we saw of it, it was floundering in the brush, making unsuccessful attempts to fly.

Of course, we never saw it again. And Jack never mentioned it again.

## *Dr. David Schless*

I keep the transcript of the trial in my study. All twelve volumes. Rita gets annoyed with me for poring over them two or three nights a week. She says I'm exhausted enough from the long hours on my feet at the office, and that I should start playing golf regularly, swim every day at the YMCA. Hell, I tell her, my anger keeps me healthy.

We've made preparations to fly to Joshua a day before the weekend events start. I want to spend some time with the organizers of the faculty Committee for Justice, Tom Finnegan and Harriet Blochman. Rita isn't too thrilled with the idea. Joshua gives her the creeps. Who can blame her?

Although I had sat through the entire trial, I'd forgotten some of the choice morsels. Like the business about the sniper. And here it is, in cold print.

You may recall that all policemen accused of firing weapons claimed they heard sniper fire before they started blasting the students. They swore to it under oath, before the state grand jury, before the federal grand jury and in court.

Yet no sniper bullets were ever found. No sniper was ever seen anywhere, not in the campus buildings, on ground level, on a roof, from a car. Zero. Zilch. Expert analysis of the tapes of the firing and the fifteen minutes surrounding it disclosed no shots of any kind prior to the shootings.

It's gotten so that three years after the trial I can't believe what I'm reading. Merritt Winnington, the chief defense lawyer, kept this sniper horseshit going for *hours* in front of the jury, in spite of objections by the prosecutor. Every time Kalt tried to contest Winnington, old Frankendorf stopped him in his tracks.

*Sniper!* It was an out-and-out lie. Same variety of lie as the gun Kazinski said he found on Jack Christopher. Another bald lie. But time and time again, the defendants mentioned the sniper. I'm convinced the jury believed them. *Hell, yes, one of those foul-mouthed kids fired a weapon! Did the troopers have any choice but to shoot back? Isn't that what law and order is all about?*

At one point Dennis Boyle, the youngest of the cops, admitted under cross-examination that maybe he heard no shot. All six of the troopers admitted that they *saw* no sniper at any time. But the judge and the defense lawyers knew how to cut the cross-examination short, block any attempt to follow up the line of questioning. And finally Frankendorf told the jury to ignore the tape recording and to disregard our expert witness's interpretation of it.

Rita came into the study. She put her arms around me, kissed the top of my head. We stared at the photograph of Andrea smiling, full of life and ambition.

"Should I pack for you?" Rita asked. "Anything special you want to take along?"

"Packing already?" I asked.

"You know me, always a day ahead. It's liable to be hot down there. Summer suits and short-sleeved shirts?"

"Yeah," I said. "And my outrage."

"I'm worried that you'll be angry all your life. That's why you don't cry."

I kissed her arms and her cheek. "It keeps me going."

On the plane I noticed a dark, chunky guy—maybe thirty or so—sitting across the aisle from us reading a magazine called Manifest Destiny. He had a strange look about him—intellectual but rugged. Thick glasses with black frames, a brown jacket so tweedy it looked like it was woven out of twigs, a blunted nose, heavy brows, jutting jaw. I couldn't see his eyes. They were mangled by the lenses. A few times he glanced over at me as if to say something, seemed to think better of it, returned to the magazine.

"Know that guy?" I asked Rita.

"I've seen him on television. Sheck, or Shneck. Something like that. He's one of those new-conservative spokesmen. I think he writes for that magazine."

"Manifest Destiny," I read. "Whose?"

"Oh, you know that crowd," Rita said. "All government is bad except the police and the army. Get government off the backs of the corporations and onto the backs of the muggers."

I wondered what Mr. Sheck, or whatever his name was, was doing coming to Joshua. Maybe to tell the country what most of the people already believed: that my daughter got what she was asking for.

## Colonel Gregory Offitt

Marge got the tickets from the travel agent today. That's fine with me. At first I thought it would be viewed as an act of what—cowardice? Evasion? That is, leaving Joshua during the remembrance, or whatever they plan to call it.

56

But there's no reason in the world we have to make excuses for going to Tucson to see our daughter and our son-in-law and our wonderful grandchildren. Cowardice? I earned a Silver Star and three Purple Hearts when I was a company commander in World War II. I paid my dues in Korea and 'Nam. I never backed away from a fight, never refused to face up to a moral issue, never failed to do what I thought was right and fair.

You can go back and read my instructions to the troopers under my command at Joshua College.

*Weapons will not be aimed unless the intent is to fire them, and then only upon the order of the commanding officer. Weapons will remain unloaded until an order to load is given. Force will be kept to a minimum, and only appropriate force to protect lives and property will be used. In the event of the firing of weapons, such weapons will be sequestered, ammunition recovered, and a full investigation made . . .* And so on. I was always a stickler for details.

I regretted that we had to be summoned to Joshua College. But the local police and the campus cops were undermanned, and I can't blame the governor for his reluctance to call in the National Guard. My men were infinitely better trained than the guardsmen. Mature, competent, not given to panic, capable of handling mobs.

That's why what happened hurts me so much. Not a night passes that I don't fall asleep with images of those dead and wounded young people swarming in my brain. The Christopher boy, crumpled in front of the hedge. Lucy Terragni, her chest a great dark splotch, her arms outthrust, like a young female Christ. The Schless girl, face down, looking as if she were asleep, with her head resting in the crook of her arm.

Life is filled with ironies. I was a commanding officer with a reputation for being sparing of my men. In Germany, in the worse of the fighting, I don't believe I ever foolishly or needlessly sacrificed my soldiers. Things like winter-issue clothing, hot meals, R&R were always paramount in my mind. It's why I respected Ike so much. Enlisted men knew he cared about them. He was not the kind of high-ranking officer who looked upon his lofty position as a way of lording it over others. Just the opposite. He knew that anyone in uniform deserved respect, that the basis of any military command is fairness, decency, concern for others. And discipline, of course. Both in the army and in my last post, commandant of the state police, I tried to keep these precepts in mind.

I went even further. Not only did I insist on fair treatment of my boys, but I insisted that they in turn behave politely, helpfully, always observing the amenities of civilized behavior. That is why the Joshua College affair has so upset me, and why, after a decent interval, I resigned my command. Do not believe the stories that I was under fire. The governor repeatedly asked me to stay on. But my mind was made up. Whatever the reason for that terrible occurrence, I had played a role in it, and I felt it best that I step down.

(The governor knew what it was to feel the fire. Under pressure from certain senators, he agreed to seek the federal grand jury probe. It destroyed his career. From his position as a popular chief executive he quickly fell into disrepute, failed to be renominated by his party and was repudiated by all but a fringe of radicals. I felt it was unfair. He was a decent man and did not deserve political oblivion because of the Joshua Massacre.)

Marge told me about the confirmation of our airline reservations while I was working in the garden. I'd turned the earth over, added topsoil and fertilizer. Tomorrow I'll plant herbs before we leave. Last year we had a bumper crop—sage, marjoram, oregano, rosemary, chives, turmeric and bales of basil. When I was stationed in Italy after the war, Marge and I learned to love Italian cooking. We use a great deal of basil and other spices. I like to cook. After the Joshua business, the few interviews I gave out were conducted in our kitchen. "The Colonel at the Cuisinart" was the title of one newspaper article.

Marge found me mixing the dark topsoil into the pale sandy earth of the garden. Deer flies buzzed around my head and nipped at me. I could hear a mockingbird going wild at the morning sun, chortling his foolish head off. (I know all about mockingbirds. They're fearless and aggressive. Be careful not to get too close to their nests because you'll be dive-bombed. I like all natural creatures, have never enjoyed hunting.)

"You look happy," Marge said.

"Yes, I am. The garden is nice and moist. All the spring rain. We should do well with the vegetables."

She kneeled and kissed me. "Old Ironpants," she said. "They should know you the way I do. A softie."

"I can be tough."

"Don't I know it. I'll phone Laura and tell them it's all set. Five days is better than none. We can go to the Desert Museum and Mount Lemon. I think I'll buy presents for the little ones. Want me to pack for you?"

"No, no. The old campaigner travels light."

I watched my wife leave for the rear door of the house. Her frail figure and her crown of white hair filled me with love. She has stood by me through much trouble. Marge has made this home and all our homes warm, loving places.

I got up, surveyed our two acres of bottomland, the pond in the hazed distance, where the Shawnees used to fish, the low-lying blue-green mountains. Digging in my garden I often find arrowheads. This is as good a place as any to wind up my life. Laura and Hal, my daughter and son-in-law, have often asked us to move to Arizona. I don't think I'd be happy there.

Except lately I've begun to wonder if maybe I'd be better off some distance removed from Joshua. I'm getting sick of crank letters, requests for interviews, innuendo, rumors, raking over of the coals.

Colonel Gregory Offitt, USA, Ret., has nothing to hide. I'm ashamed of nothing I did. Had I not left my men for five minutes to confer with President Cudlipp in his office—that's when the shooting broke out— it's remotely possible I might have prevented the deaths. That is true. By the same token, a field commander cannot be in touch with line soldiers every second. There were forty-two trained troopers out there protecting the administration building. Sergeant Kazinski was a veteran of riot situations. Who could have guessed that a wild shot, some inexplicable breakdown of discipline, would have caused the death and wounding of so many?

Maybe Bates Woffler, dead these past two years, had the right idea. *Don't confuse the major issues. Law and order. The right of society to protect itself. Threats from radical mobs* ... A man like me spends his life dedicated to duty, honor and service. Did Bates do the right thing? I have to think he did. After all, he saw things differently than I did, and he was a persuasive arguer. We really went at it hammer and tongs in his office. I'm glad no one else was present ...

Later, when I'd finished turning over the garden, I went into my study—Marge was napping, she hasn't much energy—and glanced at my file on the Joshua case. For some reason I was thinking of my men, especially the six defendants.

Four were still on the force—Adam Kazinski, the old sarge; Wallace Markland, a quiet fellow; and two younger men, Dennis Boyle, who was taking college courses, and Kevin Case. Two had resigned and had lost contact with me. One was Louis Trippi, who had had some kind of personal problems after the shooting, and the other was Francis Hofheimer. Hofheimer was the one they called "Stub," I guess because he'd once worked as a ticket-taker at county fairs and carnivals. They were the six who'd been indicted and acquitted.

Funny thing, I was always regarded as a close partisan of the six. Well, I was certainly convinced of their innocence, and I did so testify. But *close* to them? I don't think so. There's a gap between enlisted men and officers that must be maintained. This is not a matter of snobbery but one of necessity. For some time I kept in touch with the fellows. But lately I'd been letting those old associations wither. Perhaps that was as it should be. In fact it was only recently that I learned that Lou Trippi and Stub Hofheimer had resigned and left the state.

They were all good men. They were sucked up into a terrible situation. Our police had an excellent record of restraint, community relations, efficient riot control. How this awful thing came about still eludes me. *Damn.* If only I'd been on the portico when the shooting began. (As it happened, my subordinate, Captain Owen Durham, was injured a few minutes before while using the bullhorn, telling the students to disperse. So much for the peaceful intentions of the mob. He was hit in the face by a rock and was getting medical treatment in the parking lot. This left Sergeant Adam Kazinski in command on the porch of the administration building.)

I've heard reports that a committee of parents and the wounded students are trying to bring a civil suit for damages. I have nothing to fear. Did my job, told the truth, informed the media afterward that there was absolutely nothing left to say about the so-called Joshua Massacre.

And my men, the six defendants, Captain Durham, and the other troopers on duty that fateful day (the ones who did not fire) have observed a discreet and manly silence about the events. The courts have had their day and they have found no guilt. I know for a fact that some of the men who were indicted, notably Boyle and Markland, were truly saddened by the deaths, and said so early on. Since then, they and the others have remained silent. And rightly so.

Reporters, investigators and self-appointed crusaders never seem to tire of digging up the Joshua case, refusing to let it die. Don't they have any feelings for my men and their families? Isn't it possible that they too were hurt by the three deaths, that they have been wounded in body and spirit?

## Dr. David Schless

After a cardboard dinner at the Joshua Motor Inn I telephoned Tom Finnegan and confirmed the meeting for tomorrow in the faculty club. Finnegan and the Reverend Al Jensen would co-chair it. Harriet Blochman would be there, as well as most of the wounded kids. Even Wilma Overstreet in her wheelchair. Rita and I were tickled to hear Wilma was engaged to be married. Gutsy girl.

Of the other wounded students, all but Lyle Pulsifer were coming. Lyle was researching a glacier in Alaska. Crazy kid. He'd gone on, after a year of rehab for the bullet in his left knee, to get a master's in geology. A skinny, bushy-haired boy. I had always thought of him as a kind of hippie freak, so I was glad he was on track.

The Terragnis were due Friday night. Joe couldn't take a day off from work. I felt sorry for them. Four more kids to worry about, the grief of Lucy's death, the crap they had had to take from their fellow townspeople in Flagg City. I'd be happy to see them.

What the hell, Rita and I, we're outsiders in many ways. We give money to the NAACP and we backed George McGovern. That makes us red radical atheist secular humanist pinko weirdos. Anything we do is suspect. Joe and Sally Terragni are so American no one can lay a glove on them, I used to say. But they'd been ostracized and punished too. For what? The death of their child?

As yet Finnegan had not heard from Helen Christopher. When he'd last talked to her, she was dubious about coming. Dan didn't approve. Poor guy, half-stewed all the time. Any man who wrote the kind of letter he did about his own son has to live under a cloud. Or in Christopher's case, inside a bottle.

I guess Helen feels she has to prop him up. *She* is quite a dame, if ever she could get over her shyness, that apologetic manner. Rita and I've always felt she's a woman of intelligence and courage, except she's had to put up with that pickled herring, encourage him, tell him he's great, worry about his next promotion. No wonder their daughter has a guru.

Anyway, we'd had our Sanka and I was about to start stoking my pipe when I saw this tweedy fellow, Arnold Shreck, sitting across from us in the restaurant and sort of smiling at me. He'd been on the plane with us.

"Good evening," he said.

We greeted him. He got up.

"You folks look familiar," he said. "May I join you?"

"Sure," Rita said. "We can have another Sanka."

Shreck came to our table. He was husky and moved like an athlete. I guessed he must have boxed when he was younger. The flattened nose and the gait, the corded hands.

And he was surely Jewish, all of which gave me a favorable first impression. Jews should learn to fight with their hands, stay in tip-top physical condition, cultivate athletics and athletes. *And know when to hit back.* Like I've said, all this eternal blubbering and lamentation and asking the *goyishe* world for sympathy doesn't mean doodly. Knowing how to box, how to stuff a basketball, drive a golf ball, throw a block —these are important. You think I'm kidding, that I'm naive? I was chairman of our local B'nai B'rith Sports Lodge, and I know what gentiles think is important.

I'll go further. Do you know what keeps the true bigots, the Kluxers and the killers, from getting the upper hand, what prevents the gun-carrying assholes, the professional racists from running America? *Black athletes.* That's right. God bless them all—the heavy dudes, the main men, the slam-dunkers, the hotdogs, the Hank Aarons and Moses Malones and Earl Campbells. You can't wipe out a people who produce such exemplars of what America loves. Nor can you create native fascism with black jocks on TV every night.

Same with Jews. No better image of Jews was ever projected than the one presented by the Israeli army after the Six Day War. No amount of weeping, wailing, breast-beating, praying, all the brotherhood conferences in the world, all the Holocaust remembrances didn't mean a thing compared to what Moshe Dayan did to those Arab *mamzerim.* And the rest of the world *loved* it . . .

"I've seen you on television," Rita was saying. "On William Buckley, right? And on the David Brinkley Show? You're the writer—"

"Arnold Shreck."

I shook his hand. We introduced ourselves.

"New Right," I said. "Neoconservative. I've never met one of you guys up close. I must say, you've really shaken things up."

Shreck must have realized we were the parents of one of the Joshua Three, but it didn't embarrass him.

"I hope you won't consider me in the enemy camp," he said. He had a loud, gravelly voice. I learned later he lectured a great deal and taught a course in Modern Ethics at St. Elmo's College in Newark.

"I can guess where you stand," I said. "Mr. Shreck, I don't mess around. I'm no intellectual. One word about Andrea—"

He smiled. "Give me more credit than that. Have you read what I've written about Joshua College?"

"No."

Rita said she hadn't either. But she could not imagine that an intellectual like Arnold Shreck would possibly side with the authorities.

"It's not a question of siding with *anyone*," Shreck said. "I am in sympathy with you both. And with the other parents. I think it shameful that you lost a child. That the Terragni girl and the Christopher boy had to pay with their lives because of the manipulation of radical terrorists, connivers who needed a cause and egged your daughter on —no, no, please don't interrupt . . ."

I had to hand it to him. Damn few people can tell me not to interrupt and get away with it. But there was a sort of hypnotic fascination about this right-wing character, and I had to listen. Never saw myself as a rabbit paralyzed by a cobra, but there I was. Rita looked upset.

"Hear me out. I've researched the case. Your daughter was a splendid young woman. Mildly liberal, perhaps radical on a few issues. But hardly an agitator. She wanted to work with emotionally disturbed children, had a boyfriend, loved nature. A wonderful girl. Why in heaven's name should she try to storm the college president's office? Or hurl curses and stones at policemen who were doing nothing more than their jobs? Protecting lives, property, the fabric of society?"

"Is that an excuse for murder?" I asked. My fists were clenching. I wondered about him. As tough as he looked?

"No. Not at all. I believe in dissent. I believe in free speech. But others do not."

"Like the cops? The courts?"

Rita kicked me under the table. She could see my neck turning scarlet. I figured Shreck was in his thirties and in good shape.

"One of my colleagues researched the Joshua College matter," he said. "There is no doubt that for six months before the riots, a cadre of extreme left activists, a mix of Black Panthers, Weathermen and other revolutionary groups, occupied a house near the campus and were working secretly to cause an eruption of violence in the spring. We have their names, their backgrounds, and we know precisely how they arranged to get innocents like your daughter and others involved and—"

"You goddamn idiot," I shouted. A waitress dropped an armload of plates. Diners turned to stare at me.

"Dave, Dave," Rita said. "Let's leave. There's no point to all of this."

"Yes there is. I know all about the secret house. I know all about those left freaks on campus. Did you know that not a *single* one of them ever turned up at the riots? That neither the FBI, nor the prosecutors, nor anyone involved in the investigation found the remotest connection between the radicals and the riots? The riots started after a beer party at a fraternity house when the campus cops beat up a jock. The jocks started it. Someone burned down an old prefab and more cops came on campus. Heads got cracked and the kids went wild. It's a tradition on college campuses. Cops show up, kids riot. Then it escalates. It was no more a political act than the Pillsbury Bake-Off, except for some hollering about the rise of tuition."

"You are naive, doctor. It's precisely what the agitators wanted. A seemingly innocent event. Martyrs. A cause. Well, they got it. But it backfired. It aroused the country against liberalism, and in favor of tough police methods. No wonder the government lost its case. Dr. Schless, I'm on your side. I mourn with you—"

My fuse is a short one. I suppose all the hostility I've saved up over rotten teeth, implants, root canal work, all the stuff I really hate doing because I wanted to be a radiologist but couldn't get into medical school, all these resentments make me boil over quickly.

"I would hope you and I could be friends someday. That out of this understandable anger we can reach understanding. You should be on our side—"

The fuse blew. "*Your* side? What the hell is your side? Ass-kissing the bigots? Taking it out on blacks and Hispanics, so *your* hide will be safe when *Der Tag* comes? Shreck, do you think the chairman of the board of General Motors or the president of Dupont sleeps more soundly at night knowing that Arnie Shreck and all the other right-wing Jewish hotshots have told him that they're good Joes, that anything they do is nitsy so long as they don't hate Jews? You *jerk*. I'm no radical. I'm no communist. But I see what you guys are up to. I can see you and all your pals hidden in a secret room in William F. Buckley's Jacuzzi, while the stormtroopers parade up and down the street looking for you. Oh, you're so pure and conservative! You hate Mrs. Roosevelt and affirmative action and busing and you think school prayer is okay and abortion is murder. So you'll be spared in the new Christian America—"

"That isn't funny, doctor."

"Dave, I want to go," Rita said.

"I'm not finished. Peddling his reactionary horseshit so he can score points with the future fascists of America. The funny thing is, you may be right. You may just be able to save us. Maybe I owe you a vote of thanks. You've pressed the right buttons. One says *black*. One says *liberal*. Deflect the hatred from us Jews—look, look, we're okay, we hate quotas and Martin Luther King and street crime and we're all for your Christian prayers and your born-agains, and let it land where it usually does, on the *schvarzers* . . . But I tell you this, Schreck, the day that the majority gets *bored* with dumping on Afro-Americans and wants more blood, they may decide *I'm* next. Oh, not you, of course. You hate commies and long-haired kids and rock music and teenage sex and street crime and faggots. You're so pure and anticommunist, no one could possibly want to stick you in a concentration camp in Alaska."

Shreck got up. Behind the thick lenses he looked pale. The sallow skin was splotched. Maybe he had high blood pressure. But he was a big bastard, heavy in the chest, thick in the thighs.

"I misjudged you," Arnold Shreck said. "I thought you and I might have agreed upon aspects of this tragedy. I can see that the loss of your daughter has made you irrational and that nothing I can say will make you understand."

Moving slowly, faking old age, I got up too. And I hit him as hard as I could. I'd learned years ago, on the streets in Brooklyn, that when you want to surprise a guy, never throw a roundhouse punch. Keep it short, fast. No more than eight or ten inches.

Rita screamed. It was so charmingly dark in the restaurant that only a few people saw what happened. Shreck went ass-over-teakettle into an unoccupied booth, hitting the table and pawing the air.

The manager, a squirt with a waxed mustache, came running over to inquire if anything was wrong. By then Shreck was sitting up in the booth, mulling over his neoconservatism. I'd belted him in the sweet spot, under the sternum and above the *kishkas.*

Rita was dragging me away. She was furious. "Dave, Dave, you're not a kid anymore . . ."

Shreck did not hit back. He weighed his words and patted his jacket. I guess he was making sure all the twigs were in place. "Dr. Schless, that was a stupid act. I will charge it to your emotional state. You suffered a terrible loss. I don't think I can discuss the matter with you again."

I told him he'd be well advised to keep his theorizing to himself, at least around me. "Listen, Arnold," I said, "reserve your political opinions for all those terrible people that are threatening you. Welfare queens, homosexuals, busing advocates, nuclear freeze bishops and conservationists. But lay off my daughter, understand?"

"Someday," he said ominously, as the manager performed little dance steps around me, "someday you will see that I'm right."

Outside the restaurant, en route to our room, Rita gave me hell. Crying, trembling, she said that if I couldn't control my temper she'd leave.

Rita fell into a deep Tranxene-aided slumber. I sat up in a hard chair and began to wonder if maybe Arnold Shreck and other fellas who have joined him in his crusade to keep America safe from long hair and pot and food stamps and gays had something on the ball.

In some screwy way, they may be right. Not that I agree with their ideas. But suppose the country goes crazy? Suppose some kind of fascism takes over? Suppose the worst elements on the right get the upper hand, or at least are in a position to challenge the authorities— the government, the courts, the whole tradition? Wouldn't it be a good idea, a bit of insurance, for Jews to say—look, look at *us,* we're very conservative, we hate gun control, we love school prayer, we want to keep blacks in their place, we want bigger nuclear bombs to blast the commies, we want everything you want? Just lay off *us*. We're Jews, get it, but we're also like you.

Would that be the scenario that Arnold Shreck and his pals, at three o'clock in the morning, envision? And what if they're right and I'm wrong?

## *Helen Christopher*

Tom and Judy Finnegan met me at the airport in Flagg City. Joshua has no commercial airport, just a private landing strip. Flagg City has heavy industry—a ball-bearing plant, a rolling mill. It's a rough town, peopled largely by European ethnics and migrants from the hill country to the south. Many of the local police in Joshua and many of the state police come from Flagg City.

I was cheered by the sight of Finnegan's bearlike figure and his bristling red beard. Judy looked like one of his children, tiny, dark, carrying their newest addition (Brian? Cullen?) in a knapsacklike sling. Three other Finnegan children and a mixed retriever occupied the rear of their rusty station wagon.

Tom kissed me and Judy introduced the fat baby as Kevin. I thought they had already had a Kevin, but I was wrong.

"God, Helen, we're happy you made it," Tom said. He took my flowery print bag and hefted it into the rear amid the children and the dog. "Who could ever call Helen Christopher a radical trouble-maker?"

I sat up front with Tom. Judy nestled into the rear seat, popped out a white breast and fed Kevin, who sucked contentedly.

Finnegan left the airport and turned onto the interstate that led to Joshua. I noticed that the smoke stacks of the rolling mill were idle.

"Yeah, the recession is still here," Tom said. "The Japs are giving them fits. Joe Terragni says the plant's been a loser for a long time. Obsolete machinery. They're talking about some new high-tech facto-ries, but so far it's only talk."

Flagg City with its smoke-stained brick walls was light years removed from the loveliness of Old Surrey. Beth says Old Surrey looks like a stage set, a town built for a movie.

"It doesn't help us to have the nearby industrial center full of anger," Tom said. "These people don't want to be reminded about Joshua. They've got other things on their mind. Like jobs, food, rent money, hospital bills."

"Does it matter whether they're sympathetic to us or not?" I asked. "Suppose you and Al Jensen took another new poll. Suppose you found that fifty percent of the local people now feel that the killings were unjustified—"

"Never happen, Helen."

"Well, suppose it did. What would it mean?"

Judy hefted the baby. "It would mean we'd have a much better atmosphere for the civil suit."

"Dan says there won't be any," I said. "He says Dave Schless is dreaming. There's no way the Supreme Court will let us sue state personnel as individuals. It's never been done."

Finnegan said, "Yes, Dave is optimistic, but Brian Dooley, our new lawyer, is a tiger. He won't roll over like the feds. They saw which way the wind blew. Their case was a strong one, but they took a lot of crap from Frankendorf and didn't fight too hard. No reversal, no new trial, *nada.*"

It had been a short flight from New York to Flagg City but I was exhausted. My nerves were taut. Dan had taken an early train, making sure to kiss me before leaving. He told me he loved me and assured me that even though he didn't want me to go to Joshua, he'd respect my decision. His stiff tolerance made me feel guilty, and worried me.

Tom began to talk now about the program—a meeting tonight, the press conference tomorrow, the workshops, the sessions with local officials, students, perhaps police representatives, everything leading to the all-night vigil at the site—but my mind wandered.

The truth was I was terrified at the thought of divorce. For all the problems Dan and I had, I sensed I would be unhappy without him. I saw myself in a one-bedroom apartment on the edge of town, forced to go back to the daily chores of classroom teaching.

To be honest, teaching had been wearing me down, especially after the loss of Jack. Facing those TV-benumbed, unhearing tenth-graders was getting to be more than I could stand. It seemed that every term there were less good students, more dull-eyed, disruptive ones. I think

I was conscientious and dedicated, forever looking for ways to pique their interest, but with little to show for it. Reaching them took more than my talents as a teacher, I'm afraid.

No, I did not want to be a divorced woman. I saw myself growing heavy, hair graying, yearning for the companionship of a man. Dan, for all his faults, had shared a great deal with me. I could not imagine a life without him, or the loneliness . . . I don't make friends so easily. I am not a flirt. And despite my "good looks," I have never used them to attract men. If anything, I downplay them . . .

"Yeah, it should be a worthwhile experience," Finnegan was saying.

"I hope so," I said. My voice had little conviction.

" 'Those who forget the past,' " Judy said, as she separated a small boy from the dog whose ear he was twisting, " 'are doomed to repeat it.' Who said that, Tom?"

"Santayana. But the bad guys don't forget the past. They learn from it. They can be bad all over again, maybe improve their act. And if victims remember the past, too often there's damn little they can do to change things. The Jews knew all abut persecution. A couple of thousand years of it. But memories didn't save them when the SS came around. Hitler and Himmler sure as hell remembered the past and they didn't feel at all doomed. The past taught them. It isn't a question of remembering, it's a question of acting. If you don't act, if you don't have a game plan, you just may be next."

Tom's field of sociology is often characterized by double-talk, abstractions and what his old professor at Columbia Graduate School, William C. Casey, referred to as "Y" language—language that obscures, says nothing. Finnegan was not a dealer in "Y" language. He dealt in Casey's "X" language—*a-square plus b-square equals c-square.*

"Wouldn't it be great if we got big national coverage?" Tom asked. "We could get Cudlipp so wound up, he'd okay a memorial statue. Better yet, suppose something came out of this that helped Dave Schless get his show on the road?"

"It could work the other way," I said. "Get everyone angry again, all the old hatreds. Isn't it true that there was some kind of pact among the police and the state's attorney and the college officials never to discuss the case again? They won't even give interviews."

"But there are also laws that have to be obeyed. The whole country isn't Joshua."

I hoped not.

We'd left the shabby outskirts of Flagg City—pea-green trailers where people made their homes next to patches of hardscrabble farmland—and climbed to the foothills where Joshua nestled.

I was glad Tom did not cross the campus. It would be an effort for me to look at the red brick buildings with their green copper roofs, the maples and hemlocks and tulip trees, the white columns of the administration building and the stretch of lawn in front of it, where my son was killed.

Mercifully, he went right to his home, where I was plunged into the chaotic Finnegan scene—two more dogs, several cats, jam-smeared children, an older boy slamming tennis balls against a garage door, a weed-choked lawn.

At night, after too much chianti and too much talk at dinner—Harriet Blochman, Tom's co-chairman, was present—I was troubled and sleepless in the "guest" bedroom . . . one of the older boys had been dispossessed to make room for me. I made my mind up to move to the Joshua Motor Inn the next day. Dan, who had never stayed overnight at the Finnegans but had visited there, had observed that every available horizontal space was covered with eight to twelve unrelated objects. "Don't ever put a toothbrush down in the john," he said. "You'll never find it again."

I missed Dan. Grouchy, gloomy, he was still someone I knew better than anyone in the world. Uneasiness at being without him, out of Old Surrey, kept me awake throughout most of the night. I tried listening to a radio on the night table, but could get only country music and evangelists.

## Colonel Gregory Offitt

See by the papers and the local TV news that they're arriving already. Dr. Schless and his wife. The Italian couple from Flagg City, nice people, I feel especially sorry for them. The mother of the Christopher boy. And the wounded ones.

I never looked on them as enemies. Some of my troopers could have been their fathers, some were almost young enough to have been students. Dennis Boyle had attended Joshua. The day doesn't go by that I don't think of that tragic accident. Some of the more irresponsible members of the press tried to depict me as some kind of bloodthirsty monster, aching to shoot down students. Nonsense. Marge and I thought of suing a TV station at one time, then thought it best to let the whole thing run its course. Never explain, never apologize, that's my belief.

I'd finished packing for our trip to Tucson when the phone rang.

What I especially enjoyed was arranging my camera bag—the Nikon for color film, the Pentax for black-and-white, rolls of film, my set of lenses, filters and so on. I use an exposure meter after all these years of built-in meters. I find I get more accurate readings with it, rather than with the electronic hocus-pocus of the new cameras.

(Maybe that's why I had studied the photographs with a professional eye. In private moments I'm forced to admit that the photographs tell a damning story. But only part of the story. A photograph is not the ultimate truth. It's a one-dimensional reflection of a moment, nothing more.)

To my astonishment it was Professor Blochman calling me. That would be Professor Harriet Blochman of the Joshua College department of mathematics. I'd never exchanged a word with her. She's a skinny spinster. Graying hair, long sad face, an activist on campus and, along with Finnegan, one of the people who are intent on keeping the issue alive. I was sorry Marge was in the garden and hadn't taken the call. She'd have gotten rid of her.

She was, it turned out, extremely polite. Amazing the way all these people who defended the "rights" of students to indulge in atrocious acts of violence, to use the foulest language, to scream with hate and rage at others now find it expedient to speak politely and weigh their words. Once or twice I've chatted with the Reverend Alvord Jensen. The man is the essence of civility. I wonder how he—and this Blochman woman—continue to excuse the behavior of those they seek to defend.

I was stunned. Professor Blochman wanted *me* to participate in the conference and to chair one of the "workshops." They would have present a police chief from a New England city, and a chap from, of all places, Singapore, who was an authority on "riot control." As if I needed to be lectured to. Her audacity rendered me speechless. I had darn near been a *defendant* myself. Only pressure from the attorney general's office in Washington had kept federal prosecutors from indicting me. The Lord knows what went on inside that federal grand jury.

Then I recalled that Harriet Blochman herself had been indicted by the state grand jury. If it hadn't been for Judge Althouse, *she'd* have been in the dock. You'll recall the burning of the state grand jury findings, and the bawling out that Bates Woffler took from the judge.

It did not surprise me—I've a considerable reserve of self-control tested under fire—that I was polite to Blochman.

I believe I mentioned that she's a mathematician. She got right to the point. No long speeches. Of course I replied in the negative.

"I see," she said. "You won't participate?"

"I'm leaving Saturday for Tucson."

"That's too bad. If I may be candid, Colonel Offitt, many of us thought you could add balance to the program."

"How should I take that word *balance?*"

Professor Blochman laughed. "We wanted the view of a law enforcement officer, and you've always seemed to have maintained a level and fair view of the event."

"Level and fair . . . Yes, I believe I did . . ."

"You never made charges about a radical-led mob goaded on by outsiders. And the shootings took place while you were in conference with President Cudlipp. Nothing you said indicated you condoned the shooting."

"I did not condone," I said carefully, "but I also did not *condemn*. My men were justified. Now, if you'll excuse me, Professor Blochman . . ."

But she was not to be put off. If I was leaving Saturday, perhaps she could meet with me for lunch today? Discussion that involved me might come up at the conference. It might be useful, and fair to me, if I gave her my updated view of the Joshua College affair. And would I mind if Dr. Schless and his wife and Mrs. Christopher met with me at lunch?

I still don't know exactly what got into me. Common sense, of course, dictated that I rebuff her. Reviewing my acquiescence (after that odd luncheon), I think it may have been the mention of Schless that piqued my interest. Something about the man had earlier aroused my admiration, though not without qualification. He *had* lost a daughter, an only child, apparently a talented and very pretty young lady. Sad. Terribly sad. But he did not take it lying down. He was a fighter. He had intestinal fortitude, no question. I knew the story about his confrontation with a gang of armed vigilantes, and I had to respect him for it. I must say I've often found this kind of courage in Jews. God knows they have had reasons for developing it over the centuries. I had Jewish officers and enlisted men under me in World War II and they were good soldiers. My exec—before he was blown apart by a land mine outside Aachen—was Hal Epstein. A better officer never served in the Twenty-ninth Division.

At any rate, I told Harriet Blochman I'd meet her in a rear booth at Ricci's at one. And I told Marge a white lie. I said I'd be doing some last-minute shopping at the Joshua Mall and that I'd finish packing when I got back.

## Dr. David Schless

Rita was in better shape this morning. So was I. It isn't easy coming back here. We can handle Andrea's death by now. Well, almost. But the notion that damn near everyone in this town welcomed it, cheered when they got the news . . . Maybe I'm a masochist at heart. I was sorry

I'd socked that schmuck writer the night before. No, I wasn't. I was sorry I'd upset Rita.

We drove around the campus for about a half hour. Seemed to us the kids had changed. Subdued, soberly dressed. A marked absence of long-haired boys and short-haired girls. No crazy Indian costumes, no beads, headbands, tattered cutoffs. They looked vaguely preppy. Sweaters, slacks and saddle shoes. The fifties were making a comeback.

Finnegan had told us the students were apolitical. No racial overtones. There never were many blacks at Joshua, and there are even fewer now. The smart black kids get scholarships to places like Amherst and Columbia. The average-smart ones go to state universities. Joshua's few blacks were always a quiet group. When all hell broke loose five years ago there wasn't a black face among the demonstrators. Not *one.* They knew. The brothers had gotten the message. When you see the fuzz, split. They did, and they weren't touched. Who could blame them?

Tom says his students don't care all that much about nuclear disarmament, or Central America, or ecology, or the decay of the big cities. They tend to be conservative or indifferent. Biggest political organization on campus? Young Americans for Conservatism. A lot of them oppose busing, advocate school prayer and would like us to invade Cuba. Funny the way things go.

The campus looked lovely—bright green trees and hedges, the fine old brick buildings, the new gymnasium and stadium. And that stretch of flawless lawn—someone said it was like the century-old turf of England—in between the president's office, a Federal-style mansion, and the round pantheon-type curiosity, Dexter Hall.

"Where she fell," Rita said. She didn't cry.

We stared at the seamless undulating lawn, bordered with pin oaks and red maples. There was a small baroque fountain, a grotesque bronze monstrosity depicting dolphins and a bearded water god spouting streams, halfway between Dexter and the administration building. It was in front of this fountain that the students had made their furthest advance. Well, not really an advance. More like a ragged skirmish line. No leaders, no organization, no plan. They threw stones and bricks. Then cursed and chanted.

I stared at it again. Hard to believe. It was three hundred feet from the fountain to the portico of President Cudlipp's office. Three hundred feet! Where was the swarming, charging mob that was about to over-whelm the cops? The facts had become irrelevant. Hatred and fear had ruled, buried our evidence.

But not forever, if Dr. Dave Schless had his way.

"Right there," Rita said, pointing. "There's a little outcropping of rocks next to that big oak tree. She was hit there."

I blinked at the site. Morning sunlight edged the leaves and the brown-gray trunk with a rim of gold. A handsome old tree. Birds fluttered in the upper branches. I caught the red flash of a cardinal and heard the scolding of jays.

"A clear menace to society," I said. "A clear and present danger. One nineteen-year-old girl who threw a rock. And a bullet through the lungs and the aorta."

"Stop, Dave."

"It helps me to spit it out."

I held her hand. She was cold. She turned her head away from the tree, the lawn, the scene of green perfection.

"I can't face that man," she said. "I don't want to have lunch with him."

"You sure? He's the only one who ever said he was sorry—"

"To save his neck. Dave, I'm not as strong as you are. I'm not up to it."

I wouldn't force my will on Rita. I love her. We need each other more than ever with Andrea gone. Sometimes I think she can't tolerate my obsession with the case. Once after I'd spent a whole day and part of the night on the phone, hounding editors, bawling out Brian Dooley, busting my back trying to get the civil suit off dead center, she had hysterics.

"Dave, let it rest. I can't handle it. It's me . . . or that damned trial. You know what they told us. We'd never win it . . . we can't win it."

She almost convinced me. Almost. By God, someone will answer for murdering my child.

You could have knocked me down with a pipe cleaner when Harriet told me that Offitt had agreed to meet with the enemy.

I dropped Rita off at the motel. She said she'd read and watch TV until the meeting this afternoon at the faculty club. Meanwhile, I'd go to lunch with Harriet Blochman and Colonel Offitt. As far as I was concerned, Offitt was the key to the case. Or at least a key that could open a door leading to other doors. Dooley had been insisting all along that Offitt knew something, something he'd hidden. Of course it could all have been latrine rumor. (Both sides had plenty of that, except that *theirs* were accepted by the public. Did you know that a story circulated around Joshua that our daughter was a notorious lesbian, and that she had scribbled notes about assassination attempts on public figures who had opposed the Equal Rights Amendment? That showed up in some "conservative" rag. My letter to the editor never made it into print. They wanted it both ways, these infernal bastards. Andrea was a lesbian, *and* she was rumored to be pregnant.)

Downtown Joshua had changed. It used to be one long street of wood-framed stores—Karlinsky's Jewelers, Fein's Hardware, numerous bars and pizza joints, DeNardo's Tailoring and Dry Cleaners. A crumbling movie house, the Joshua Showcase, was now a Publix supermarket. They were still there but they looked seedy, except for the supermarket. I soon saw the reason. At the traffic light marking the intersection of College Avenue and Washington Street (Washington Street was a state highway, 119 North and South), several blocks had been cleared and turned into a vast shopping mall.

It was enormous. I wondered how a college town with little industry was able to support it. But it seemed to be thriving. A Sears, a local department store, boutiques, a gourmet shop and a "communications plaza" with three theaters and a huge video-computer-appliance store. The plaza—stark concrete blocks and much glass—also housed the offices of the local radio station, KJOS, and the afternoon paper, the Joshua *Clarion-Ledger*. The mall was modern and spotless, and to judge by the afternoon crowds, enormously popular. I felt sorry for old merchants like DeNardo and Fein, who were surely hurting. Five years ago the poor guys had seen their stores trashed by a mob of wild kids (no, I never approved of that kind of outrageous behavior) and now they were being phased out by shops selling quiche and poster art, places dealing in designer jeans and a video arcade, where kids could numb their brains with mindless games.

Ricci's was located in a cul-de-sac at one end of the mall. A discreet red neon sign in a beige-curtained window. It was a step up from the old pizza parlor and greasy spoons that had been favored when Andrea attended Joshua. Glancing at the menu in an illuminated wooden box, I could see why students might avoid it. Cheap, it wasn't. And who

76

could believe that Mr. Ricci, whoever he was, could really generate a legit *veal cordon bleu* or *pesto genovese?*

I was led to our booth by a ravishingly beautiful dark girl with an Italian accent. Mrs. Ricci? The usual decor, imitation dark grained wood (plastic) and imitation red leather booths and banquettes (vinyl). It was even darker than the motel restaurant where I'd belted Arnold Shreck last night. My knuckles still hurt.

Harriet Blochman and Helen Christopher were seated on one banquette facing Offitt. All three looked like they wished they were somewhere else. Of course, Helen is so controlled and discreet that it was hard to tell. Except for a slight vertical crease in the middle of her lovely forehead, she is a marvelous-looking woman—naturally curly light brown hair, small firm features, blue eyes. And a serenity overall. The mouth gives something away. It's sensual, lips slightly parted . . .

Harriet, as plain as the binomial theorem, was her usual drab, determined self. As for the colonel, he already seemed sorry he'd come to confront his old enemies. I wondered what had changed his mind.

I was also surprised Helen was there. That morning I had to plead, damn near threaten her to get her to agree. She said she had no stomach for seeing Offitt. True, he had not pulled the trigger that killed Jack, but his men had. And he had defended them. What was his quote after the trial? "The system works," Offitt had said. "The trial proved my men were innocent."

How in God's name, Helen had asked me over the phone, could I possibly sit near that man? Believe me, it took some of Schless's best arm-twisting to get her to agree. I explained that Offitt would be more susceptible to someone like her. I was a loudmouthed dentist. Harriet was an old maid. We were both, let's face it, Jewish. (Not that the colonel was a prejudiced man. I'd researched him. But I had to use everything on Helen.)

They were indeed a frosty threesome. Harriet is by nature taciturn and prim. Helen was all but shrinking against the maroon vinyl of the booth to get as far away from Offitt as possible. The colonel was trying to be cordial, relaxed in a tweedy jacket and shades. He was a good-looking man, younger in appearance than his sixty-odd years. I continued to wonder why he'd agreed to meet with us. I had a random thought. Could it be he remembered what a beautiful woman Helen Christopher was?

I greeted the ladies and extended my hand to Offitt. He rose, gave me a hearty handshake and allowed as how he of course knew me but didn't recall being formally introduced. I sat next to him. Harriet was seated opposite him, and Helen was opposite me. Her eyes kept darting toward the kitchen door, the bar, across the aisle—seemingly anything to avoid Offitt's gaze.

Myself, I was curious about him. Lean, fit, polite, soft-spoken. A guy with a distinguished combat record. A well-regarded commander of the state police. Under tough cross-examining by Walter Kalt, he couldn't be shaken. He handled himself so well that there were times when he seemed annoyed by Judge Frankendorf's intervention in his behalf or Merritt Winnington's crudities. I could swear Offitt had winced when Winnington needled Kalt as "one of those smart New York lawyers." (Translation: *Jew.* Kalt, in fact, was a Lutheran).

Offitt was working on a vodka-tonic. I ordered a Heineken. The women were sipping iced tea.

"You'll forgive me if I don't feel at ease with you," Offitt said. "And I will understand if you, doctor, and Mrs. Christopher aren't especially friendly toward me."

Helen said nothing. I gave a noncommittal shrug.

"I'm really not certain as to why Professor Blochman invited me to this lunch," he went on. He was not put off by our failure to respond. He hardly expected us to kiss him.

"Colonel, we would like you to participate in the workshop on police-community relations," Harriet said. "I wanted Mrs. Christopher and Dr. Schless here to try to convince you there would be no effort to pillory you. We want to look ahead, to learn from what occurred five years ago—"

"My feeling is that I can contribute very little. I've said all I have to say about the Joshua College affair—"

Suddenly Helen was talking. I'd gotten the feeling that her feelings about the guy would keep her silent. But now she had leveled those cool blue eyes at him. "Colonel, those were *your* men who fired the guns. Surely there's more to be said."

He smiled at her. "Perhaps so, Mrs. Christopher. But not by me."

"Why?"

"The courts have settled the matter. Why pursue it forever?"

"Because," Helen said, with a fine edge of ice in her genteel voice, "little has been learned up to now."

"Rules for riot control have been changed, largely at my urging. Men no longer are allowed to enter a riot situation with live rounds in their weapons. Tighter controls have been imposed on junior officers and noncoms—"

"None of this will bring my son back."

"I am aware of that," Offitt said.

Proper Helen Christopher. I was amazed at the way she'd taken aim at him. Good for her.

"Are you saying there is no way we can persuade you to attend one of our workshops?" Harriet Blochman said.

"I'm leaving for Arizona tomorrow, but even if I stayed, I could not join you. Mrs. Offitt is not too well, and she doesn't like these unearthings—"

I must have turned a darker red than I am normally. Helen stiffened.

"Sorry," Offitt said. "A bad choice of words. I meant to say my wife is easily upset. Besides, I don't think I'd add anything to what will be discussed. And I have the feeling I would become a target. It doesn't appeal to me."

"Would any of your men appear?" I probed. "Captain Durham, perhaps?"

"I'm sure they would not. They have all taken a vow of secrecy, or rather silence, about the events. Not to hide anything, but they have suffered too. They have simply had enough. I assure you they are as regretful as I am about the tragic outcome. It was a terrible, unforeseen accident. No one set out to kill or hurt anyone. But things happen in riot situations . . ."

He must have caught the glance that passed between me and Helen, because he began to rattle on—sounding odd in such a self-controlled man—about his men not being monsters, that they were family men, good policemen and good citizens, and that some had even gone to school at Joshua and weren't much older than the students, and so on.

I noted that he was directing his defense at Helen.

"I believe the six men who were defendants and all of my men have been sufficiently punished," the colonel said. "They are proud and dedicated men and I see no reason to subject them to further examination. It is time to let matters lie."

"And let the dead be dead?" I asked.

"Dr. Schless, my sympathies go out to you and Mrs. Christopher and the other family . . ."

"Terragni," Harriet said.

"Yes. Their little girl. I have offered my condolences. What more can I do? Or contribute?"

Helen turned loose an almost wistful smile. Damn, she was working on him. But her eyes remained cold. "What would you have to fear?" she asked sweetly. "You were not indicted. You were not really blamed by anyone. The press accounts spoke well of you."

Gratefully, Colonel Offitt returned her smile and thanked her. Forgive me if I am blunt, but I had the distinct feeling that the two vodkas our colonel had by now imbibed, along with Helen's calculated appeal, were having their effect.

"I respect your plan to hold this observance," he said. "It may do some good. But then, it may not. Why not let it go away—accept the courts' decisions, accept the public verdict?"

"We don't want it to happen again," Harriet said.

"Campuses are quiet these days," he said. "Law officers have learned a great deal. Kent State, Jackson State, Columbia, Joshua College. Tragedies, to be sure. But it is my belief that both factions have learned from them—the authorities and the students."

"Could be the students are afraid they'll get shot," I said.

"I don't believe so," he said. "Today, when demonstrations are held, ground rules are agreed upon in advance. There are parameters, limits."

President Cudlipp, I reminded Offitt, had testified that ground rules had been established at Joshua five years ago.

"True," he said. "But they were broken."

"By whom?" Helen asked.

"The students," he said quickly. "The march on the administration building was such a violation. A serious one. They had been warned in advance, and three times at the site, not to pass the fountain line. Dr. Cudlipp and the leaders of the demonstration—I forget who they were —had such an agreement."

I'd never heard about this, but that didn't mean he was faking. God, here sat the guy who commanded the men who killed my daughter, and I could not get really mad at him. I was angrier at that reactionary little creep Shreck than I was at Colonel Offitt. At least he seemed to show *some* regret, sorrow over what had happened to our children.

So we ate salads and sandwiches, and talked, but we could not get the colonel off the dime. At the same time I noted he was increasingly directing his talk to Helen, ignoring Harriet and me. (I suppose Harriet is easy to ignore; she's used to students sleeping through class. Me, I am large in heft and voice, but the colonel did a good job of looking past me, trying to win the approval of Helen. She wasn't, of course, buying it.)

"I certainly begrudge no one their right to mourn," he now said. "But from my standpoint the Joshua College events are a closed book."

I let him gaze winningly into Helen's unrewarding eyes—again she'd shifted her slender body so that she was a bit more removed from his line of sight—and I let fly.

"Not as closed as you think."

"I beg your pardon?"

"The Joshua case isn't over. We're planning a civil suit."

He wasn't fazed. Say what you would about Offitt, there was no ki-yi in him. Frankly, I didn't enjoy trying to work him over. But I kept thinking of Brian Dooley's notion—that the colonel knew things he wasn't telling, that he and the late Bates Woffler had maybe sat on evidence.

"On what basis?" he asked.

"Damages. That's all you can collect in a civil suit. Nobody goes to jail, but at least people will have to pay." I called for a check.

"I was told there's no legal basis for it, that it won't get into court."

Helen was no longer smiling. She seemed to be thinking—so you're not so sure of yourself, colonel . . . checking your lawyers to make sure you're safe . . .

"We're going back to the Supreme Court," I said. "And the state legislature could pass a special bill letting us get around so-called sovereign immunity."

"I believe that will not happen."

Helen crossed her legs. She looked like she'd had enough. But a plot was brewing in the Schless brain. Lord, what bait she was . . . I am old enough to know when a man is developing a bad case of the hots for a woman.

"Don't bet on it, colonel," I said.

He allowed a smile. "Well, then I'd best be careful as to what I say. Who will be sued?"

"Maybe you, among others. We'll do what our lawyers advise us to do. It's not personal—"

He shook his head. "You must recall I was not on the portico when the shooting started. I was in Dr. Cudlipp's office trying to find a way out of the morass. The firing began. Captain Durham was at the ambulance, having been severely injured by one of those *peaceful* demonstrators. I ran out to the veranda and halted the shooting at once. I physically wrestled weapons from some of the men—"

"Colonel," I said, "I agree you testified openly at the trial. And you've never said anything contradictory to the press. But I was wondering—"

"My testimony and my reputation support everything I said."

"How about the things you didn't say?"

"I don't know what you're talking about."

"I hear tell about unrevealed testimony. Suppressed or lost—"

"Not mine, I assure you."

Helen looked uneasy. Harriet blinked.

"Maybe not testimony," I pushed on. "If it was in the grand jury records it would have come out by now. Obviously the feds had access to the proceedings of both grand juries. So nothing could be suppressed forever if it was important enough. No . . . I mean something else . . ."

Was I imagining it, or were his creased neck and flattened ears turning faintly purplish? Maybe I was being stupid, shooting my ammo this early. We weren't even sure we'd have a case. But he was getting to me. Whatever else he was, this was also the guy who, after all the charges against his trigger-happy cops had been dismissed, had said to the TV cameras: "The system works." And Andrea was dead.

"I have no idea what you're talking about."

"You name keeps coming up. Yours, Woffler's, Judge Frankendorf's."

"Dr. Schless, I respect you, but I remind you that there has been more false rumor, calumniation, innuendo, wild speculation and uneducated guessing connected with this case than anything I've ever heard of, including the John F. Kennedy assassination. May I remind you that some of *your* supporters contended that agents provocateurs set the fire in the hut to provoke the state into a response. Never proven. Not remotely. We think we know the students who torched the hut.

"There were also rumors that an unidentified civilian, a man in a black leather jacket, gave a signal to the police to start firing when I went into Dr. Cudlipp's office. No such man was ever seen. He appears in no photographs. He was a fiction. And the recurrent rumor—lie, I should call it—that some kind of cabal on our police force had decided that morning to force the issue. These lies persist. They disturb me, they torment my wife. If you're embarked on another such fishing expedition and expect me to help you, you have the wrong man. Why is it that people in your position always assume that *all* the virtue is on your side?"

"Perhaps it is," Helen said.

"Yes, unproven theories kept popping up," I said. "And I don't hold with the stuff about the guy in the leather jacket. Or the alleged spies who burned the hut. But let's look at the other side. Your people not only invented theories, you tried to stick us with them. What about the sniper nobody heard or saw until some of your cops swore this phantom fired at them?"

"I never accepted that thesis."

"You talked to the press the day after my daughter and Helen's son were killed and you said, I think this is a direct quote, 'There appears to have been sniper fire prior to the response.' "

His ears seemed to give off heat. "I retracted the statement as soon as I knew more about the circumstances. After I studied the photographs and listened to the tapes."

"No sniper? You're certain?"

"I said so at the trial."

"All right . . . both sides went in for some cockeyed theories, though your guys were more inventive. What about that rusty gun that Sergeant Kazinski said he found on Jack Christopher's body?"

"I was not party to that."

"You didn't stop Kazinski and the defense lawyers when they went public with that fraud. You didn't say a word. Then they changed their story four times and finally admitted they'd perjured themselves and that no gun of any kind was ever found on any student, dead or alive. They came up with an arsenal of sticks and stones and a Swiss army knife."

"Those are weapons too."

"Against rapid-fire automatic rifles? Colonel, I'm talking about a cheap throw-down."

"I was not involved in that incident. I knew nothing about it. At least give my men credit for the courage to tell the truth."

"After lying for three months. And after the federal prosecutor threatened to put them away for perjury if they didn't tell the truth."

He clasped his hands and straightened his back, oddly like a schoolboy. "How did you know that?"

Was he a little rattled?

"Grand jury testimony is supposed to be secret and privileged but sooner or later it leaks out. Not that it made any difference. It was after the fact, after the acquittal. Judge Frankendorf was pretty cute. The way he handled the evidence—what he allowed, and what he tossed out."

Offitt touched his lips. "I'm not a lawyer but I've read several professional analyses of the judge's handling of a very emotional and difficult case. Every commentator upheld him. It was his responsibility to decide what was admissible and what was not. He can't be faulted, doctor. My men are free of taint and back on the job."

"Do you see them?"

"No. Why should I? I'm retired."

I bore in. "Like reunions, get-togethers?"

"No."

I'm not sure if he knew where I was leading. If the rumors about what he'd told Bates Woffler were true, it was possible that his former brothers-in-arms might not be interested in pursuing the friendship.

"I'm afraid I have to go," Offitt said. "This has been a learning experience for me. I suppose as one gets older one tries to ameliorate differences of opinion . . ." He was looking at Helen, still talking with her.

*Differences of opinion.* Three dead, six wounded.

He refused to let me spring for his lunch, carefully counting out bills and change to pay for his share, plus fifteen percent tip. Then he damn near saluted us, turned on a crepe sole and left.

"Struck out," I said.

"Well, it was worth a try," Harriet said. "But it's funny. He's sort of two people. He knows it was wrong, but he stands by his men."

Helen inhaled deeply. "I don't want to go through this again," she said. "Dave, Harriet, please forgive me. I'm a little sick to my stomach. The way that man can sit here, all friendly and rational and polite—

and know in his heart that he wrongly supported those murderers under his command. He's supposed to live by a code of honor. Dave, if I were you, I'd watch out for him. He's going to warn everybody to be on guard."

"Maybe so . . . I just couldn't resist the needle . . . Well, at least he'll sweat a little. He's still caught up in this mess. Who knows what it's like for him, knowing it was wrong, rotten wrong, and he had to go along with it. Or thought he did . . ."

Helen looked green around the gills, and drew stares from some business types in polyester suits as she walked determinedly in a firm tread to the ladies' room.

"Did we do any good?" Harriet asked.

"Can't be sure. But something happened that makes me feel I'll be calling on Helen Christopher to try out the colonel once more."

Harriet understood. "Really, Dave. Don't torture the poor woman."

I didn't answer. Later I gave Rita a report on the lunch. She was surprised that I had anything good to say about Colonel Offitt. Truth was, I told her, I believe he meant it when he said he deeply regretted what had happened.

I didn't tell her that his obvious interest in Helen offered possibilities. I'd been playing it light when I said to Helen she might have to make the supreme sacrifice, but I felt that if she could keep the colonel in town the next few days, we . . . she . . . might learn something from him that could turn this thing around.

## Sally Terragni

Joe and I, we don't like coming back to Joshua College. Too many memories. Whenever we enter the campus—it's so pretty in the spring, all green and fresh—I see that stone bench where we sat with Lucy the last time we saw her alive.

We were so proud of her. We'd driven her back from Flagg City after Easter vacation. She looked adorable—her hair long and shiny black, her face so sweet with her large brown eyes and the smiling lips. She was wearing a tan blouse and a dark brown skirt. How could she have been part of that mob? Witnesses said later she was shouting at the police, but no one saw her throw anything.

It was near the end of her junior year. As usual, she expected an A-minus average. She had her summer all planned—working at the rehabilitation center three days a week, then three days waiting on tables at Papa Frank's Italian restaurant. She had a new boyfriend, Milt Nawaski, and Joe and I liked him. A big blond boy, what the girls call a "hunk," but gentle and thoughtful. He wasn't in Lucy's class in the brains department, but he was good to her, brought her gifts. And was always polite with us. He played varsity football and was going to be a gym teacher. After she was killed he stopped calling us. He didn't even come to the funeral. I was shocked. His father was in the same union with Joe, and they stopped talking to each other. Steve Nawaski was an officer of the National Rifle Association and the American Legion, and he was quoted as saying that the state police had every right to defend themselves from commies and dope fiends, and he thought they deserved medals.

Anyway we'd sat on that bench—I think it says on it, "Gift of the Class of 1918"—and we talked, and laughed, and shared a picnic lunch I'd made up, chicken sandwiches on rye bread and pickles and peanut butter cookies. Joe told Lucy that if she wanted to go to graduate school for her master's, he'd find the money somehow, and she said, dad, don't worry, I'm a Terragni, and that means I know how to work, I'll work nights and summers and get a student loan and it won't cost you a thing . . .

We hugged her and were so proud of her. Mr. Shapiro, her old high school adviser, told us he'd heard she might make magna cum laude. I often wondered where the brains came from. Joe and I aren't stupid, mind you, but we aren't educated, and only Bobby, the youngest of our surviving children, seems interested in college. Top scores in math and science. He has that same alert look in his eyes that Lucy had . . .

"Don't look at it too long," Joe said, as we drove on to the campus.

"Look at what?"

"The bench. Where we sat with her that day."

"It doesn't hurt so much any more, Joe. I mean, she was so good. The memories are happy ones, really."

"Not for me."

He burned inside. It was not just the murder of his favorite child. It was the way so many people put the blame on *her*, on us. *We* were suddenly guilty, and *they* were innocent. I told you what the union did to Joe, the way he was snubbed and insulted. Once he invited Steve Nawaski into the alley to fight it out, and the other men in the shop had to restrain him. I must say, a lot of the younger metalworkers, the fellows with mustaches and long hair, the ones who brought radios to work or had been in Vietnam and a few who went to college, they were friendly.

I don't understand it. I always thought that workingmen, what they call blue-collar people, were sympathetic to protests and strikes and people saying what they thought. Not the guys in Joe's factory. It was the better educated people, like the teachers at Joshua and the newspaper reporters and TV people, who looked at it differently.

Joe parked our Chevy on the asphalt lot in back of the gym and we walked around the concrete fieldhouse to Dexter Hall, where the meeting was going to take place. I wondered why we had come. Maybe it would have been better just to show up for the vigil and pay our respects to Lucy and the others. We really had nothing to say to Professor Finnegan and Professor Blochman.

I felt better when I saw some of the students who'd been wounded and who'd come back for the anniversary. We'd gotten to be a sort of family during the terrible days after the shooting, and even more so during the trial. We were all five years older, Joe and me heavier. But the young people looked terrific.

Except for Wilma Overstreet, of course. She was in a wheelchair. I knew she'd been paralyzed from the waist down. I'd heard she'd been having rehabilitation therapy. She looked strange . . . skin very smooth, blonde hair thinned out, the upper part of her body looking kind of, well, inflated . . . Her legs were covered by a thin blanket even though it was a warm day.

"Mrs. Terragni! Mr. Terragni!" she called out.

We walked over and kissed her. I noticed she wore a big gold cross around her neck. I never knew Wilma was a Catholic. She saw me look at it and she squeezed my hand.

"I'm born again, Mrs. Terragni. I've accepted Christ. I believe in Him. He's blessed me and He has blessed my coming marriage to Timmy."

A gangly bespectacled young man with a chinless face and straight black hair was standing in back of the motorized wheelchair. He wore a stiff white shirt, black tie, tan jacket, brown slacks. In one lapel of the jacket was a button that said, "WE ALL NEED JESUS!"

Wilma introduced us to her fiance. He shook our hands firmly. He said he'd heard about our Lucy from Wilma, how everyone was so fond of her, and what a good Christian life she had led.

"Actually we're Catholics," Joe said, sounding a little irritated.

But the young man smiled. We'd heard that some of these Protestant born-agains aren't too friendly to Catholics, but Wilma's Timmy was all grins and nods.

"How do you two feel about this thing Finnegan and the others have planned?" Joe asked Wilma.

"If the Lord approves of it, so do we," Wilma said.

"How can you tell if He does?" Joe asked.

Timmy's Adam's apple bobbed as if it were a bouncing ball. "He will manifest himself to us. You see, He has so much love. He loves the state police as much as He loves Wilma. He loves President Cudlipp as much as He loved your daughter. In this love, we all are one."

"Yeah . . ." Joe mumbled.

Others arrived. I was happy to see all of them. Bernie Hoch, the little Jewish boy who'd been shot in the chest and miraculously survived, came with his wife and a baby in a stroller. Bernie was a doctor now, specializing in dermatology. He had a huge mustache and was quite bald, and as usual was full of fun and said how much he missed our Lucy and Andrea. He hadn't known the Christopher boy.

And there was Keith McCandless, from a wealthy family downstate, looking prosperous, with a tall blonde wife on his arm. Her name was Gloria. Keith had sort of separated himself from the rest of us. He'd been wounded in the left shoulder, said he wasn't part of the riot, was just crossing the campus when he was shot.

I saw Hubie Colson, a farmboy from Staffordville, with a beer belly at age twenty-seven, and wearing coveralls and a "Gimme" cap, and finally that little guy Billy Mallory, who'd become some kind of writer.

Mallory was the only real radical in the group. He made no bones about it. "I'm anything you say I am," Billy told the reporters. "Weatherman, SDS, Black Panther, Commie, Workers' Party, name it. You want it, you got it."

Joe and I didn't much like Billy Mallory at first, but then we realized a lot of what he said was, you know, kidding people.

Billy Mallory was what Joe called a "squirt"—skinny, undersized, with a smirk on his face. You couldn't tell whether it was a smile or a sneer. But you got used to it after a while. The funny thing was, Billy didn't belong to any of those radical groups he claimed he did. But by shooting off his mouth he sort of made all the students look bad.

Well, the truth is they did behave badly. But not to overthrow a government or anything or kill anyone. Joe said they should have arrested a hundred of them, locked them up and stopped the rioting. And used tear gas.

But shooting bullets out of automatic weapons? Into a crowd that didn't even get near them? That wasn't the worst of it. It was the words, the talk, what people said afterwards, the hatred . . .

"Hey, Joe Terragni," Billy Mallory said. "You look lean and mean, Joe. How's the bowling team? They take you back?"

"They never kicked me off, squirt."

They hugged each other. Billy kissed me. I could see under his blue denim jacket he was wearing one of those T-shirts that were popular after the shooting. It showed a big black target, the round black circles, and over it, "JOSHUA COLLEGE, AIM GOOD."

Billy said he was living in Boston and working on an "alternative food newspaper," whatever that meant. He was also writing his own true version of the massacre, he said.

"Hair's too long, skin looks lousy," Joe said. "You guys don't realize the revolution is over and you didn't score a point."

"We got *you* on our side."

"Like hell you did. I lined up with you to get some justice for Lucy. I hated your guts. All you dirty-mouth freaks."

I was afraid Joe was serious. But he was smiling and so was Billy. It was funny how we'd been drawn together by what happened.

Dr. Bernard Hoch and his wife Sandra and their baby Jonathan joined us on the steps of Dexter Hall. I kept calling him "Dr. Hoch" and he kept shaking his head, saying he would always be "Bernie" to us and all the people who'd stuck together throughout the terrible days.

Bernie reviewed the injuries for us, like a medical report. Wilma was getting therapy, but his guess was she'd never get out of the wheelchair. She'd had her spine shattered, a clean shot from the rear as she was turning to run away, three hundred feet from the police. Bernie said he was convinced someone was aiming at her.

"She's got her faith," Billy Mallory said. "Maybe that'll get her on her feet again." He sounded a little cynical.

"Yeah, laying on of hands," Dr. Hoch said. He squinted across the campus at the ugly stone arch donated by the Class of 1894. It was peppered with little white scars. Bullet marks. All the shots that had not struck the students. Beyond it, visible through the archway, was the white administration building with its white columns. It all looked so peaceful. Tulips, daffodils and phlox were in bloom.

Bernie said his own wound, a bullet in the right thigh, had healed fine. He jogged and played tennis and he and Sandra were planning a second child. I felt as proud of him as if he were my own son. He was a poor boy, on full scholarship at Joshua. When Bates Woffler had him indicted as a ringleader five years ago (how do you indict someone who has been shot?) Bates tried to have his scholarship cancelled. Bernie fought back from his hospital bed and threatened to get the TV reporters on the story. He kept his scholarship. Even with his bald head and black mustache, he looked young and full of fun. I was glad he'd made a success of his life.

"Looks like you sold out, Bernie," Billy Mallory said. "Christ, the way you waved that red flag five years ago. I figured we had a real revolutionary on the first team. Now look at you. Big practice in skin diseases, family. Bet you charge exorbitant fees, huh? Got a house in the suburbs?"

"Georgian red brick. Sandra and I are fixing it up ourselves. You need a job, Billy, come down and you can start scraping paint."

Joe and I laughed. Billy Mallory hated to work.

But I was so proud of Bernie. He'd sat next to Lucy in biology class and had always been helpful to her.

Billy said that the bullets he took in his side hadn't slowed him down much. Ribs shattered, damage to the tissues in his chest wall, but miraculously his lungs and heart were untouched.

"Take more than those comedy cops to bring down a Mallory," he said. "I told my old man that it was all the dope I took—pot, acid, toot. Gave me a natural immunity to hot lead."

"Lay off," Bernie said. He glanced at us, back to Billy, as if to say, *Think of Lucy.*

The McCandlesses, both tall and blond, were talking to Wilma Overstreet and her young man, Timmy, and I wondered what they'd have to say to one another. Keith McCandless and his wife looked like suburban types—station wagons, horses, golf, the kind of things I associated with Helen Christopher, not that I don't like Helen. Poor Wilma with her born-again faith and her strange-looking fiance didn't seem their type. But as I said, the shooting joined us all together, and we were really a kind of family.

"Yeah, big Keith," Bernie said. "Making megabucks in reinsurance, but he couldn't explain to me what it was. Married a state senator's daughter. One of the guys who petitioned the governor to make Cudlipp expel us and lay off the fuzz."

Bernie said that Keith had fully recovered and had become a handicap golfer. I guess Keith McCandless wasn't a bad sort, but he was never one of us, and I was kind of surprised that he and his wife Gloria had shown up for the memorial. I wondered whether his father-in-law approved.

Fat Hubie Colson was doing fine, Bernie said, running tractors on his pig farm, active in the farm lobby, ready to forget the whole thing but loyal to his friends at Joshua. He'd been seriously wounded, one of the most serious. A bullet had torn up what Bernie called his "plumbing," but Hubie had made a miracle recovery.

"And Lyle Pulsifer?" I asked.

"Doing okay, Sally," Bernie said. "Investigating a glacier in Alaska. Part of his graduate work in geology. Limps a little from where he got hit in the foot. But he wrote me the Eskimos don't seem to mind a gimpy geologist. Lyle sends his best."

That accounted for the six wounded students. Five were present, some with their wives, kids, fiances. It was a very good turnout, thanks to Tom Finnegan's hard work.

We started up the steps into Dexter Hall. The Hoch baby, Jonathan, was bawling, and Bernie picked him up while his wife Sandra—she was a perky, birdy woman—wrestled with the stroller. Joe went to help her and carried the stroller since she was burdened with the baby's bag.

"Thank you," she said. "I've heard a lot about Lucy. Bern says she was terrific."

"Yeah," my Joe said. "At least we've got good memories."

I could see his eyes were wet, his mouth turning down, holding it back, like he wanted to be a real man, one of the boys in the union hall, the softball league, the bowling team, a tough guy who never cried. But no one ever gets over what happened to us. It tore Joey apart. I wonder how I keep going. There are days when I stare at Lucy's photograph and let myself cry for an hour or more. Please God, I hope she never knew what was happening to her . . .

And then I hear their voices and their sneers, and the lies they told . . .

There's a story going around that Dr. Schless punched some writer fella the other night, hit him in the jaw for making remarks. Sometimes I wish I could punch someone. It's nothing to be ashamed of. Joe said to me after the trial he wanted to hurt someone, punish someone, make people suffer for what they did to our Lucy, what they said about her when she was dead. Actually he said he could *kill*.

And I said to him, no one's on our side, no one believes us.

We took seats up front with the Hochs and Billy Mallory, and we said hello to Keith McCandless and his wife Gloria and smiled at Wilma and her boyfriend again, and laughed when Hubie Colson turned his "Gimme" hat on backwards and made a crazy face.

Then Professor Finnegan and Professor Blochman and the Schlesses walked onto the platform. Reverend Al Jensen joined them.

Joe said to me, "I wonder if we should have bothered." His voice was thick. "Maybe it'll just hurt more."

"It will always hurt, Joey."

"I'm wondering if we want to be part of this."

"You told Dave you would."

I could see Helen Christopher walking in, looking beautiful and thin, taking a seat in a rear row. It's funny how seeing her gave me confidence. I knew her husband was against the whole idea of the anniversary. Alvord Jensen's wife said she'd heard that Dan was even threatening to leave her . . .

"Yeah, but this business of a lawsuit," Joe was saying. "No judge or jury in this state will ever do anything to the police. Why bother?"

"To get justice for our Lucy."

"Justice, hell. There ain't no such animal."

Dave Schless wanted me on the dais but I said no. I feel better here in the rear row with some of Jack's old teachers, even with the handful of Joshua students who seem to be here more out of curiosity than anything else.

How terribly young they look. And innocent. I must say, they're very neat. Ties and jackets, clean sweaters. Their faces have a pale, bland quality. I'm told that since the rioting, academic standards have declined. Tom Finnegan says that a lot of the more "progressive" faculty have resigned or been eased out. But Harriet Blochman says there are so many excellent teachers available these days, especially in the humanities, that the college has no trouble finding good replacements. Maybe things work out. Some things.

I can't imagine these clean-cut people ever throwing rocks and cursing the police or trying to storm the president's office. I'm still not clear how Jack ever got caught up in that mob. All that useless anger and aimless violence . . .

In the front rows were the "survivors"—Wilma, Keith, Billy and Bernie. I should say Dr. Bernard Hoch. And a group of people who looked like reporters. One of them was a burly dark man in thick eyeglasses with a bandage on his chin. Harriet whispered to me before I sat down that he was a writer and that Dave Schless had hit him the night before because of something he said.

There were also two TV crews with video cameras, two people with tape recorders and some other press. Most of them were from Flagg City and the college newspaper and radio station. They all seemed young. I recall that Jack went through one of his phases as a budding journalist. Tried out for the newspaper at Joshua, lost interest after a few weeks and went back to his dorm to listen to records.

Dave began introducing the people on the dais—Reverend Alvord Jensen, Tom Finnegan, Harriet, and Hubie Colson, who'd agreed to act as the "survivor" member of the committee. There was also a representative of the present Joshua student body, a blonde girl named Amy.

Dave made some general comments about the weekend. He welcomed all of us—it was a rather sparse group, the room less than a third filled—and talked about the events. The climax, he said, would be a candlelight vigil at the site of the shootings.

"I volunteered to reenact my role," Hubie Colson said. "Billy Mallory and me, we go into our falling-down routine at midnight."

People laughed, a bit nervously. A young reporter, a boy with the campus paper, raised his hand. Dave recognized him.

"Dr. Schless," he began, "what do you really expect to accomplish by this ceremony? I mean, the talks, the seminars. What good can they do?"

Dave said he hoped we could learn something from it.

A girl from the Flagg City TV station asked if it wouldn't just stir up a lot of bad feeling. After all, the communities were getting over it, the college was making a comeback and what would be gained by reliving the tragedy?

Dave asked Reverend Jensen to respond to this. Al got up. He's a bald, sort of bulky man. He was wearing his turnabout collar for the press conference. Usually Al favored business suits, but I guess he wanted to make sure everyone knew he was a minister.

"We seek understanding," Al said. "Bridging the gaps. If people had talked more, reached out to one another rather than resorting to anger and violence, the Joshua Massacre might have been avoided."

"Are you saying," the TV girl asked, "that there was blame on both sides? That the students, through their use of violence, played a role in starting the shooting?"

"Not quite," Al said carefully. "We on the committee have never defended the excesses of the students. We have never excused their violent acts, the foul language, the threats. But we have to ask what impelled agents of the state to shoot them down? Why was public opinion so strongly in favor of the killings? What went wrong?"

The man named Shreck was on his feet. He had a deep voice. "Reverend Jensen, will this memorial observance take into account the general phenomenon of radical infiltration of campuses? Of the *continuing* attempts of the extreme left to subvert student groups and encourage violence? Or will you just raise the usual liberal complaints about the police?"

"Mr. Shreck, we hope to be as openminded as possible. All aspects of the incident, as well as the broader picture of student unrest, will be discussed. And you, sir, are invited to participate in the open discussions."

94

"Thank you." Shreck stroked his bandaged jaw and sat down. I recalled that Dan often approvingly quoted Shreck's articles about "the new conservatism." I told Dan that they seemed to me to be based largely on fear and hatred of blacks—not overtly but in subtle ways— so as to gain the allegiance of people on other issues.

Other questions were asked. Would there be any famous names? Dave and Al said no, they weren't interested in celebrities, although anyone who was interested could attend. The importance of the occasion, Reverend Jensen said, was not to reopen wounds but to speed the healing process. They did not want to accuse or embarrass anyone, just try to find some answers.

The girl from TV was on her feet again. "But how can you help but open old wounds? People want to *forget* the Joshua Massacre. They're sick of it around here. Why all this fuss?"

"The fuss is over three dead people," Dave said. "We don't want them forgotten."

"Or me and my five friends who got pinged," Hubie Colson said. "You think Wilma wants to forget?"

Wilma's voice, loud and firm, rose from the wheelchair. She was in the middle of the first aisle, holding hands with her Timmy.

"I can't forget," Wilma said, "but I certainly do forgive. The Lord Jesus has told me to forgive, and I forgive everyone. I mean it, Dr. Schless."

"We respect you for it, Wilma," Dave said.

But the TV girl persisted. "If Wilma Overstreet can forgive the people who shot her, why can't the rest of you do the same?"

Several tried to answer her at once. Bernie Hoch got up and said it was a matter of legal rights, civil rights *and* justice. Reverend Jensen said there were a lot of unanswered questions. Billy Mallory shouted that the revolution wasn't over, and he was so mad he felt like burning down a few buildings just to remind people it could still be done.

Jensen and Schless tried to stop the camera crews from focusing on Billy, who was having a fine time taunting the reporters. I could see he was kidding. The only trouble was a lot of people in Joshua (and around the country) would take him seriously. Billy would never learn. He was baring his chest, displaying the bull's-eye target.

"Billy, for God's sake . . ." Dave was saying.

The undergraduates laughed at Billy's antics. Hubie, waving his "Gimme" cap, was shouting at Billy to shut up.

My mind drifted. I saw Jack with Dan and me on our first visit to Joshua College, during Jack's junior year in high school. Jack was shy, slow-talking. We had gone to a welcome breakfast for high school students, listened to President Cudlipp speak, wandered around the campus. Jack had been silent, almost sullen. Dan had kept asking Jack, "Do you like it here? Think you can cut the mustard?" Jack didn't answer, just kept mumbling that it looked pretty nice.

I knew what was bothering him. Dan wanted him to go to Amherst or Princeton or some other prestigious place. Dan had struggled to work his way through the University of Connecticut, laboring at odd jobs, staying up nights, borrowing money. He badly wanted to have a son who would be a "Lord Jeff" or would join an eating club at Princeton. And it showed. We could tell that Dan was not impressed with the dark red brick buildings and rolling hills of this obscure college.

He said as much to me at night in the motel after we'd put out the lights. "It's a jerkwater school, Helen. What does it mean to be a graduate of Joshua? If the kid had studied harder, or had been an athlete . . ."

I reminded Dan of what he knew but had trouble accepting. Jack simply did not have the natural gift for learning that our daughter Beth had. He was not a self-starter. He'd been a slow reader. And was it his fault he was uncoordinated? I felt sorry for Jack, alone in the room next to us, confused by what he'd seen, aware that his father was disappointed in him. It was a sad trip, though we tried to make the best of it. I remember praising the attractive campus, the nice-looking students, the reputation Joshua College had for its music and fine arts departments. I'm afraid there was a hollow ring to what I said . . . I don't dissemble very well.

While Dan was checking out the next morning, and Jack and I were packing our valises in the rented Ford, my son said, "I know the old man is pissed off at me. I can't help it. Beth has all the brains. I wish dad would understand that." And now, of course, Dan lived with his guilt, understanding but not admitting . . .

Voices rose and fell around me . . . someone asking Dave Schless if he anticipated violence . . . Billy Mallory saying he might torch the new football stadium . . . Al Jensen trying to shut him up, if in ministerial fashion . . . one of the reporters challenging the people on the platform to produce evidence that there was any "conspiracy" to shoot the students, that there was anything that could be reasonably pursued after the courts had dismissed the case against the police over and over . . .

But I only heard half of it. I was thinking of a glorious three weeks Dan and I and the children had spent at Truro on Cape Cod. We'd rented a small house. We swam and fished and hiked around Provincetown. I could remember Jack and Beth with their eyes opening wide when they saw for the first time an old-fashioned penny-candy store, and loaded up with twists of licorice and colored sugar buttons, and got the sticky stuff smeared all over their faces. How happy we were during those three weeks. Jack was four or five, Beth two years older . . .

No sooner do the memories cheer me with their bright hard-edged pictures of a summer's day—blue sky, darker blue water, yellow sand, dark green shrubs and trees—than I'm saddened as I see Dan and the kids fishing from a rowboat on the placid pond near our rented cottage, Dan pulling in a wriggling silvery fish, Jack recoiling in fear while Dan tries to reassure him the fish is harmless and won't bite him. Dan *had* been a loving father, no question. And I believe he always loved Jack . . .

I'm also thinking about that officer, Colonel Offitt. I didn't appreciate his efforts to be friendly. The way he stared at me. For all his superficially good manners there was, I felt, a clear and presumptuous message in his smiling solicitude. How dare he act like that, especially when he must know how I feel about him.

Somewhere I'd read that political prisoners often develop a dependence, almost an affection, for their jailers and torturers. I assure you, I felt no such emotion. To me, Colonel Gregory Offitt was a bad memory. A living one, as distinct from my son Jack.

A male reporter had asked about reports that we were planning a civil suit.

"Where did you hear that?" Tom Finnegan asked. He and Dave were at odds about whether to go public with the plan to sue people.

"Courthouse rumors, Tom. You and your committee are supposed to be revving up to sue the troopers for a hundred million dollars."

Tom left the lectern and went to confer with Schless and Jensen for a moment. The audience stirred. Apparently the story had not gotten around Joshua College. The reporter appeared to be the only outsider who had gotten wind of it.

Dave Schless now came to the microphone. "Such a lawsuit is being considered. We've not settled on a figure. We aren't settled on who we'll sue. But we're talking about it. You realize the state has ruled we can't sue any employee of the state. There's something called sovereign immunity that prevents it. But our lawyers have appealed to the United States Supreme Court to let us sue individuals. That's where it stands now."

"You say you've filed with the Supreme Court?" the reporter asked.

"We have."

"Have they granted *certiorari?*"

"Not yet. But we're hopeful. That's all I can tell you."

The woman reporter with the TV crew got up. "But why pursue this? You've lost every time you've gone to court. *Do* you have new evidence?"

Dave smiled. "Can't comment on that. But if we go into court to sue for damages, you can be assured we'll have a strong case."

"The old stuff?" the newsman asked. "The photographs? The tape recordings?"

"And more," Dave said enigmatically . . .

## Colonel Gregory Offitt

The evening news ran a long piece on the press conference held by the so-called Memorial Committee.

Marge missed most of it. She was packing and on the phone with our daughter, making plans for our visit to Tucson.

Several things interested me. I'd learned at that lunch about the civil suit against us. Judge Frankendorf feels it is nonsense, that the Supreme Court will never allow these people to bring a lawsuit in our state. I have to believe him, although Schless and the others seem pretty cocky.

Well, I have nothing to fear, even if they try to make me a defendant. For one thing, I've only my retirement pay . . .

I saw Helen Christopher during the TV report. Shots of her sitting with the sparse audience, and later a brief interview between her and a woman TV reporter.

I must say she *is* an attractive woman. *Elegant,* too. And she's got a graciousness, a delicate yet strong quality.

I was attracted to her at lunch. She seemed to stand for something I've missed in my life—not that I don't love Marge. But Marge has always had her problems. The bottle . . . John Barleycorn, as my father used to say. It has affected our life. I'm young and vigorous enough to be attractive to women. I'm afraid passion died in our marriage many years ago—so far back that I can't remember.

Why deny it? I engaged the services of, shall we say, professional women during my tours of duty overseas. They say one does not love these hired partners. But I'm convinced that I could have loved an Italian girl I spent a week with in Salerno during the occupation.

Her name was Assunta. Dark, petite, wide-eyed. She said she loved me, murmured it over and over when we were together in the broken-down hotel we'd commandeered for our officers.

*Assunta.* Knowing no English, ripe and sweaty, with skin like fine tan silk, lush black hair tumbling around her shoulders. Why lie about it any longer? I loved her. But marriage was out of the question. She was a street woman. A nineteen-year-old professional. I've never longed for a woman as I did for her. I couldn't wait for the moments when she would knock at the door of my room, or when I would meet her in a bar or a cafe, loaded down with G.I. rations for her family, PX stockings and toiletries for her . . .

I was so lost in my passion for her I don't think I gave a damn if an unexploded shell detonated under us and obliterated us both in one deadly burst. At least I'd die in ecstasy, in the fullest bloom of love. Yes, *love.* I'll be damned how we distinguish between lust and love, or why we try.

To myself, here in the privacy of my study in my retirement home, I admit that I have *never* been happier than when I was embracing Assunta. Soft skin, whispered love words, the wonderful sense of one-ness, of two people alien in so many ways finding in their passion a magic that blends their souls, forms a new amalgam.

I'm rambling, I know . . . When I was reassigned I lost contact with her. Well, she was a prostitute by training and inclination. I suspect she found new lovers. Perhaps some G.I. married her. Or maybe a local

Salerno bravo and they raised a family of lusty dark-eyed kids. I shiver when I remember her . . .

Now the funny thing is that when I sat across from Helen Christopher, I experienced some of these same feelings. Not purely sensual, but some kind of inner flutterings, as if part of me had come loose, or my heart were learning new rhythms. Can't explain it. Two women could not be more different than my lost love, that uninhibited child of the Salerno slums, and the elegant, modish woman of forty-odd years whose legs I ogled like a schoolboy, whose subtle perfume actually dizzied me slightly. Women from different planets. And yet they both affected me in such an overwhelming fashion . . .

Am I losing my hold on reality? I hear Marge's nasal voice in the bedroom, envision her in scuffs and housedress—she is only sixty-two but looks much older—and wonder about her next round with the bottle. I've lived through it all. A.A., church groups, encounter sessions, drying-outs, Antabuse, psychiatric care. And then after a month of cure, finding her spraying her mouth with cologne or an aerosol hair-set or even an underarm deodorant. Anything that has a trace of alcohol. The last doctor we saw said it was chemical imbalance. Thank God she's seemed stable these last six months. No backsliding. Now I wonder if the fuss Schless and the others are raising will set her off. There was a time five years ago, when I was under fire from the provokers and apologists for the students, when she went into one of her worst declines. Did those people calling me a killer and a liar have any *idea* what they had done to my wife?

I'm glad Mrs. Christopher was not part of the group that Finnegan and Blochman led, all those New York lawyers, civil-liberties types, and behind them, the righteous federal prosecutors egged on by political hacks who wanted to nail our hides to the door. Over what? A tragic accident?

I hope Helen Christopher appreciates my personal sorrow. If I had been on the portico when the shooting began it is possible it might never have happened and her son Jack would be alive today. I wish I could just sit quietly with her, hold her hands and explain it, make amends in some way. She was only at the trial for two days. Her husband was with her. Gray-haired man with a ruddy face, dark eyes. A corporate executive. I'm jealous of him. He was the one who made her go back to Connecticut. He'd written that letter saying his dead boy had been wrong and had paid the price.

He went too far. Even if he thought these things he should have spared Helen. God, here I am calling her by her first name! My mind wanders. What kind of underclothing does she wear? Is she passionate? Shy? How would she respond to an advance? Or suppose I told her some of the things I know and have never told anyone—except for Bates Woffler—and said I told her these things because, well, because I respected . . . liked her enormously . . . wondered if . . .

No . . . It isn't fair to Marge. I must hide my thoughts from her. A crazy notion seizes me, insanity in a man of my age. I want to run off with Helen Christopher. Know her the way I knew Assunta, share things with her, tell her how I won the Silver Star on D day, led my troops into the heart of Germany, fought off a Waffen-SS armored division . . . And see her clear blue eyes smile at me, all full of admiration and love. I'll stroke her light brown hair, caress that high forehead, kiss her neck—stop it. Except I couldn't.

As soon as the TV news ended the phone rang. It was Adam Kazinski. He was one of the Six, as they were known. (Our opponents called them the Sick Six. Those who were on our side referred to them as the Superb Six.

"Colonel, you saw the news?"

I said I had.

"That stuff the dentist is talking about. Is that guy for real?"

I replied that there had been reports that some of the parents of the deceased, along with the wounded students, were trying to find a way of bringing a civil suit. My feeling was that Adam and his five buddies had nothing to worry about.

Kazinski said he was in Gaffney's Bar and Grill, out of uniform, with two of his pals, also members of the Six. They were Wallace Markland and Denny Boyle, who had been in the front line where they had taken the most abuse, weathered barrages of stones, sticks and concrete.

"Give my very best to Troopers Boyle and Markland," I said. "You fellows will always be in my heart. You know that."

"That's why I called, sir," Kazinski said. "We sort of feel we need to talk to you."

"Right now?"

"Well, before those people start making any more accusations."

Gaffney's is not the kind of place I frequent. It's not really a dive, but I know a bit about Matt Gaffney and the bookmaking business he runs on the side, the loan sharking that his brother-in-law Nick Santangelo indulges in. Neither Judge Frankendorf nor President Cudlipp would patronize it, and in fact, even the students from Joshua College seem to avoid it. It's a workingman's hangout, drab, depressing. In the fall you can see the hunters' cars parked outside with dead deer strapped to the fenders. Not my taste, at any rate.

I wondered what the urgency was about. Again, I asked Kazinski if it could wait until my return from Tucson.

He seemed to be chuckling, or clearing his throat. "The way we heard it, colonel, is that that guy Schless and the others, they're going to hang it all on *you.*"

"Where did you hear that?"

"Oh, it's around. I can't give no names. Denny and Wally and me, considering we're fifty percent of the guys who took the fall, we figured it would be a good idea to get our stories straight before that dentist and those others, like that prick Finnegan, start running off at the mouth."

"Back up a minute, Adam," I said. "No one made you take any fall. Not me. Not the governor. Nobody. You were indicted by a federal grand jury—"

"Full of coons."

"Be that as it may, Adam, you were indicted. But you never had to, as you put it, take a fall. You were, after all, acquitted. Thanks to Judge Frankendorf's courage, and may I add, thanks to the support you got from me. We would not let our men be railroaded, especially when there was no case against you. We still won't—"

"Hey, colonel, this civil suit thing is something else. Maybe they'll get a bleeding-heart judge like Althouse, and maybe we'll be the suckers. That bastard Schless . . ."

It dawned on me that Kazinski was at least slightly drunk. He was slurring words. There was a hint of a drunkard's threat in his voice. During my military career (and my second career as a law enforcement official) I developed a knack for measuring men, gauging their attitudes by a change in voice, a movement of their eyes, their choice of language. And what I detected now in Adam Kazinski's ramblings was, indeed, nothing less than a *threat.*

"So you want to talk to me now?"

"Yeah, colonel. Just me and Denny and Wally. You see, you going off to Arizona, which is your privilege, and leaving us here . . . who knows what Finnegan or Schless or Joe Terragni will say? They even got that snooty Christopher dame here. They're liable to make wild accusations, and you know the rule with the Six. Not a word. Silence. Not to no one, no reporter, no lawyer."

"I'll stick with you. I always have."

"Might be better if you went to bat for us. You can answer these people when they start hollering that their precious little brats were so innocent, so sweet, and we pumped bullets into them. You know, like we're Nazis or something. After what those kids called us? The filthy language, what they said about . . . about our *wives?*"

The truth was I had always maintained proper distance from these men. And not just because I was their highest ranking officer, or had a long career as a combat soldier, or because I was never a defendant in that mistaken trial. No, we *were* different. I'm not sure I can explain it. A matter of . . . what? My origins are humble. My parents' farm in northern Vermont. West Point? My choosing to stay into military as a professional soldier? That was some of it . . . and always hungering for education, improvement, expanding my frontiers. Still, not for a moment did I doubt that Troopers Kazinski, Boyle, Markland, Case, Hofheimer and Trippi were anything but honest, well-trained, courageous policemen. Yes, policemen. We *were* different . . .

"It's getting late," I said.

"It won't take long," Adam said. "And we better not do it on the phone."

I agreed to have a beer with them.

Marge was surprised that I was going out. She knows me as a homebody, an early goer-to-bed. She was puzzled so I told her the truth. The fifth-anniversary observances, the threats from Schless, had worried the troopers. They wanted to talk to me.

"But it doesn't involve you anymore, dear."

"I think it does. They were my men. I stood by them and I should now."

"Well, I wish Dr. Schless and the rest of those people would just take their medicine like everyone else does."

"None of it means a darn, Marge. In three days it will blow over."

She was folding clothing into a valise. She looked old and tired, worn out by a lifetime of too many changes, different countries, different homes, a husband away for too long. "I guess so," she said tonelessly.

"And you be good, sweetie," I said. "You know what I mean. The old man is in your corner every second. He loves you."

She turned and smiled. Her back is getting bent. A faint hump is developing under her neck. Again I realized she was aging a lot faster than I was. I kissed her cheek, put on my brown tweed jacket and left.

## Billy Mallory

Colson and Bernie Hoch and his wife and I went out for pizza tonight. Hubie Colson is really a pistol. Ever meet a pig farmer who's also a stand-up comic? Colson actually thinks he's funny, with his pot belly and that collection of "Gimme" caps he carries around with him. The one he was wearing tonight said "CRAB APPLE VOCATIONAL." He said it was a faculty cap from the local vocational high school. Would you believe Hubie teaches pig-breeding to teenagers?

I always liked Bernie Hoch. His wife Sandra was okay (I'd never met her before), except she seemed a little unnerved by my antics. What the hell, I told her, I survived two slugs in the chest that would have killed a normal person. I figure I got to live every minute.

Sandra kept asking me about the weekly paper I write for in Boston. She acted as if I was some kind of bomb-thrower. Truth is, I'd like to be. And another truth is, I've thrown a few things. Not bombs but flares, torches, rocks and some interesting return fire, like the tear-gas canisters that the fuzz unloaded on us.

"I had no idea you were that fearsome," Sandra Hoch said. She was cradling the baby in her arms, giving him the bottle. The kid was well-behaved. Any minute I expected it to ask for a chunk of pepperoni pizza.

"Want to know a secret? All of you? I was the dude who torched the Quonset hut. Me and Lyle and two bikers from Flagg City. They showed us how to do it. Some gasoline-soaked rags wrapped around a broomstick. So what? Once the state cops came on campus, it was no holds barred."

Dr. Bernie Hoch stroked his mustache. "I'll be damned. Is this a confession, Billy?"

Hubie sputtered. "Ah, I bet they knew all along."

"Who knew?" Sandra asked.

"The state police." Hubie laughed. "I've even heard they had the nine of us picked out. Knew who was going to get shot." Colson pushed his cap back. It was dark blue and gold, the colors, I guess, of Crab Apple Vocational. "On second thought, maybe they just started shooting. Teach us a lesson. I got a lesson, all right. An advanced course in a ventilated gut. I like the way the newspaper said I was hit in the *hip*. Hip, hell. It was my belly."

"An inviting target," Bernie said.

We started to talk about Doc Schless's obsession with the civil suit he was trying to lay on the cops. Everyone felt it was a whore's dream, something that kept Schless alive. Sad, that tough-guy act. He'd never get over Andrea's death. I knew Andrea slightly. A really cool girl, even though she was a little bit of a JAP. Wrote poetry. Not a bad-looking head, either. Rosy skin, light brown hair, green eyes. She didn't date anyone steady, but she had a few of the more intellectual types after her. I'm pretty sure Andrea was a virgin. But that didn't stop locals from starting the rumor that she had VD, that when they undressed the body in the morgue they found her covered with syphilis sores. Jesus.

Bernie was looking at me. "Billy, I swear I never knew you and Lyle were the guys started the fire."

"Yeah, a revelation."

"Does Schless know?" he asked.

"What's the difference? You think if Schless and the rest of us go to court again it'll matter? So the cops can say, yes, we shot William Francis Mallory twice in the chest because we heard he torched the Quonset C–1009?"

"No," Bernie said. "It's just that the burning of that old dump was what brought the state police on campus in the first place."

Hubie agreed. "Yeah. Cudlipp went into orbit after that. Said he was dealing with a mob of revolutionaries and arsonists."

They were ganging up on me. "Wait a minute, good buddies. So I threw a torch into an old storage building. Guilty. Me and Lyle. I admit it. What's that got to do with bringing an army of cops with automatic weapons onto campus? And firing them."

Sandra Hoch lifted the kid and burped it. A soft white bubble appeared on its fat lips. I'll never have kids. Okay, I'm selfish. Charter member of the Me Generation. I like sex, and I like Colombia red brick, and I know I am a leftover from the late sixties and early seventies. A vestigial freak, as a professor at Boston University called me during a debate. Big deal. I'm still allowed not to like marriage or kids. Women, of course, are something else. They serve useful purposes. (Robin, my girl, would kick me in the *cojones* if she heard that.)

"Billy," Sandra said, after the kid had sputtered and heaved up a world-class burp, "why didn't you ever fess up before?"

Hubie Colson was turning the ring on his pinky. It was from some kind of Farmer's Lodge, some rural society of pig lovers. "Sandra's got a point, Billy. Jesus, after the way Bates Woffler tried to hang us. Maybe if you'd said it was me, folks, me and Lyle Pulsifer, a lot of heat would have been cooled—"

"I said a lot. Jesus, what d'you want, blood? Anyway, it wouldn't have helped," I said. "Woffler and the governor and that prick Offitt, they wanted it to go the other way. They *had* to make a case against the three students who were killed. Besides, that state grand jury report went into the toilet. It was a load of crapola. Not even a local jury would believe the junk they put in it."

Bernie said, "You could have leveled, Billy."

"Yeah, that sure would have helped." I was getting real antsy. Bernie and Hubie and Lyle and I were considered the radical members of the student wounded. Me, because I admitted it. Hell, there were so few radicals at Joshua College that *someone* had to volunteer. It was like those interfaith conferences on campus where only Jews show up. So a couple of Jewish kids usually volunteer for "role playing" as Protestants and Catholics. I think they overdid it one semester when Irving Malkowitz, a rabbi's son, was asked to be the representative of Islam.

Anyway, I was regarded as the ringleader of the radicals. Bernie Hoch was included, because he was a Jewish premed and had a mustache. And Hubie . . . I'll be damned if I know why. Hubie was a farmboy. Oh, I think I know why. He was an A-student in the Aggie program. Knew all about hoof-and-mouth disease, how to pull a calf out of a cow's insides. But his old man worked for the Small Farmers' League, a slightly liberal group. That was enough in Bates Woffler's book. Hubie was tagged as a red in spite of his pickup truck. And poor skinny Lyle . . . he'd been something of a pothead, so he was included.

*What a revolutionary cadre we made* . . . We couldn't have started a revolution in the men's room of the Elks Club in Flagg City. But, you see, they had to believe. *They.* All of them out there. Eighty percent of the country. Andrea, Lucy and Jack deserved to get killed. They had earned their bloody deaths. And so we, not the cops or the governor or Cudlipp, had to be blamed . . .

Still, I guess it's about time I stopped feeling sorry for myself. It's not what happened to me, or Bernie, or Wilma, or the three dead kids that bugs me. I mean it. It's the way the whole thing was turned around. What it revealed about *all* of us.

"I got my own theories about why they shot us," Hubie said. He ordered another round of beer, explaining that his wife Vera (she preferred to stay down on the farm) rationed him to one beer a day. Whenever he was away from home he made up for it. Actually, Hubie told me, he didn't care whether Doc Schless and the Terragnis and Mrs. Christopher got their civil suit going. He just liked the chance to ditch Vera and beer up.

"Let's hear it, Hubie," Bernie said. He took the baby from Sandra, cradled it in his chunky arms. You had to like Bernie. He was basically a simple uncomplicated guy. A good doctor, a loving husband and father, a surburban type. He was not one of those intense Jews, full of anxiety, guilt, pain and breast-beating, like the kind I usually rapped with in Boston.

"Hear what?" Hubie asked.

"Your theory. Why they started shooting."

"Oh, what we started shouting when they warned us on the bullhorn to stay clear of the line past the fountain."

"We were shouting a lot of things," I said. "Pigs go home. Pigs off campus. Cops eat shit. Excuse me, Sandra."

"No, something else," Hubie said. "Sandra, is it okay if I use dirty words?"

It's funny. Five years ago, in front of *any* coed in Joshua College, maybe even the president of the Newman Club or the Junior League, Hubie and I would not have hesitated to use the words George Carlin says are forbidden by the Supreme Court. And here we were, five years older, and me, a frazzled radical, worrying whether Sandra Hoch (who I'm sure had heard it all) would be shocked by dirty language. Maybe it was the baby who made Hubie and me so solicitous of Sandra's ears.

"Me?" Sandra asked. "You must be kidding."

"Okay," Hubie said, "maybe you guys don't remember, but a bunch of us on the front line, the guys throwing stones and canisters, we started chanting, 'Who's fucking your wives?' "

The word "fucking" hung like a fart in the air. Sandra's brown eyes opened like morning-blooming tulips. Bernie said, yes, he recalled we were hollering that at the cops. But it started only after the first barrage of tear gas, and after the cops had grabbed a kid who got too close to the administration building and beat the shit out of him with their billy clubs.

"Yeah, it comes back to me now," I said. "The kid wasn't even a Joshua student. He was some pothead high school kid, and was with a bunch of townies. Near where the path from Cudlipp's office winds down to the parking lot. Boy, did they let that dude have it."

"Right," Bernie said. "Beat his ass red and finally his buddies dragged him away."

"Then we let loose with the stones," I said. "I guess I threw some of the first rocks. Jack Christopher too."

"Christopher?" asked Hubie. "That big kid who never said anything?"

"Helen Christopher's boy. One of our glorious dead," I said. "It surprised me, because he was nonpolitical. Almost nonanything. I mean, a good guy, lend you money, buy you a beer, but he didn't know which side was up. From that WASP Connecticut town. Jesus, I went there once to see a girl I knew and the place looked like a stage set. *Our Town.* Disneyland."

Bernie hefted the baby. "Christopher. I can't even remember it. Hollering at the cops?"

"Yeah, yeah," I said. "Me, and Christopher, and Hubie here, and a few other guys. Also Pulsifer. Not just politicals. Jocks, fraternity doodahs, nerds. It just seemed like a good idea at the time. We got caught up in it. Sort of jerky, I admit."

"And that's when the guns went off?" Sandra asked.

"Nearly as I can figure." I closed my eyes, tried to remember the humid afternoon, the trees a paint-box green, the air thick with the blue smoke of gas grenades, the double line of state cops in plastic helmets, gas masks, shields, boots, and the bright orange flashes from the black-blue automatic rifles. HK–91s. Oh, I read all the accounts, all the testimony. Hell, I was part of it. The weapons were not supposed to be loaded. State regulations. No order had been given (so the cops testified) to load and lock. Then how in hell did all those bullets, two of which violated my frail chest, get into the chambers? Judge Frankendorf made sure that line of inquiry never made it to his courtroom.

Bernie said, "That could be it. Part of it, anyway . . . I often wondered why they opened on us when we were so far away."

"They had rabbit ears," Hubie said. "Yeah, bad language . . . nobody likes to hear his wife insulted like that . . . leastwise not in public, and from a bunch of snotty kids. Still, you can shout back, not shoot back."

I said I agreed there.

Bernie and Sandra decided to take the baby back to the motel and sack in. Hubie and I stayed and rapped for another hour. I enjoyed watching him inhale beer as if it were tap water. And never get drunk. Me, I'm into macrobiotic foods, organics, granola and herbal teas these days. If you live in Boston it's a phase you have to go through. Like learning to like whale blubber if you're adopted by Eskimos.

"I wonder, does Helen Christopher know her son was one of us who taunted the cops?" Hubie asked. "I wonder whose idea was it, 'Who's fucking your wives?' "

"I'll take credit," I said. "I have for everything else. It might as well be me."

## Helen Christopher

While I was dressing to go out to dinner the phone rang. I imagined it was a member of our group, Tom Finnegan perhaps, asking me if I'd reconsider giving an interview. Or maybe it was one of those reporters who'd been at the conference.

"Hello," I said. "This is Helen Christopher."

"Mrs. Christopher, I'm calling for your own good," a strange voice said. It was husky, muffled.

"Who is this?"

"Get out of Joshua. Pack up tomorrow morning and leave."

He hung up before I could answer.

A threat. An obvious threat. Dan had always said I am the coolest and calmest of people, that there was some kind of genetic code in me for handling scary situations, confronting tragedy. Once Dan and I came home and surprised a burglar in the house. A teenage boy picking up TV sets, tape recorders and jewelry to finance his drug habit.

We came upon him as he was trying to get out of the kitchen door, fumbling with the knob, terrified and pale. Dan was all for killing him on the spot. He grabbed the poker from the family room and warned the boy to stand still.

I talked the young man into returning anything he had that belonged to us (he was a pretty inept thief, he'd only taken costume jewelry). He broke down, begged that we not tell his mother. It developed that she was divorced, a drunk, and struggling to keep her household together. Not a poor family, just a disintegrating one.

Dan wanted to call the police but I persuaded him to let the boy go. All through the crazy incident, Dan disagreed with me, but he said I was cool as a veteran marine on patrol; he was proud of me.

I'm not sure why I seem to have this capacity for such reaction. It took me a week before I cried over Jack. Bred in the bone, I suppose. Four generations of Mount Holyoke women, and a mother who used to assure my brothers and me that we were a natural elite. And being members of that elite, "proper modes of behavior" were required of us. It didn't take with all of us. My older brother Angus was caught cheating on exams at Trinity College and asked to leave. He had a checkered career as a sales representative for dubious manufacturers and was almost tried for mail fraud.

But our family, the Potters, was not dismayed by Angus's defection. He was regarded as a mutant. Mother did teach us to be courageous, truthful, helpful. We weren't rich but we always were given to understand that we were people who by dint of a birthright I never fully understood—it wasn't money or status or special achievement—had an obligation to do the right thing. It was almost mystical. "Damn Yankee conceit," Dan used to call it. Dan's folks were late nineteenth-century arrivals in New England, poor farmers from Cornwall. The Potters were teachers, lawyers, ministers . . .

Where was I? Oh, the threatening call. It did frighten me, but not for too long. Cranks, fools. Dan had warned me that this sort of thing would happen. I thought of calling Tom Finnegan and telling him. Or Dave Schless. But I realized they could do nothing. The police certainly wouldn't care. The cops had made clear their lack of ardor for the weekend observances and the return of the "victims."

I decided I wasn't that hungry after all, read Time for an hour, listened to a light rain falling outside the motel room and tried to sleep. I confess I slept poorly, if at all. I had a series of brief dreams. They were upsetting and unclear. Most maddening, as soon as I awakened, I forgot most of what I had been dreaming.

Do you know how hard it is to recall the details of a dream? How frustrating? One thinks the images will come to mind. They seem to be on the verge of revealing themselves, than they vanish, vaporize.

So this dream kept tantalizing me and I wondered if it had anything to do with the presumptuous colonel. But he wasn't either of the men as nearly as I could remember. In fact, as I thought of him—not at all in any sympathetic way—it seemed that if he'd been a part of my dream he would have found a way out for me. He'd certainly found an out for himself and his men. And he apparently had been a successful military leader . . . I had this persistent notion that he was one of those people who can control their lives, and other peoples' too . . .


## August Karl Frankendorf


That Schless person has been all over television, threatening, making dark hints, reviving long-dead issues. I confess I am revolted by his lumbering figure, his beetling brow, his harsh accusative tone. His Jewishness has nothing to do with my disgust. I have always gotten along splendidly with Jews. Like me, many of them support the arts. I can always count on the Karlinskys and the Feins and the Wachtels to back the fund drive for the chamber music society, the magnolia art festival and so on. I never wanted Dr. Schless to be my enemy; I rather respected the man at first. But his thirst for vengeance I find repugnant.

It's strange, very strange. In some ways I suspect that he and his wife are more like me than the likes of the late Bates Woffler or Merritt Winnington. You'll recall that Merritt's father-in-law, Duke Everson, used to humiliate me in high school. And I now remember—as I watch Schless being interviewed on our local TV news—that it was usually Milton Cohen, one of the few Jewish lads in our class, who came to my rescue. He was a burly dull boy who later died in the Argonne forest, but I'll never forget him.

The truth is I am a sensitive man, and I do not seem to develop a tougher skin with age. That is why I'm so uneasy these days. I don't like conflict and tension. I wish they'd get their memorial weekend over with. Perhaps what I need is a long visit to New York, some days in the Museum of Modern Art, the Metropolitan, the Whitney. Were I not so exhausted I might even essay a trip to Paris. Just to look at my favorite Bonnards and Vuillards once more before I pass on.

I checked some of my colleagues today and they assured me that no judge worth his salt would ever let me take the witness stand in a civil suit. The state may have sovereign immunity, but judges exercise an unspoken bond that is perhaps even stronger. Schless and his New York attorneys may decide to subpoena me (if this matter ever comes to trial, which I doubt) but my fellow justices would laugh the notion out of court . . .

Still, I suppose the *possibility* remains.

But of course I am totally in the clear, as they say. Cleaner than a hound's tooth. There are no notes, no tapes of my conversations with key people like Governor Hasslinger or Bates Woffler or the defense counsel.

I wonder if Bates left any notes on his pretrial investigations? He spent hours with the colonel. I had the feeling that Offitt, a West Pointer and a true war hero, detested Bates.

Woffler was shrewd, ingratiating. Many women regarded him as handsome, with his glistening chestnut hair and narrow mahogany eyes. He had satiny skin, as if he never shaved. He wore black vested suits, and before he worked for the state he was said to be one of the best negligence lawyers in Flagg City. He had a disarming smile, and he always seemed to be a step ahead of you.

When he began his work on the case he would present to the state grand jury, he cornered me at the courthouse one day. I should have refused to listen to him—actually I let him do the talking and offered no opinions—but I saw no harm in it. I'd known him a long time and respected his talents, even though the man was a bit of an enigma.

"You see, judge," Woffler said, rather patronizingly, "the issues here are far greater than the accidental deaths of three young people. The issue is, where does it stop? How can we stop the country from sliding downhill?"

He told me that Adam Kazinski had discovered a pistol on the body of the Christoper lad. This was news to me. A sweep of the area had turned up sticks, stones, knives and other missiles, certainly proof positive that the mob was armed. But a pistol?

He was also investigating the backgrounds of the three dead students and the six wounded. The Mallory boy was a confessed revolutionary. He admitted that he belonged to all sorts of subversive groups. And there appeared to be serious questions about the associations of the Hoch boy, the Schless girl (they said she had syphilis) and the Terragni girl (pregnant, it was rumored, with a black baby).

Woffler said he would produce witnesses from New York and Chicago who would pinpoint radical attachments, and who would establish that a secret cabal had ordered the bloodshed at Joshua.

"You have found these people?"

"We will," Bates said.

I pointed out that I understood a rise in tuition and some heavy beer drinking were claimed to be behind the riot. Bates said that was a made-to-order situation for the radicals . . . kids shot down for nothing . . . except, he said, they weren't all that innocent themselves.

"Look, judge," he said softly, "the philosophical issue, the overarching political issue will be behind my presentation. Society must defend itself. Any and all measures are, under such circumstances, permissible. Not only permissible, but obligatory."

He certainly had a point. Still, there were varying opinions on the state grand jury's findings. I refer to its refusal to indict the troopers, and its indictment of students and teachers. Which leads me to recollections about my judicial brother, Judge Herman Althouse.

My fellow jurist Herman Althouse is an odd duck, but I respect him. We have wonderful friendly arguments as to the merits of Italian versus German opera. Herman, being of Germanic descent, is a Wagner buff, while I lean to Bellini, Donizetti and Verdi. My antecedents are German also, but the Italian mode has always appealed to me. I adore *Norma* and *I Puritani*. In the depths of despair, my spirits can be elevated by listening to the sublime Sutherland singing either of these gems. Bellini died at age thirty-four. Has anyone, in so short a span of life, given the world so much joy, so much love? Mozart, perhaps? Keats?

Herman has a Teutonic strain of bullheadedness about him, and when the state grand jury indictments were presented to him by Woffler, he consulted with me in my offices.

He came alone and asked that our meeting be "between us boys."

He showed me the famous master shot of the students' farthest advance to the so-called fountain line. You can see the hatred on their young faces . . . their arms arching as they hurl missiles, the police raising their automatic rifles.

"What do you make of this, August?" he said.

"Obviously it is some time before the shooting took place."

"Wrong. The guns are about to be fired. We checked it out with an enlargement of the clock in the Dexter Hall tower."

"But . . . there is no mob surrounding the police. The nearest students —two of them are all I can see—are about twenty feet away. Then a small group is a hundred or so feet away. But the mob looks to be more than three hundred feet away."

"Correct. See anyone being rushed? Overwhelmed?"

"No, Herman, not at this moment. But the officers have sworn over and over they were surrounded and feared for their lives."

Althouse looked grim. "I think I know what I am going to do about those indictments of faculty members and students," he said.

I said that perhaps the photos were forged, or a technical mistake made. The enlargement of the clock could be misleading.

"There is nothing misleading about any of this."

I made some comment about larger issues, the rights of society, the *perception* of danger on the part of the police. The heat, the shouting, the abuse, the missiles . . .

"No one is being overrun. No one's life is threatened. There are many more photographs like this one, taken by different people. I think I know what my duty is, August."

I replied that the new issue of a stable society might be an overriding factor. That photographs could deceive, and that he should not act too hastily.

I was glad when Herman changed the subject and we talked about the Metropolitan Opera's last radio broadcast of *Tosca,* which both of us enjoyed enormously.

## Colonel Gregory Offitt

It was close to ten when I got to Gaffney's. I was grateful that no one recognized me—neither Matt Gaffney, the aged owner, nor the fat bartender nor the waitress. On the other hand, why should they? It had been some time since my picture had been in the paper or on TV. I felt out of place among the denims and T-shirts and work shoes in my tweed jacket, tan cavalry twill slacks, tan shirt, knitted brown tie.

At the rear of the bar I found the three policemen who had served under me and who wanted to see me.

Kazinski appeared a bit the worse for wear. His broad face was beet-red and sweaty. He was always a bit sloppy. Dennis Boyle and Wallace Markland were younger men, excellent officers with good records. (After the incident I went over their personnel files with a fine-tooth comb. I knew a great deal about all the men, especially those who had discharged their weapons.)

Boyle was a slender long-jawed man with dark, red-brown hair, greenish eyes and a pleasant manner. He was in his late twenties. It was hard to imagine him wanting to shoot anyone unless absolutely driven to it. It was one of the reasons I stood by all of them. Boyle was not trigger-happy or angry or narrowminded. He had three years of college and wrote the best reports in his section.

The third officer in the booth, Wallace Markland, was less well known to me. He was burly, broad-chested, with a sallow face and a shock of black hair. His appearance suggested Indian blood. He was rugged but not ugly. My recollection was that he was in his early forties, father of five children and, like Kazinski, a high school graduate.

Kazinski insisted I have a beer. I agreed. I've never been one of the boys and I prefer a decent wine to beer, which I find doesn't relieve my thirst.

"How can I help you fellows?" I asked.

Kazinski cleared his throat. "Colonel, that guy Schless. I mean, he's got to be stopped."

Somewhat less emphatically, Boyle and Markland agreed. I felt sorry for them. They were decent men who had been placed in an impossible situation. After the trauma of the trial, endless investigations, lie detector tests, the bullying of the federal prosecutor and the FBI, to have it all reopened, the wound bared again, the old hatreds rising to keep them awake at night, torment their wives and children . . . it wasn't fair. They deserved better.

I said that it was unlikely that Dr. Schless or his supporters would get anywhere. They would need a court ruling to be allowed to sue the police as individuals. And I wasn't so sure that the wounded students or the other parents were united behind Schless. Mrs. Christopher, for example, might be a weak link. At least her husband—the fellow who wrote the letter—was opposed to a civil suit. His absence from the "memorial weekend" told me a great deal. Moreover, I told them, she impressed me as an intelligent person and I had the feeling she might be opposed to the suit. I also said I doubted that Wilma Overstreet would lend herself to a campaign of vengeance. She had become a born-again Christian and appeared to be full of forgiveness. She'd said as much on the TV news.

"That isn't what I heard," Adam Kazinski said. His nose glowed red. His broad forehead gleamed with sweat in the half-light of the booth. A jukebox had begun to blare. Kazinski went on, his voice getting louder over the beat of a guitar. "The Overstreet girl, those wounded kids, they made a pact. Some lawyer got to them. Some New York guy. They'll back Schless. That Hoch kid, he's a *doctor* now. How bad hurt could he be? And that little prick Mallory. He's a goddamn revolutionary, a dirty-mouthed liar. Him and Hoch and Pulsifer and that fat Colson. All of them. They want our blood, colonel."

Markland agreed. "My doctor knew Hoch when the guy was an intern at JFK Memorial Hospital downstate. He says Hoch talks about it a lot. As if he hadn't asked for it. He admitted he threw a canister at us."

Boyle had said little. He was the youngest and the best educated. At the trial he had been a strong witness. The prosecutor had never gotten him to hedge on his version of events, to shake his testimony. Of course, Boyle was not involved in the matter of the Christopher boy's gun or the rumor about a sniper.

Boyle said, "Our feeling, colonel, is that we have to be ready. The press will be asking questions. Adam and Wally and myself contacted Hofheimer, Case and Trippi. We're all in agreement."

"As to what?"

"A united front, colonel."

"I thought we always presented that to the public."

Boyle sipped his beer. "We want to make sure it stays that way. Suppose we get a judge less sympathetic than Frankendorf? That's what Schless and his people will angle for. Their lawyers will try to get the case before someone like Althouse."

"My guess is it will never come to trial, the issue will be moot—"

"We ain't so sure," Kazinski said. "All this memorial crap, and the TV people nosing around. Hippie bums, most of those reporters. They were always on the kids' side."

"I don't see what you're getting at," I said.

Boyle smiled. It was a cold smile. Only his thin mouth participated. The eyes were flat. "Colonel, we want to make sure we can depend on you."

"You know you can."

"On the business of the order to load and lock," Markland said heavily, "we went to bat for you, sir. I hope you remember." His Indian eyes glowed.

"Bat?"

"Yeah," Kazinski said. "We covered for you. All the guys know that. Not just the six of us. Everyone in the troop. We intend to keep it that way. Just between us."

"I'm still not sure I understand."

Boyle clasped his hands on the edge of the beer-stained table. Another jukebox balladeer wailed. "Colonel," Boyle said, lowering his voice. "We covered for you. You gave the order to load and lock."

"I did no such thing."

Kazinski was shaking his wide face. "Honest, you did, colonel. You denied it at the trial, you said you had no idea how come ten of us happened to have live rounds in our weapons. But colonel, we *heard* you say load and lock."

"There was a great deal of noise," I said. "The students were screaming and chanting. There were loudspeakers blaring at them. Orders being shouted. Captain Durham said he heard no such order from anyone. I was the only one authorized to order loading of weapons. State regulations require that. Some of you men understandably may have misheard something that was said." I paused, watching the three of them. "Or you may have taken it into your heads to act without an order. I can understand that too. The judge understood it. He stopped cross-examination on the matter—"

"We were protecting *you,* sir," Markland said.

"Protecting?"

"Sure," Markland said. "The men heard the order. From you. Oh, not all of us. But ten of us did. It just couldn't have happened, ten men ramming magazines into their pieces without an order from the C.O. We all knew it, and we decided we'd never say you gave the order."

Boyle nodded. "And it was lucky for us we had a judge who understood our problem. Sure, we loaded up. But he accepted that we at least *thought* someone gave an order, and given the violent direction that the confrontation was taking, that our response was a valid one."

"I see. Someone. Me. Or Captain Durham."

"Oh, it was you, all right," Kazinski said. He was smiling now.

"You find something funny, Adam?"

"No, sir. It's just that troopers stick together. We all knew you hollered 'load and lock' and someone passed it on to the guys in the front ranks. But we decided it wasn't right to hang it on you. After all, you didn't give the order to *fire.* You were in the president's office."

"So I was."

*What in God's name were they getting at?* This issue of my giving the order had never arisen. I knew in my heart that I had given no such command. It was against regulations. We are bound by strict standards for riot control, and it is part of every man's training *never* to carry loaded weapons into a riot situation. Every possible means of containing rioters without a resort to bullets is mandated. Tear gas, batons, massed charges, water cannon, psychological weapons, blanks, but live ammunition only as a very last resort. Moreover, such an order could only be issued by the highest ranking officer present.

And yet, as I tried to recall that chaotic day in front of the administration building, with the obscene chanting deafening me, and the barrage of stones, sticks and canisters raining on my men, I began to wonder . . . *Did* I give such an order and not remember having done so? They had heard someone else. Or imagined it. Or . . . well, to be charitable to these men, they had taken it on themselves to defend themselves and loaded their weapons. And moments later fired . . .

I told Boyle, Markland and Kazinski that the photographs showed some of the men ramming magazines home. And in none of these photographs am I present.

"Oh, you went into Dr. Cudlipp's office soon as you gave the order," Kazinski said. "Isn't that right, Denny?"

"That's our recollection."

Inhaling, I sat back and studied them. They had been through hell. They had spent a terrible day, cursed, struck, insulted, threatened. An awful tragedy had followed. Not their fault. Not my fault. A concatenation of unforeseen events.

I said, "I see nothing to be concerned about. You brought me here to tell me that you intend to stick to your version. I regard it as the truth. But I gave no order. Captain Durham gave no order. You thought you heard someone—perhaps me—give such an order. Is that it?" I found myself, oddly for me, struggling to control the situation. I even felt defensive.

"Only part of it, sir," Boyle said. His voice had flint in it.

"And the other part?"

"There's stories going around. About things you said to Mr. Woffler, and maybe the judge."

"What kind of things, Dennis?"

"About what happened on the steps," Markland said.

"What am I supposed to have said?"

"Nobody knows for *sure,* sir," Boyle said. "But that's the rumor. Mr. Woffler was always on our side. He appreciated what this was all about. But we've heard you had some arguments with him. Things you told him about us. Statements that would make us look bad."

"I assure you I did no such thing. The prosecutor and I discussed the events in great detail. We reviewed the photographs—"

"Yeah, and we're fed up with those photographs," Kazinski interrupted. "As if they mean a damn. As if they tell everything about the truth—"

Boyle silenced him with a hand wave. "Save that, Adam."

"Every time I hear photograph I get steamed," Kazinski said. "You can bet Schless will drag them out if he gets us into court."

"Dennis, since you seem to be the spokesman here," I said politely, "perhaps you can channel the discussion. Get to the point."

"Okay," Boyle said. "One hand washes the other."

"What does that mean?"

"We won't say anything about you giving the order to load up, and you don't say anything about . . . well . . . what you told Woffler and maybe Frankendorf."

"About us," Markland said.

"Yeah," Kazinski added. "*Us.* The guys whose heads were on the line. Colonel, you were always aces with us. We respected a guy with a combat record, who treated us fair. But it wasn't *you* went on trial. It wasn't *you* got dirty letters and threats. It was *us.* And if that civil suit goes through, it'll be our bare asses again."

"Maybe mine too, Adam."

"All the more reason, sir," Boyle said, "to play ball."

I wasn't sure what to say, how to explain my position. How much did they know about the conversations I'd had with Bates Woffler? Obviously they had some information. But exactly what?

"All of you should be reassured that I've testified fully on the events of May fifteenth. There have been no deals, no hidden testimony, no suppressed evidence. As a career military man and an officer of the law, I could do no less. I am with you fellows all the way."

Markland grabbed my hand. "I knew we could depend on the old man. I always said you were on our side."

Boyle and Kazinski also voiced their appreciation, though I still sensed the hard edge of a threat. They were telling me that if I changed my testimony, or if I said certain things publicly or in front of a judge, information on which I had hitherto kept silent, they would drag me down with them.

After I left them I began to wonder. Did it matter—those . . . observations I made to Woffler and the judge? Rather strong opinions. Reflections on what I'd heard that day, things I'd witnessed. Judge Frankendorf made clear to me that what I'd said to the prosecutor, Woffler, had no bearing on the case. I wonder if he was right. At any rate I could not let my men down. They'd suffered enough. I'd stand by them now.

Driving home, for reasons that elude me, I began to think of Assunta. And of Helen Christopher.

## Dr. David Schless

Bad night last night. Rita crying a lot, saying she's sorry she came here. We had a threatening phone call. Some imbecile with a muffled voice, calling me a "Jew fuck" and telling me to get out of town while I was in one piece. I told him to meet me in the lobby of the motel in an hour, just the two of us, bare fists. He called me a commie prick and hung up.

Rita started to bawl. We did the sleeping pill routine again and told the desk clerk not to ring the room.

The pill knocked her out. But it made me ill. Brought on a low-grade migraine, a gnawing at my left temple and left eyeball.

There was a ballgame on TV, the Atlanta Braves and the St. Louis Cardinals, and I huddled in a corner of the room with the audio off, enjoyed watching Ossie Smith perform acrobatics at shortstop, and silently applauded the way Andujar worked batters over before fooling them with the high hard one.

Then I started to feel my eyes moistening and I knew why. Andrea was a baseball fan. Our only child. Sure, I wanted a son too. But . . .

I taught her to throw and bat, and she was a pretty good softball player in high school. She loved the Mets. Tom Seaver was her idol when she was a kid. Pretty good choice, I told her, a combination of athletic talent, brains and good manners. I used to tell her about the athletes I'd admired. DiMaggio, who never sulked, never blamed anyone, never argued with an umpire, never badmouthed a teammate or an opponent, just went out and was spectacular every day. I was sorry she never saw the great Joe D. in action. He showed the world you could have all the talent, all the fame, all the fantastic skills that the law allowed—and still be a *mensch.*

Andrea loved my stories about Jackie Robinson. Before her time, of course, like Joe D. But what a man. I'd tell her about Jackie stealing home, taunting pitchers, battling for his honor and dignity. Where are the likes of him today?

It's more than I can take sometimes. Andrea and me—Rita was never much of a baseball fan—sitting in a box in Shea Stadium, watching Seaver or Koosman or McGraw work their magic. And the batters. Tommy Agee and Cleon Jones and that third baseman . . . what was his name? Not Ezzard Charles. He was a boxer. Ed Charles.

She had dozens of sets of bubble-gum cards, her heroes. Each team was neatly packaged with a rubber band, the little stacks of cardboard rectangles stored in an old metal tackle box I'd given her. "They'll be worth a lot of money someday, daddy," she said. "But I don't think I'll sell them. Isn't Ron Swoboda cute? I love him. And I love Bud Harrelson, and Al Wise, and Gil Hodges." Her innocence choked me up now.

How did *she* get marked for that awful death at age nineteen? What did it prove to anyone? Whom did it satisfy? Why . . .?

"Daddy," she used to say to me, "don't buy me toys."

I'd ask her why. She said they weren't any fun. What she loved were colored papers to cut up, crayons, paint boxes, scotch tape, scissors, stuff she could make things with. Once I spent a July Fourth, when everything was closed, tearing around Westbury to find a notions store or a drugstore where I could buy a bag of glitter so she could make me a holiday card. *Glitter*. God, the little things that make kids happy. She must have been six, maybe seven. Do kids understand the perfection of their lives? How when they're older they'll never be made as happy by far more expensive gifts than a twenty-five-cent bag of glitter?

I sat up and stared at the screen—as with most hotel TV's, the predominant colors were paris green and deadly purple—and didn't know who was winning, or why they'd yanked Andujar. The names of the players mean less to me every year. I don't have Andrea to clue me in on the new outfielder or the young pitcher with the fast slider.

If only we could have our day in court. Rita says I'm obsessed and that it's bad for me. Too much hate boiling inside of me. Maybe she's right. But it's more than hate. It's goddamn *outrage*. How could they get away with it? Why do so many people think it was a wonderful idea to shoot down three kids who were three hundred feet away?

I must have fallen asleep in the chair with the TV on, a smear of sickly colors, when I was awakened by someone rapping at the door. Looked at my watch. Jesus, it was nine o'clock. Rita and I had been zonked by the pills. And having left no wake-up call, the desk assumed we didn't want to be bothered.

Figuring the lynch mob was paying me a personal call, I edged the door open, keeping the chain bolt secure. I saw no angry bum with a club, but Tom Finnegan's bearded hulk.

"Up and at 'em, Dave," he said. "Good news."

I told Tom that Rita and I would meet him in the coffee shop in fifteen minutes. She was exhausted and said she couldn't handle much more of this. Rita had been a tower of strength. But she kept the agony inside. Don't believe what you hear about us Jews letting everything out, wailing and hollering and lamenting all the time. It's not just the Helen Christophers of the world who handle personal tragedy in a stoical manner. Yet sometimes I wonder if some day Rita would pay for being so self-controlled. Maybe she was paying already.

"Let's go, kiddo," I said. I kissed her neck. "Finnegan has news."

She hugged me. She was slender and soft under the silk gown and I loved her as much as I did the first night I dated her at Syracuse. But our lives had a void in them. It would never be the same. She tolerated my mania. It kept me functioning, but it was tough on her.

Over coffee Finnegan said he'd gotten some positive readouts from a group of state legislators—two assemblymen and a state senator—on the chances of our civil suit.

"The lawyers kept telling us that only the Supreme Court could give us what we wanted," I said.

"Not so, Dave. These people I met with—one of them's on the state judiciary committee—say that the legislature can pass a bill giving us the right to start a civil suit."

"In spite of sovereign immunity?" Rita asked.

"Apparently. The constitution says that the state can't be sued if it refuses to entertain a suit. But the legislature is also empowered to pass a special bill permitting such a suit against individuals."

"How come we didn't know this?"

"The law was passed during the Civil War. Everybody forgot it was on the books. Had to do with permitting former slaves to sue state officials who liked the idea of bondage. Anyway my contact at the capital, Assemblywoman Peggy Sharpless, says it's worth a try."

"Tom, you're smoking rich stuff these days. Do you and Miss Sharpless honestly believe that both legislative houses of this state will ever pass a bill letting the families of the Joshua Three bring a civil suit? That would be something like getting the Politburo to vote for free speech."

"It's worth a try, Dave. Peggy says a lot of the guys in the legislature are sick unto death over this thing. Not that most of them give a damn about what happened. A lot of them still favor shooting wild kids. But it's given the state a black eye. They figure a good way to lay it to rest would be to give you and the Terragnis and the Christophers a final day in court. So a few cops will have to stand trial. The guys at the capital figure you'll *never* win. Not a dime. Not a word of sympathy. Peggy will be at the opening session this afternoon and we can talk to her. She's good people."

The more I thought of it the less likely it seemed. Those country lawyers in the legislature giving us another crack at their troopers? Yet crazier things had happened.

"How do we go after this?" The gleam was in my eye again. The urge to hit back, to make someone suffer the way Rita and I and the Terragnis and Helen had suffered, the way our kids had been snuffed out. It was no longer just the crime that angered me, pumped blood to my head, caused my heart to race, but even more the notion of a conspiracy of hatred, a united front of cruelty, a crippling of simple justice in the interest of . . . what?

"Peggy should have some ideas," Finnegan said. He stared at me. "Take it easy, Dave. You're turning the color of red dye number two. Rita, can't we calm the dentist down?"

"I want them all in hell," I said. "Why try to fake anything? Not just for murder . . . but for lying and covering up and, yes, *laughing* at us all the way."

# Billy Mallory

Keep bragging to everyone that those slugs I took in my chest don't bother me anymore. It's part of my act. Maybe I should shut up. If we ever get to court again it might look better if I complain that I've been disabled for life.

Truth is, in the morning my ribs hurt like hell. As if I've been beaten with two-by-fours. The bones and the tissues have healed, the doctors say, but for some reason they can't explain, I still have morning pain, wet-weather pain, pain after I exert myself.

All-night beer drinking doesn't help. After Bernie and Sandra went back to their hotel, Hubie and I matched Michelobs for another hour until we were both zonked.

Every campus has a few beat-up old houses where hippies, radicals, junkies and assorted freaks crash. I'd located myself at one on the south side of town, a creaky gray dump on a bombed-out street in the black section. I didn't know a soul there, but the house had been in business five years ago as a kind of counterculture center, or at least what passed for the counterculture at Joshua College. I'd holed up there part of my junior year, trying to revive the glorious years of the late sixties and the early seventies, and pretty much falling on my face.

What few people know is that at the time of the riot I had dropped out of school for a semester and was working as a bartender in a dump called the Command Post. A lot of Vietnam veterans hung out there. The owner, Doug Willis, was a one-legged bearded graduate of the Second Cav. He was a cockeyed combination of gung-ho boonie rat— claimed he'd walked point more times than anyone in his battalion— and dropout pothead. He was a really cool guy. I enjoyed tending bar with him, and I respected him.

Anyway, this house. It had three slanted floors and an attic, and at any one time it could be housing ten to twenty-five people, students, hangers-on, dealers, radicals. Very few blacks. They never trusted us. For that matter they didn't trust anyone and who can blame them? If you look at the photographs of May 15, you'll notice that there isn't a single black face, not even a brown one, in the crowd outside the administration building. The bros knew when to split. They smelled it, felt in their bones that this was going to be a bummer.

So now I was back in what had come to be known as Idiot House. What used to amuse me, and still does, is that the place was depicted as a center for revolutionary plotting. Jesus, the people I knew there, myself included, were no more capable of creating a revolution than Bernie Hoch's baby. A more inept collection of airheads, nerds, losers and dim-bulbs I have never met. Half the time they were stoned, or pretending to be. And these cripples were the enemies of society? Would overthrow the government?

Although the press was generally sympathetic to the students and critical of the police (I think this is what especially infuriated the locals) a lot of BS was written about the sinister things coming out of Idiot House.

One account said that it all started as a plot by campus radicals, a cadre of professional agitators and revolutionaries, a combo of Weathermen, Black Panthers, SDSers, Christ knows what else. Was ever such garbage written? To begin with, the people identified as being the leaders of such groups (I never saw a black for more than ten minutes in Idiot House and usually he was some dude peddling dope) had lived there *five years earlier.* The only quasi-radicals in the dump were me and Lyle Pulsifer. Poor Lyle, he didn't know what he was. He was so full of pot and hash and acid that he wasn't sure if it was winter or Tuesday.

Writers spent pages analyzing the dangerous radicals at Idiot House, who they were and what they said, and decided that *they* had set off the riots. That, friends, is bull of such a high order it deserves another name. The brawling started when some jocks got pissed at being thrown out of the campus beer hall, the Ram's Horn. And there was also a mini-demonstration against the tuition increase. (Did you know our athletic teams are known as the Jerichos? And that our mascot is a ram? Get it? Joshua Fit the Battle of Jericho, right? Well, the walls sure came tumbling down five years ago.)

Anyway the public came to believe this was a commie revolutionary plot to destroy the country. I suppose I did no good shooting my mouth off about all my counterculture connections, flashing the black power salute—the bros regarded me as a honky clown—and mouthing off about what we'd do next time. Frankly I'm ashamed of myself. But I've got this perverse streak in me. If that's what the public craves, William Francis Mallory will be pleased to supply it.

If anything, Idiot House had gone downhill in five years. There were the old faded pictures of Ché and Mao and Rap Brown on the walls, but they seemed forlorn and irrelevant. And the resident students seemed more interested in tofu and carob flour, TM and psychic phenomena. Nobody was reading *The Urban Guerrilla* any more, nobody knew who Franz Fanon was, and the closest thing to a political discussion was when I overheard two girls talking about a petition to abolish pay toilets in the Joshua bus station.

Not that we talked about anything so much more important five years ago. You see, that whole radical, anti-Vietnam, anti-Nixon, off-the-pigs stuff was dead even then. At its height it was a curse for any politician to embrace it, or even be tainted by it, as George McGovern found out. We were lepers. But mostly we were just a wart on the ass of the body politic. People hated and feared us. How in God's name could the student leaders of that era have ever believed that they could make any *lasting* impression on the American people? All they did—I include myself, even though I came five years late, when the stage had collapsed on the actors and the audience had fled into the street—was make certain that it would be easier for the haters and bigots and greed merchants to take over the country.

Sitting in the crud-encrusted kitchen of Idiot House, I sipped Roast-aroma and found myself sick of my role as the jester of the Joshua Massacre. Enough. As my old man back in Worcester says, *Billy, you got to grow up some time.* The old man's right. But I don't seem to find it that easy. Guess I'll be a more or less free spirit for a long time, maybe all my life. When I'm sixty I'll be peddling ginseng tea and macrobiotic prunes door-to-door in Boston, crawling home to a tatami mat, where I can do my two hours of meditation and feel the pain drain out of my old bones . . .

Two young foxes were sitting in the kitchen. I was only six or seven years older, but I felt twenty years their senior, in my faded cutoffs, my target T-shirt, my beard and ponytail, and the morning aches shooting out of my chest to my throat and into my gut.

They had long frizzy hair, wide eyes, pale skin. They kept staring at me. They were unaware that I'd crashed there last night, and had just found out who I was. The infamous Billy Mallory. One of the Joshua

Nine. Interviewed on TV, quoted in the newspapers, indicted, acquitted, and now back to the scenes of his greatest fuck-up.

"Gee, it's really you," one of them said. She was eating homemade yogurt with a plastic spoon.

"Wow," the other said. She was wearing a patched Mother Hubbard and granny glasses and nibbling dry granola.

"Yeah, it's me. The commie hippie bomb-thrower William Francis Mallory. The Worcester Wildman."

"You look pretty cool to me," the yogurt-eater said.

"You guys going to bust the place up again?" Granny Glasses asked.

"My days of anger are over. I'm a burnout. I was late even when I was trashing buildings and hollering at pigs."

"It must've been neat," said Granny Glasses.

"It stunk."

"But I mean, you guys really made a statement," the yogurt-eater said.

"What was it?"

"Well, like, you know, it was really cool . . ."

Granny Glasses wandered off into these burps and ejaculations that pass for conversation among the young. We weren't much better, I guess, although at least we had a political vocabulary. They just seem to meander and stutter, like an old car not getting full compression from a cylinder. It's as if they need mental valve jobs.

Television is to blame. They grow up, even the bright ones, watching that talking box hour after hour, until they're incapable of speech, thought. It's all signals coming out, impulses being thrown at them. And nothing has to be returned. No need to rap, communicate, hash ideas around. They think television is the real world, that the real world is another sitcom. And TV sitcom *has* to end happily.

"Could you show us your wounds?" yogurt-eater asked.

"Hey, Olga, that's embarrassing," Granny Glasses said.

Feeling like Lyndon Baines Johnson when he showed *his* postoperative scar, I rolled up my T-shirt and revealed the roadmap of white scars, the old stitch marks and entry marks that described a broad *V* on the left side of my rib cage.

"Oh, wow."

"Gross."

"Yech."

"Oooh. Can I touch it?"

So there I sat, getting what passes for a high on herbal tea, while two unformed girls stroked my starved chest and fondled my repaired ribs. Thus a campus hero comes to glory. Sometimes I wish that that old fart Woffler had gotten us into court and tried us for sedition, riot, arson and attempted murder, as he had planned. Instead of sitting here, a relic of a campus shit-storm, a twenty-seven-year-old has-been, I could have become a legend in my time. Léon Blum defending himself against the Vichy swine. George Dmitrov giving the Nazis hell at the Reichstag fire trial. I'd have been Darrow in Tennessee. John Peter Altgeld championing the Haymarket bombers. (As you can guess, I was a modern history major. But all my hopes got blown to hell that morning five years ago. Can't explain it. Bernie Hoch seems to have gotten a handle on his life. Colson and McCandless are on track, and even poor Wilma has the Lord.)

Sitting there, letting self-pity rise around me, wishing someone would offer me a joint—Idiot House was so drug-free now, so hooked on natural diets and TM that you couldn't find the remains of a roach anywhere—I was coming to the conclusion that I'd screwed up my life. The lathe work peeking through the walls of the stained kitchen, the sink overflowing with crap, the aroma of uncollected garbage, the girls with their vulnerable faces . . . Jesus, there had to be more to life than this.

It dawned on me that at age twenty-seven, helping manage a macrobiotic alternative restaurant in Roxbury and freelancing for an organic food newsletter, I wasn't much better off than I was five years ago when I torched a Quonset hut and gained brief fame as a clay pigeon for Trooper Kazinski and his colleagues. Well, if I was feeling sorry for myself, at least I didn't lay the blame on others. Not the cops, not President Cudlipp (who expelled me), not even Woffler or Frankendorf. And certainly not my good Irish Catholic parents in Worcester who wanted their Billy to become a lawyer and work with his uncle Patrick Emmett Mallory in his law office. It is a wonder that my old man and my mother tolerate me when I come home to get my laundry done. Yeah, I admit it, I'm not too neat, and I don't live too well, and I sponge on them. You can see why I'm jealous of Dr. Bernie Hoch, and even that stiff McCandless, and Colson, and Wilma . . .

A tow-headed, downy-skinned boy in farmer's overalls—his name was Ollie—wandered into the kitchen and stared at me.

"Sir, are you Mr. Mallory?" he asked.

*Sir.* You can see what I mean by what had happened to Idiot House. These were the cleanest, sweetest kids in the world. The legacy of the massacre had neutered them. Keep your mouth shut, be polite and maybe we won't blow you away.

"That's me. But no autographs, folks. I have a full schedule."

Ollie smiled. "There was a phone call for you last night. I wrote it down."

He handed me a slip of paper. It was from my main squeeze, Robin Shapiro, owner of the Krishna Cafe. I'd left the phone number of Idiot House with her. But I could not imagine why she'd want to call me. Robin is ten times brighter and emotionally stronger than I am. She actually makes money out of her stewed lentils and *chapatis,* not to mention crisp health salads, tofu loaves, and whole grain breads. She is thinking of koshering the kitchen (Robin serves no meat or milk products) and influential Orthodox personages have expressed interest in favoring her eatery.

"Any message?"

"She wants you to call her, sir."

If Ollie called me *sir* once more I'd have to kick him in the nuts. What had happened to the radical pothead freaks I had come to love? All those cunning plotters the folks told us about (none of whom were on campus the day of the riot) and most of whom had bailed out of Joshua College three years earlier?

Granny Glasses advised me that the phone was a pay phone and I'd either need a pocketful of change or a credit card.

"All I need is a dime. I'll call collect."

They stared at me with awe, like tots studying an alien from space. You see, I was also part of a TV program to them. Not real. Not someone who'd damned near been killed by cops. Not a participant in a shameful bit of history. But a sitcom character. Fonzie Mallory.

The wall phone was in the front hallway. I had a view of the dirty end-of-town street. Sad-assed blacks moved by. Black kids whooped and shrieked and smashed empty fruit crates. They were all wearing their felony shoes.

Robin was brisk and businesslike, getting on my case to come home in a hurry since she was operating shorthanded, she'd just had a big fight with the tofu supplier, and the board of health was threatening to serve a summons if she didn't clean up the organic vegetable bins.

"Is that all you called for?"

"No. You got a registered letter from your friend Pulsifer. The envelope says it came from Fairbanks, Alaska."

"That's Lyle."

"Want me to read it to you? He scrawled 'Urgent' on the front. Isn't he that creep who disappeared after the trial? Dropped out of school with you?"

He had dropped out. I had more class. I was booted out. I told Robin to read it.

She complained that it was a collect call and could run into money if it was a long letter. Would I prefer to wait?

"No. It may be useful. Read it, Robin."

"Okay. I'll deduct the call from your paycheck."

Can you see why I'm crazy about her? People think those health-food alternative whole-wheat types are dummkopfs. Believe it not.

"It says,

> Good buddy William, Hope you and the other martyrs are having a wild time in Joshua. I'm camping out on glaciers trying to protect my pure white body from grizzly bears. Didn't have the heart to return to the scene of the crime, but I hope you are holding up my end of the business. Me, I'm lean and mean, off drugs, living in the open air and waiting for my money to run out. People think I'm a geologist, but as you know I never got a degree. I pick up a little dough doing manual labor, pipe-fitting, driving heavy equipment, demolition, anything that'll pay me a few weeks wages. Then I move on. Expensive here. What you earn, you spend, so it is a good thing I'm off cigarettes, pot, beer and booze.

Robin stopped reading. "Why is this so important?"

"It isn't. What else does he say?" I could hear Robin's chef shouting in the background. Sitar music leaked from the stereo set. I wonder how the Hasidim, our future customers, would appreciate Ravi Shankar.

> Billy, old comrade, I have a confession to make. It's been bothering the hell out of me. I don't mean the day we got shot. By then I was on *your* side. Pissed at the cops, the president, the whole establishment. But the night before, when you and I torched the storage hut? The wicked act that brought the pigs on to campus? I was put up to it. That's right. I was what they call a police agent.

You see, Billy Boy, they had the goods on me for dealing dope. Caught in the act by a narc as I was trying to unload decks of H. They kept me under wraps for a while, didn't press the charges because, they said, they might be able to use me. You'll recall the campus scuffling they'd had over the nuclear power plant on Sparrow Hawk River? I was the guy who started the fighting when the cops moved in. The idea was to make it more than a peaceful bust. Make it a violent incident provoked by radicals. That was me. Playing a role. They'd go easy on the dope charge if I gave good performances.

I halted Robin. "That son of a bitch. *He* was the one. He was the one got *me* to go to the bikers and ask them for the soaked rags."

"You were suckered, Billy. This creep Pulsifer was your best friend?"

"Yeah . . . Any more, Robin?"

Certain interested parties on the side of the law decided the rioting at Joshua had gone too far. Too much nasty language, rock-throwing, threats. Poor Cudlipp kept saying the campus fuzz and the local gendarmes couldn't handle us. He wanted state troopers. So his pals obliged. They threatened me with the heroin arrest and pretty soon Pulsifer was in the middle of the mob, following a script. They even picked out that Quonset hut because they knew it was worth nothing and would make a hell of a bonfire. Sorry about that, Billy, but I had other worries. Hey, man, they could have sent me away for six to sixteen, and I don't think I'd be too good at jailing. I was never exactly a stand-up guy.

I can't tell you who my employers were, but maybe you can guess. Sure, you can use this information. Give it to Dr. Schless, or Tom Finnegan or the newspapers and TV. Maybe they'll ask to extradite me from Alaska, but I don't care. Maybe someday I'll say who put me up to it. I never thought it would get so heavy, with kids getting killed. Maybe I should have taken one of the slugs that got Jack Christopher or the girls. Anyway, you can't reach me. I float around a lot, use a different name and look different. I even use a fake Social Security card. You'll oblige me by keeping this last piece of information to yourself. If Schless ever gets his civil suit into court, what I've told you may be useful. Hang in there, Mallory.

—Lyle

"Christ," I said. "I can't believe it. Old acidhead Pulsifer. He told me he got off seeing things burn."

Robin said a pox on both of us and started to get on my back again about running off when she was shorthanded, and so on, and that she was sick of the Joshua College crap. Robin is an ideological dropout. No politics, no causes. Except for additive-free diets, holistic medicine and the relaxation response. She claims she can relax her entire system —mind, body, soul—in six seconds.

I leaned against the peeling wall in the hot narrow hallway, half-listening to the black kids outside. Not certain what to do with Lyle's information, I found myself grimly amused. Here I'd always thought it was a secret that Pulsifer and I, aided by some pimply-faced bikers, were the heroes who'd burned the building. Crazy. Last night, when I confessed my role to Bernie Hoch and Hubie Colson, I'd come on *macho,* a runner, a bomb-thrower. What was the expression Lyle had used in his letter? *A stand-up guy.*

It was almost as if Lyle, that six-foot-three, one hundred-thirty-pound atrocity with his mop of yellow hair and nose like an anteater, maybe the ugliest man on the Joshua campus, had somehow overheard me bragging. Now I was duly informed that I'd been set up. Part of some scheme—the administration, the D.A., the cops?—to lean on students. Me, Billy Mallory, the original radical wildman, doing *their* job.

Question now was, what do I do with Pulsifer's confession? He had to be telling the truth. No guy would admit to being a fink for the pigs. It was like admitting you stole from the poor box at St. Aloysius church or tortured kittens. Unless Lyle was a little nuts. (I always figured him as a wide-eyed, innocent jerk, a former jock who'd gotten dumped from the freshman basketball team for exotic smoking habits.) Lyle didn't seem to care much about anything.

As I left Idiot House I had to laugh at myself. The fierce revolutionary. The nearest Joshua College had to a real-live radical commie bomb-thrower. And suckered by a police plant! My best friend, at that!

The image came back to me in mocking splendor. Lyle and me, and the bikers, racing up to the abandoned hut, smashing a window, tossing in the gasoline-drenched rags. The bikers had showed us how, opening the tanks on their bikes, wrapping the rags around sticks to make missiles.

Oh, we thought we were hot stuff. There must have been lots of cardboard and wood shavings on the floor of the Quonset. It took some time to burn, but when it did, it took off with a lovely orange burst. Sunrise at midnight.

Come to think of it, it took the firemen an awfully long time to show up. By then the metal walls were collapsing, and Lyle and I shared a friendly joint on Charity Hill, fifty yards away. Our secret laughing place.

I never suspected that other people—smarter and tougher than I could ever be—were also laughing.

## Helen Christopher

I was still in my bra and panty hose—I admit it, I was admiring at my figure, the absence of flab—when the phone rang.

Tom Finnegan or Dr. Schless, I imagined. Or a reporter. They'd been showing up in greater numbers, trying to get us to make provocative statements.

"Hello."

"Good morning. This is Colonel Offitt."

I was stunned. He was the last person I expected—or wanted—to call me. At the lunch yesterday I'd formed a distinctively negative impression of him, never mind his obvious attempts to butter me up, appeal to me. There was something too proper about him, too rigid. And he *was,* after all, the commander who had stood by his men, made excuses for them, told the world that "the system works" when they were absolved of killing my son.

"May I see you, Mrs. Christopher?"

"I beg your pardon . . . why?"

". . . I want to talk over some things with you . . ."

The gall of the man left me breathless. I also heard in his voice a pleading tone. He *sounded* contrite, apologetic. "Can't we talk on the phone?"

"I'd rather not. May I please pick you up at the motel? In about an hour?"

"I have a busy schedule this morning. The opening session is due to start in a few hours—"

"I won't take much of your time. *Please,* Mrs. Christopher."

Dan says I'm too accepting, too tolerant of others. I knew I should have insisted he tell me on the phone what he wanted to talk about, but I ended by agreeing to see him. What can I say? There was a sense of almost hideous fascination with the man. The so-correct upright bearing, the quiet commanding voice, the steady gaze . . . *and* a man who rationalized the killing of three young people, including Jack.

## *Colonel Gregory Offitt*

It was not easy . . . was, in fact, impossible . . . to explain to Marge why I had decided to postpone my trip to Tucson. The reasons were . . . complex, mixed.

"The children will be disappointed," she said gloomily, "and I don't feel like going alone."

I told her I insisted that she go. I would leave on Monday if all went well. Then I told her (in edited fashion) of my meeting with Troopers Kazinski, Boyle and Markland. I made it sound as if they needed me, that they were concerned about what might develop at the memorial observances. I had stood by them, backed them to the limit, and if they were troubled about things that might be said about them, I felt I should be on hand to defend them.

"You aren't their C.O. any more," Marge said. "You've done your part. But if you stay, I stay."

It took some convincing to get her to agree to leave without me. Careful of her frail feelings, I had to keep from her the sense I'd had last night of some not-too-subtle threats from the men. I could not explain to Marge that one of the reasons I wanted to be in Joshua during the anniversary was that I not only wanted to defend them, but if necessary, defend *myself*. Who knew what Schless had in mind?

Watching my wife at the breakfast table, her face creased and powdery, her white hair tangled, her mouth set in that eternal down-turning of the lips, her hands corded and misshapen from arthritis, I was full of guilt.

Never, *never* would I tell her the other part of my motivation for remaining in town. True, I was concerned about the troopers, and the odd relationship we now had—partners and yet potential antagonists. But I could only tell Marge certain things . . . Part of the reason I wanted to stay on was, undeniably, my need to see Helen Christopher again.

## Helen Christopher

He was driving a black Chevrolet sedan. Immaculate, anonymous. He got out in front of the motel, bowed stiffly, smiled and opened the car door.

In the morning sunlight, brighter than the dim confines of the restaurant, I could see he was a man who carried his years well. He was wearing dark aviator glasses. He was lean, straight-featured, flecks of gray in his close-cropped light brown hair. He would have fitted in well in the bar car of the New Haven Railroad, or a town council meeting in Old Surrey. I believe Tom Finnegan had told me he was sixty-five. He looked younger.

"Thank you for agreeing to see me, Mrs. Christopher."

I said nothing. I didn't smile. I edged away from him, getting as close to the automobile door as I could. He glanced at my knees as I moved. I tugged at my tan skirt.

His voice was a trifle shaky. "This means a great deal to me." He seemed ill at ease. Yesterday, at the meeting with Dr. Schless and Harriet Blochman, he'd been stiff, authoritative—the commander, the drill field martinet.

"I have to be back for a meeting at eleven," I said.

"I'll have you back before then. We can ride out to Lecky Park. The azaleas are in flower."

I resented his attempts to make our meeting—which I had already decided I shouldn't have consented to—as a kind of date, an excursion to look at the azaleas in bloom. On the other hand, he didn't seem conniving or dishonest. Difficult to reconcile with his support of his policemen. His testimony at the trial. His refusal to ever make public statements about the awful events that had led to my son's death.

We drove in a wide circle across the greening campus. The newer modular red brick buildings looked flat and uninspired against the older heavy cut-stone edifices. Classes were not in session, and apart from a lazy Frisbee game or a pair of coeds strolling by the college appeared nearly deserted.

He drove us through the square granite pillars and the opened iron gates with the plaque "JOSHUA COLLEGE FOUNDED 1877." He mentioned that this was the reverse of the route he had taken five years ago when he came with his men in response to the request from President Cudlipp, and with the approval of the governor.

"It never dawned on me," Offitt said, "that it would be the saddest day of my life."

"And mine."

"Of course. Your grief is infinitely greater than mine, Mrs. Christopher."

I had an urge to shout at him, that if it was so damned sad, colonel, why didn't you *do* something about it? Instead of those mealy-mouthed comments about the system working, and justice being served. But I said nothing.

The streets of Joshua were almost empty. (I later learned that on weekends people swarmed to the new shopping mall.) The sun had risen, casting shadows on trimmed lawns, old frame houses. Joshua was an attractive town. It was not cute-charming like Old Surrey, which is a commuter's paradise. The average income was far lower than Old Surrey's, the homes plainer, the economic and educational level much lower, even though it was a college town. But everything seemed in proportion, balanced. White paint sparkled on old Victorian residences, bushes and trees were well tended, early flowers bloomed. I identified some superb old trees—a pair of copper beeches and a rare Japanese cut-leaf maple. People seemed to care for their homes and to have an eye for serenity. The air was still clear and clean, unlike Flagg City with its noxious smokestacks.

Colonel Offitt surprised me when he said he had decided to stay in Joshua for the weekend. "I feel I have an obligation to be here," he said.

I asked him why—although I really didn't care. When he hesitated,

I asked if he intended to take part in any of the conferences. Dr. Schless, I said, would be delighted.

"No, that's out of the question. I'm not sure I approve of this observance. Not that I would argue with anyone else's desire to do so."

The old citizen-soldier. Yes, yes, do what you want—but don't call me to account. Was the man a hypocrite or a naïf?

"Just what is your obligation? To whom is it owed?"

"My men."

So. He would stay and make sure that none of his precious troopers, those unpunished killers, would be hurt. "Then I regret having agreed to see you—"

"Please let me explain. I know you have every reason in the world to detest me. I stand for everything you must hate. I symbolize the forces that you think—rightly or wrongly—destroyed your boy. But I appeal to you to give me a hearing."

So saying, he stared at my knees again, and for a moment I thought he would (to underscore his sincerity) pat the one nearest him. I clasped my hands in my lap and looked straight ahead into Lecky Park.

It was too late to tell him that the park had painful associations for me. Dan, Jack and I had picnicked there during Jack's sophomore year. I'd made liverwurst sandwiches and bought pickles and farm tomatoes and beer for "my men." I remembered the three of us sitting on a slatted wooden bench overlooking Revelation Canyon. It was early fall, and the colors were not as flamboyant as our autumn spectacle in New England, but it was serene and lovely and Dan for once seemed pleased with Jack's progress. They talked football and discussed Jack's friends, where they were, what they were doing, and had a good laugh about the way Jack's friend Dave Gross had smuggled his golden retriever into a dorm at Ithaca College and hid him for a semester in an unused storage room.

It had been a lovely day. I identified a few birds. An indigo bunting, I recall, and a towhee, among them. Dan didn't really share my love of nature. I think his company had problems with some conservationist group. But I did manage to arouse Jack's interest in wild creatures. I remembered that little museum he'd collected in his room. "You can learn more from a robin than a soap commercial," I once told him. Dan had laughed and said, "Yeah, but there's no cash flow in it." (I think he was sorry as soon as he said it. Just as I think he was after he wrote that letter about Jack.)

Offitt parked the car on a dirt road near the start of the woodland trails. My eyes must have been wet, because he asked, "Is this painful for you?"

"It doesn't concern you."

"I have a feeling it does."

Dan says I can manifest a "formidable reserve" when I want to. I did so now. Offitt said nothing, seemed to duck his head. We walked to the edge of the canyon. Below, the Revelation River boiled downstream, shooting up sun-flecked spume, bubbling with spring fullness.

"Mrs. Christopher, I hope you won't regard me as a muddleheaded old man. But I am impelled to tell you something about myself. It may sound immodest, but at least it may help you understand me. When I commanded a company in World War Two I had the reputation of being an officer who never asked his men to do anything he wouldn't do. There were plenty of C.O.'s who never walked point. I did. I assumed the dirtiest jobs I assigned my men to. I didn't waste my men's lives. And I saw to it that they were fed and clothed and got medical treatment. I didn't hesitate to take on battalion and division if I felt my men were getting a raw deal. What happened here five years ago has been a painful end to what I had hoped was an honorable career."

"But you're alive, colonel. So are your policemen. My son is dead."

"I don't expect your sympathy. I do want you to know how profoundly sorry I am for what happened."

He was staring at me, his pale blue eyes peering from under tufted reddish eyebrows. He was asking for something. Forgiveness? Compassion? How ridiculous. It was *I* who had suffered a loss, not he.

"Colonel Offitt," I said, "you were quoted as saying that the system works and that the matter of the Joshua students was laid to rest. Do you still think so?"

He touched my hand. "I'm not sure."

I drew my hand away. "Not sure?"

"I . . . I feel it will remain an issue. Maybe complete answers will never be known. That being the case, at least we can learn from it, hope that it never happens again—"

"That seems an easy way out, a compromise. What Dr. Schless and the rest of us want is some justice."

"Sometimes we all have to settle for something less."

"I'm not ready to. Neither are the Terragnis, nor the Schlesses, nor Bernie Hoch nor any of us. Your men shot them. That isn't a difference of opinion, a dispute to be adjudicated and debated."

"You speak about justice," he said. "What you want is to punish us."

"And why not? Your policemen murdered my son."

"The courts have found otherwise."

"They can be wrong. Judge Frankendorf's conduct of the case was a scandal."

"I'm told by legal experts that his rulings on the evidence were in order."

"Dr. Schless says that our attorneys don't agree. It was an outrage that Judge Frankendorf didn't permit your man Kazinski to be cross-examined on the gun he claimed he found on my son's body. It was a *lie.* Kazinski perjured himself in front of two grand juries. And he was never even reprimanded. And those other lies about a sniper. And more lies about the so-called raging mob that threatened to overwhelm your men. *When they were three hundred feet away.* How can anyone read the eyewitness accounts, look at the photographs and then listen to the tape recordings and come to any conclusion other than that your policemen committed a form of murder?"

The colonel bent his head and rubbed the bridge of his nose. As for me, I was surprised by the outrage in my voice, the directness of my attack. I had said more to him and with a greater show of force than I'd been able to say to my own husband. But that was understandable. Offitt was a good target . . . he had asked for this meeting. It made it easier to go on the offensive. With Dan I was always a bit afraid that his contradictory feelings about Jack's death might lead to an explosion and harm our shaky marriage even more.

Yes, I thought, you have asked for this meeting, colonel, and you just may regret it.

"Colonel," I said, "do you have any guilt over what you did to my son and those other young people?"

Offitt arched his neck and ran a hand over his throat. "No one's ever asked me that. A soldier is taught not to feel guilt over killing the enemy. Of course, that was not exactly the relationship my men and

I had to your son . . . I would have to say I do feel . . . responsibility. I share the blame. A commanding officer must always assume blame—"

"Did you at the trial or in public ever say this?"

"It would have muddied the waters. I sided with my men. They were threatened. They overreacted. Perhaps they erred. But a fair interpretation of the events could, and did, lead an unbiased jury to acquit them."

He leaned back, stared at the rushing river and rocky cliffs. It was a staggeringly beautiful place. *Where every prospect pleases and only man is vile . . .* Was Gregory Offitt vile? He was surely troubled. A puzzling man. I had the feeling he was not telling me all he wanted to . . .

"Colonel, when you told me about your courage in combat, your insistence on, what did you call it—?"

"Walking point."

"I assume that's the job of the first man in an advance? The one who takes the fire?"

"More or less."

"And how you saw to it that your soldiers were properly fed and cared for. All quite admirable. But I have the impression you did the same thing after the Joshua Massacre. You also walked point for those policemen who served under you—"

"They went on trial. I didn't."

"Yes, but you repeatedly testified that they were justified in shooting students."

"I did."

"So I have to conclude that your concern for your men is greater than any sense of justice you might have. You believed that the troopers were right, that my son's death was excusable."

My voice had remained low and even.

"Well. *Well.*" He smiled at me. "You're all that I expected, Mrs. Christopher. A woman of courage and strength. I don't know how to respond."

"It was you who asked to see me. Surely you're better prepared than that."

"Touché. Shall we walk along the nature trail?"

We got up. He was studying me with more than soldierly interest. I'm not much given to self-flattery, and I am hardly a flirt. Dan says I'm not even aware when a man is making a pass at me. That's not quite true, of course, but I do tend to be surprised. It's really taking a person for granted, in a way more insulting than flattering. Once Hans Von Norden, from one of the richest and oldest families in Old Surrey, put his hand on my rear end and let it linger while we were dancing. I was surprised at Von Norden's rudeness. And presumption. I suppose, though, that I am a bit of a square . . .

It took me a moment to accept that Colonel Gregory Offitt, the man who had testified that his state police had reacted properly in firing live ammunition at my son, was actually making a pass at me. Good God . . .

He took my hand as we descended down the gravel path that rimmed the gorge.

"Colonel, I can manage." I took my hand away.

"I find you extremely attractive—"

"I think we should go back to town. Dr. Schless needs me at a briefing session before the conference begins—"

"Helen," he said. His voice was hoarse. "I ask you to accept my apology. If you want me to admit to a share of the guilt, I'll do that too."

"What about what you said at the trial? Do you still feel that justice was served?"

"What is justice? Even the lawyers aren't sure. Sometimes a social condition, an atmosphere, can decide what is just and what is unjust. I tried to keep things under control. I suppose I failed. But it was a human failing, not a desire to hurt anyone."

He had hold of my hand again. An old Sherlock Holmes story came to me—Holmes and Professor Moriarty fighting at the edge of Reichenbach Falls. Wasn't there a famous illustration of the struggle?

"Suppose I accept your apology . . . it doesn't ease the pain."

"If it were in my power I would do that."

"Would you be so *concerned* if I were Rita Schless or Sally Terragni?"

"My heart goes out to them too. But I admit it wouldn't matter as much to me if they rejected me, or accepted my apology."

"Colonel, you'll have to do better. Albert Speer, one of the few Nazi leaders who ever uttered a word of remorse, once said that the crimes against Jews were so overwhelming that any expression of sympathy that he might utter would seem pointless—"

"Surely I'm not in his category. He was the kind of monster I helped defeat."

"I was never one of those who called you a Nazi or a right-wing lunatic. But I'm making a point. Look, colonel, I can accept whatever expression of sorrow you choose. Apology, regret, remorse. I don't think you wanted anyone to die—"

"Of course not. God knows I tried to prevent it."

"Fine . . . and now I think it's time for me to get back." My voice was cold. What else could it be?

We turned and followed the winding path. The canyon was a granite gorge, bordered with evergreens, red maples and pin oaks. Offitt explained to me that further upstream the granite had once been quarried but that it had become too expensive to work the lower sections of the river. Conservation groups had fought to preserve the natural wonders of the place and maintain Lecky Park. He seemed to know a good deal about flora and fauna, identified a Red Admiral butterfly, indicated a stand of broom flower. Which again brought back memories of Jack's attempts to be a scientist.

"I once thought of a career in the natural sciences. Biology, physiology. But before I knew it I was training infantry in Georgia, then landing in North Africa. Forgive me if I seem to be bragging, but I have a Silver Star, eight battle stars and a Purple Heart with three oak leaf clusters. Sometimes it seems like a dream, a life I never lived."

I didn't say what happened to Jack was no dream. A nightmare . . .

He went on: "I led men. Gave orders. Saw them die. Was wounded. I survived. That's what made the Joshua affair so terrible. I had always conducted my life by a code. The army's code, my personal standards. Then to have it all blow up in fifteen seconds. I've lived with this a long time, you're the first person I've talked to about it."

"Not even to Mrs. Offitt?"

We halted at the edge of the woods near the parking area. We were alone in the silent green forest. Below us, the river sent out a hushed roar.

"She least of all. My wife is an alcoholic. A common ailment among army wives. A kind and loving woman, but she's incapable of sharing problems. It's been my prime duty, apart from my career, to keep her on an even keel."

I said I was sorry. Was I?

"I don't want sympathy. Perhaps I'm responsible for Marge's drinking."

"Why do you assume I've such a sympathetic ear?"

"I'm a good judge of character. I knew from the first time I saw you at the trial that you were a woman of . . . well, quality. Why should I lie? You were someone who attracted me. Forgive me, I shouldn't subject you to this."

Forgive him? I said nothing.

We got into his car. He actually appeared to be blushing under his tan, perhaps uneasy that he had revealed too much of himself.

"You must believe me," he said, as we left the park, "that I respect you very much. I'm sorry if I sounded like an old lecher. But I had to tell you how . . . remorseful I am over what happened to your son. I had to tell you I was not at fault. Errors were made that day, grievous ones, but there was certainly no intent to kill or to wound—"

"Then why did those policemen fire?"

"Panic. Fear. A need to hit back, to punish somehow. They *may* have been wrong, but not guilty."

"You believe this?"

A second's hesitation before he said, "Yes. Yes, I do."

I did not know quite what to make of him. He was breathing deeply, glancing too intensely at me.

"Well, colonel, if you feel that way, and if you're as sincere as you claim to be," I said, "then I'd like to invite you to the meeting this afternoon and have you tell everyone the same things you told me."

He smiled. "That I find you attractive?"

"You *know* what I mean. An out-and-out apology. And anything else you want to say. If you want you can defend your men, say what you said just now about panic, fear and being wrong. I think Tom Finnegan, and Reverend Jensen and Dr. Schless would like to hear this from you."

"That's impossible."

"Why?"

"It would mean that I had backed away from my support of my men."

"Would it?"

"They would think so."

"Maybe you aren't so convinced about your excuses for them. Wouldn't it be the better part of honor, that code you spoke of, to say what you believe?"

He helped guide me up the rocky slope. Colonel Offitt showed no sign of fatigue. He was fit and surefooted.

At the lip of the canyon he turned me toward him. "I am not afraid to say this. You are the kind of woman I have thought about for many years. I have an image of us—"

"Colonel, this is idiotic. I don't want to hear anymore." I could feel a flush rising on my back, my ears, my cheeks. "You didn't answer me. Is it possible you've changed your mind about those awful events that ended in my son's death? Are you sure you didn't ask me here to tell me something? I agreed to see you to give you that opportunity."

"Helen—"

"Never mind. I have to go back to the campus."

In the car he looked so sad that if he were not who he was, I might have felt sorry for him. But then he put his hand on my thigh. I removed it. He said nothing more as we drove. I felt ill, queasy, as if running a fever.

## Dr. David Schless

*Plenary.* I don't like the word. Too formal, academic. Reverend Jensen likes the title for the opening go-round. Says it keeps everything level, unemotional. He's got a point. I guess the demonstrators and counter-culturists learned that nothing is gained by hollering and cursing and insulting the American people. You've got to talk politely, reach them through their own prejudices.

The auditorium in Dexter Hall was almost filled, which pleased me. The organizational details being discussed—Al Jensen chaired the session—were pretty routine stuff. Everyone was there. Tom, Harriet, the Terragnis in the front row—our pipeline to Middle America, bless them —and Helen Christopher, more attractive than ever. She's one of those women who get better looking as they age. The tilt of the head, shape of the cheekbones and brow, the crown of light brown hair. And her eyes. Pale blue-gray, suggesting submerged passions that her lox of a husband probably doesn't appreciate.

The meeting moved along. The high point of the meeting was an address by Assemblywoman Peggy Sharpless, a sort of small-town Helen Christopher, twenty years younger. As Ms. Sharpless spoke, describing the efforts in the legislature to enable us to sue the police and the authorities as individuals, I had the sensation that if Helen hadn't fallen into that suburban round of parties, golf, Republican politics, she might have had a career like Peggy Sharpless. (It slipped my mind at the time that Helen had worked as a high school teacher for years but gave it up after Jack's death.)

There were some questions for Ms. Sharpless, including some tough ones from the reporter who worked for the newspaper whose owner was a trustee of Joshua College. He wondered how her constituents would view this attempt to open wounds, go after the troopers again, smear the college and the town . . .

I must say Peggy Sharpless handled it well. She replied that justice was never out of season, and that while a majority of the local people wanted the case laid to rest, a sizable minority felt that everyone deserved the full protection of the courts. She was making no judgment about anyone's guilt or innocence but she felt that the parents and the survivors had a right to sue.

The reporter then held up a long yellow sheet of wire service copy. (I recognized it from all the hours I spent bothering AP and UPI bureaus.)

"Ms. Sharpless," he said. "Have you seen this column by a Mr. Arnold Shreck? It ran on the feature wire this morning and it'll be in tomorrow's papers."

"I haven't," she said.

I whispered to Al Jensen, "I didn't hit Shreck hard enough."

"Maybe too hard, Dave."

"May I read some of it?" the reporter asked.

"If it relates to the discussion. Is that all right, Reverend Jensen?"

Jensen looked at me. I shrugged. Shreck's syndicated column would be in the papers, not to mention the frequent radio and TV interviews he participated in, with a certain energy and, at times, even aplomb.

"All right," Al Jensen said, "is Mr. Shreck here?"

I could see Shreck, his jaw unbandaged, raising his tweedy arm. He sat in the rear row, unwilling to get too close to the plebs. Or maybe he was afraid I'd belt him again.

The young reporter—his name was Hemlich—began to read, pushing his sliding gold-rimmed glasses up his nose. "Mr. Shreck calls the column 'A Showcase for the KGB.' "

"*Oy vay,*" I said to Al Jensen and Tom Finnegan. "Worse than I thought."

Finnegan shook his head in disbelief.

The young man read on: " 'Unimpeachable sources in the American intelligence establishment have uncovered that the fifth anniversary celebration marking the so-called Joshua Massacre has been infiltrated by the Soviet secret police, the KGB.' "

There were some hoots and boos from the audience.

Billy Mallory was on his feet. "Here I am, folks. The Kremlin sent me."

Some people at least laughed.

The reporter went on. " 'These sources state that well-meaning liberal groups, no doubt sincere in their desire to commemorate the event that shook Joshua College five years ago, have unwittingly—or perhaps wittingly?—accepted financing and support from KGB agents posing as clergy, teachers and friends of the deceased students and the survivors.' "

"Moscow gold," Billy shouted. "I got a valise full of rubles in my hotel room. Arnold, baby, I'll show 'em to you after the meeting."

As the young man read on, not a name was mentioned. But the implication was clear. We were a bunch of boobs who'd been taken in by the reds. They'd taken our show over. Just the way they took over the nuclear disarmament movement, right?

There were more boos and hisses when Hemlich sat down.

Reverend Jensen walked to the lectern and joined Ms. Sharpless. "Mr. Shreck," Al said, "since you are here in person, perhaps you would like to come forward and tell us what you know. I'm sure all of us would like the names of those of us who have become dupes of the KGB."

Shreck was standing. "Thank you, Reverend Jensen. But that would not be possible."

"Why?" I said.

"Why? Because Soviet agents don't oblige us by revealing who they are *or* who they choose as dupes. The insidious part of it is, any one of you could be doing their work without even being aware of it."

I took about as much as I could, got up, despite a restraining glare from Rita and a frown from Finnegan, who felt we should ignore Shreck. Or at least try to.

"You want it both ways," I said over the mike. "First you say we've been infiltrated and duped. But when we ask for names, you cop out. The Soviets are so cunning that none of us even *know* if we're being used. Meanwhile you've spread your poison. Why don't you telephone your sources in Washington, and ask them for the Soviet agents who are taking this meeting over and who among us is working for them?"

"You don't understand, doctor," Shreck said. "That is not how they work."

"They, *who?* Our people? *Theirs?*"

"Any intelligence operation. People are controlled and manipulated without their being aware of it."

It was, of course, hopeless. And I understood why one cannot win arguments with such people (just as one can't with communists). If you don't even know you're working for them, that they've subverted you to do their dirty work, it simply proves that they are incredibly ingenious.

Peggy Sharpless chose to ignore him after I sat down, and spoke a bit more about the people in the state assembly who had opened hearings on a bill to permit us to advance a civil suit.

I stared at Shreck, tried to catch his eye, but he was hiding between shades and chewing on a pencil. Nausea riddled me; I felt my guts trembling. Been this way since Andrea died. I whispered to Jensen that I didn't want to speak again, didn't want to chair the workshop on community relations. He must have seen the green cast on my face, understood, said fine, he'd get one of the college seniors to run it.

I glanced at Helen Christopher. She still looked cool, as though aloof from all that was going on. Maybe Old Surrey does that to a person. Anyway, who'd ever accuse Helen Christopher of being controlled by the KGB?

Me, I'm a different animal. What I want is to see someone squirm and sweat and pay for murdering my daughter. That isn't much, is it, God?

. . . and here was this big man with the prizefighter's nose and dark glasses telling us we were all some kind of communist agents. I thought all of that was over, but I guess it never is.

"Bastard," Joe muttered to me. "Leave it to that crowd."

It was funny, his saying it, because Joe used to be sympathetic to them. Joey hated long-haired hippies and welfare chiselers and radicals. I guess he still does. But what he hated even more was being accused of being a sucker for them, being used by such people, like this man Shreck was saying.

Joe stood up. "Al, I got something to say." He turned around and looked at Shreck. "You got evidence, show it to us. Put up or shut up. Who told you we were working for the reds? Give us a piece of paper."

"Mr. Terragni," Shreck said, "I shall make that clear in good time. My sources are in Washington and they are reliable. I make no direct accusation against you or Dr. Schless or Mrs. Christopher or any of the students, or indeed any of the faculty. I shall have more to say in a later column."

Shreck smiled and sat down.

Joe was still on his feet. "Well, goddammit, I'm an American Legion member with six combat medals, a registered Democrat and a Roman Catholic, and anyone says I'm a tool of commies better come up with something more than the crap you're giving out or I'll—"

"Joey, calm down," I said. I can't stand these confrontations. Why do people have to be so nasty? I wondered again if we were right to leave our nice red brick house in Flagg City for this. If it wasn't for the memory of my Lucy I'd leave now. I can't take much more of it.

Thank God for Reverend Jensen. He was calm and asked this Shreck to produce any additional information he had, and then started listing the different workshops (I don't understand why they call them that) and who'd be in charge. I was to take part in one on women's roles in the university, but I decided I'd have nothing to offer. Joe was assigned to the police workshop, which didn't have any policemen on it. The whole business seemed kind of screwy to me.

Peggy Sharpless started circulating petitions for people to sign, asking that the assembly pass a bill that would let us bring our law suit. We signed it, but it didn't make me any happier.

I know that Dr. Schless says revenge will be sweet, and he will be happy to see the people who killed his daughter on the hook, but I'm taking no pleasure out of this. I have four other children (none as smart or as good as Lucy), and I have to live in the present and the future, and sometimes I wonder if all this raking up of that sad, terrible day does any good.

## Colonel Gregory Offitt

After I saw Marge off at the airport I hurried home, trying to control the trembling in my hands. This is not like me. I'm in tip-top shape. I jog and swim, although I gave up tennis two years ago after a cardiovascular incident induced by strenuous singles under a hot sun. My wind is good, as is my muscle tone for a man of sixty-five. But I was shaking.

Marge fussed and cried a bit at the airport. I lied to her about the hours I'd spent with Helen Christopher. Told her I had to look up some newspaper articles in the town library.

Odd how women have this intuition. They sense it, they know it when you have been with another woman. Saying that, I realize it sounds idiotic. I had taken a walk with Helen, tried to make known to her my feelings about her loss. Nothing had happened beyond a touch of hands. (She didn't encourage me.) Yet I was full of guilt and realized that Marge was aware of my . . . well, *dalliance* is hardly an accurate term for my innocent hour in Lecky Park.

"I'll expect you in two days, when this foolish business is over," Marge said. She extended her withered cheek. I kissed her dryly and saw her eyes stare at me. They were gray, unemotional. Lord, lord, the bottle's worst depredations had not been to her liver and nerve endings, but to her temperament. We never slept together. We were rarely intimate. The dry kiss, the light touch of hands. I wanted more from my remaining years.

Would I be ungallant if I said I saw the plane rise into the overcast sky with a pang of excitement, of anticipation? Rid of her . . . yes, rid of her for two blessed days. I told her I had to be on hand if accusations against my men—or indeed me—were to surface. With Bates Woffler dead and Judge Frankendorf out of things—they say he's nearly senile —I am the highest ranking law enforcement officer in the area, the one most directly connected with the Joshua Massacre. She seemed to accept my explanation, even if she didn't fully believe me.

Driving into our garage, I realized that the shaking of my hands— I had it under better control now—was due to the conviction that I would see Helen Christopher again, the two of us, and that I had many things to say to her, and to ask of her. It seemed foolish, like the yearnings of a lovesick teenager, but I knew what I wanted. And I would not be diverted.

As I walked from the garage to the pantry passageway leading to the kitchen I fantasized being alone in the house with Helen.

Why not? I have never craved wealth, fame or power. But in my middle sixties, with old age beckoning, I sense my energies diminishing. The desire is in me, that need for . . . a last fling, I believe, is the popular term. Even with a wife like Marge I have been dutiful, faithful . . . with the exception I've mentioned.

But Helen Christopher means more to me than a furtive union while our respective spouses are geographically removed from us. No. I am overwhelmingly drawn to her. I watched her walk away from me one day. Her body might have been that of a woman of twenty-five.

Is it an aging boy's erotic dream? The kind of lustful craving we used to have for a favored teacher, an untouchable young aunt, the blonde girl who peered at us from a ground-floor window as we went off to school? I do not know. But I do know that I would be untrue to myself if I did not act on this need of her. It would be *dishonest.*

Not thinking of what I was about, I lowered the collapsible steps in my bedroom closet—they work off a concealed spring and are dropped into position by a rope—and went up to the attic.

It was stifling and musty, and I reminded myself to remove the fiberglass insulation from the slatted vents at either end so that the fan might function more efficiently. Neither Marge nor I, accustomed to tropical climes and humid weather, mind the Joshua summers, so we have gone without air conditioners and opted for the noisy fan that I installed myself.

I sweated liberally. It poured from my forehead, my neck, drenching my shirt. I found my old khaki footlocker and pulled it away from a folded cot and a stack of cardboard shipping boxes.

My name, rank and serial number were stencilled on the scarred lid. There was also a fading insignia of the old division. I felt tears forming in my eyes. So many good men. So many good years. I had not a damned thing to be ashamed of.

Lifting the lid, I saw my manila envelopes, maps, books, newspaper clippings, and the memories of those grand days rushed back at me, caused me to wonder how I ended up my career commanding men who shot down unarmed children—but of course that was not the case. It was not nearly so simple. I'm glad there are people like that fellow Arnold Shreck who point out that as sad as the events were, they were . . . explainable, and in a terrible sense, lessons for all of us . . .

I found a clipping that made me smile. General Gerhardt at a press conference was asked by a correspondent why the First Army had made such a point of capturing the Normandy town of St. Lô. "It's a catchy name," the old man replied. "It fitted well in the headlines and the newspapers took to using it every day. After that it became a morale factor, so we *had* to capture it." When I think of the endless questions from the press I had to field I sometimes wish I'd been able to respond as cleverly. But cleverness has never been my strong suit. Moreover, as I look at the two events dispassionately, one could probably jest during a victorious campaign against the Nazis. We were all united in fighting them. How does one jest about three young people shot dead? (Although jokes *were* told all over Joshua about them.)

I keep thinking about the Christopher boy. Helen is circumspect, closemouthed about him. At least so far as I am concerned. Some references to his desire to be a scientist, problems as a student. I gather that her husband wrote the boy off even before the rioting. I pity Helen. I could have been a good father to that boy, to any of her children. I suspect that this fellow Christopher has kept her down, frustrated her. I feel I am a better man than he is. I want to prove it. To her.

Layers of old documents revealed themselves. My West Point days. High school clippings. A yearbook. A stack of military journals. Commendations and honors from the World War—II, that is. Also my service in Korea, consulting jobs for DOD, conferences I attended, lectures I gave. Two articles I wrote for "The Infantry Journal."

Some correspondence made me smile. When Marge and I lived downstate some years ago and I was working at a vice-presidential job, head of personnel for an arms factory and wanted to quit, some local folks tried to get me to run for the state senate. After two meetings with me they decided I was too *liberal,* almost a *radical.* They discovered that I was an advocate of integration of combat units, that I willingly accepted black soldiers. As, of course, did General Eisenhower.

I found what I wanted. A thick blood-colored envelope bound with a dark red string, the sort of container favored by tax accountants. On it I had lettered: "JOSHUA." Until the outbreak, I had rarely been concerned with events in Joshua, working as I did out of the state capital twenty-five miles away, taking my orders from the governor, involved with policy, training and community relations. It was only when the situation at Joshua College appeared to be worsening that I was dispatched there. Odd that it was my home town at the time. (As nearly as any place in which I have ever lived can be called my home town. Marge says we are capable of moving in and out of new homes and environments like cuckoos or hermit crabs. Maybe that is why—apart from other traits I've already mentioned—one of the reasons I'm drawn to Helen Christopher is that she represents that rooted life typical of small New England towns. Stability, a sense of place and time.)

I did not open the envelope. I held it in my hands. Heavy. Not just with the accumulation of documents, photocopies of correspondence, testimony, meetings and interrogations concerning the events of five years past, but also newspaper clippings, magazine articles, excerpts from books.

It did nothing for my self-esteem when I realized that I viewed the blood-colored envelope as a kind of . . . well, you might call it bait. Oh yes, in the privacy of these memoirs I can be candid with myself. There was material in there that Dr. Schless and the surviving people and their lawyers—most of all, their *lawyers*—would dearly love to get their hands on. I'm certain that amidst the stacks of duty rosters and situation analyses and reports to the governor and press cuttings there lie certain unrevealed data that could be devastating in its impact on the public, the press, the courts, every single person involved in the case . . .

Is it possible, I ask myself (feeling no pride in myself) that Helen

Christopher might respond to me more favorably if I were to make this material available to her, to Schless, to Finnegan . . . But of course I never would.

I returned the envelope to the locker, covered it with old military scrapbooks, looked with a rush of memories at the tenth anniversary reunion book I helped put out for the old division, and lowered the battered lid.

## August Karl Frankendorf

Assailed this morning by what my mother would have called the "vapors." It's astonishing (and gratifying) that for one who was such a delicate child, and had such a bedridden young manhood I have lived to my eightieth year, defying colds, sniffles, aches, pains. But never a truly serious illness.

Bachelorhood and childlessness, I tell my friends with a wink. Two guarantees for long life. I like women, I do. I tolerate children. But living by myself and for myself has had its rewards. I seem to be healthier now than when I was at Harvard Law School, the butt of crude jokes because of my "hick" appearance, my midwestern nasalities, my lack of sophistication. It's always seemed to me that I have to prove myself—my manhood, my talent, my courage. I can tell you that growing up as the sissy on the street, the boy who can neither run nor fight, hardens one for life's blows.

That is why I accept my petty ailments with stoicism. A few aspirin, a tot of brandy and I'll be fine. Later I'll take my blood pressure and feel my pulse. It's a bit irregular. PVCs—premature ventricular contractions. I tend to get them when I'm tense and agitated.

I awakened feeling a bit out of sorts, probably because I had been dreaming about the trial and the verbal battles between the prosecutor Kalt and defense counsel Merritt Winnington that never seemed to end, and which I, in my best judicial and impartial manner, had to referee.

In my dream Kalt, that bearded, bald young hot shot, was taking aim at Kevin Case, one of the trooper defendants. The sharp questioning awakened me, and I proceeded to review aspects of the trial, unable to sleep.

*I ask you, sir, to study this photograph. Can you show me where you are standing, and where the nearest student is?*

Case aroused my sympathy when he balked at answering. The young officer had been hyperventilating that awful day and had almost collapsed.

Finally Case replied that, yes, he was right *there,* in front of the high double doors that led to President Cudlipp's waiting room. The door was closed.

"And now, please," Kalt asked. "show me the nearest student."

Case coughed, looked at me, looked at Winnington and said nothing. "Sir, I . . ." The lad looked terrified.

I knew what was troubling him. Those damned photographs! There was no way they could be overcome. The picture that Kalt was showing to Case indicated that nearly all of the mob, that howling, foul-mouthed, rock-throwing mob, was *the length of a football field distant* from the porch of Cudlipp's office. Yes, I am forced to admit it. There was a scattering of students closer, perhaps one hundred feet away. A few even closer. I don't recall which ones. Maybe that vile Mallory creature, the nasty one who invented those obscene chants about the policemen and their wives.

In any event, Kevin Case would have to respond to the prosecutor's bullying, that yes, it was apparent that the overwhelming number of students were three hundred feet away, with perhaps four or five of them two hundred feet closer. *He had no choice.* Not just this one photograph showed that this was a fact, but *over a hundred photographs* did. From every angle. From the side, the front, the rear, from rooftops. There was even one photo taken from (of all things) a police helicopter, a photograph that should have been destroyed but had somehow, thanks to Schless's persistence, found its way into the prosecution's hands.

Kalt was on his feet, furious. "Counsel must know that photographs are routinely introduced as evidence."

They all seemed to be waiting for me as I considered the matter of those photographs. Then I summoned Kalt and Winnington to the bench.

"These pictures," I said, "we must discuss them." Kalt should have been impressed with my show of evenhandedness. He was not.

"Your honor, the FBI has vouched for their authenticity," the prosecutor said. He could barely control his anger. "Moreover, the precise time, within fractions of seconds, at which the photographs were taken has been established."

"But they don't tell the whole story," Merritt Winnington said.

His lime-green eyes were wide, accusing. A chunky orange man, powerfully built. Truly "one of the boys." At times in my life I might have said "bully boys." His father-in-law taunted me in high school. Did that explain my sense of unease with him, even now? Like he posed some threat to me? No, no. Nonsense. On the other hand, even though young Kalt had the power of the government behind him, I regarded him as a squirt, an upstart. Which he was, I assure you.

"Your Honor," Merritt said, sensing my hesitancy, "I don't like where the prosecutor is going with these pictures. Sure, they bear on the case. But he's inviting all kinds of speculation about them. Matters of opinion, dubious readings and so on. And he's confusing and intimidating the defendants with them."

Kalt was boiling. "Your Honor, photographs are routinely introduced as evidence—"

"Not if they're irrelevant and inflammatory," Winnington said. "Possibly even doctored—"

Kalt exploded. "Counsel knows very well that these photographs were taken by people present when the shooting occurred. The photographers have testified under oath. They included students, faculty and journalists. The FBI has examined them, taken testimony, checked them against clocks and other corroborating evidence. No one has ever raised the issue that they are fraudulent or doctored."

"But subject to misinterpretation," Winnington said quickly.

"You can raise that objection to any evidence," Kalt said. "It means nothing."

"It does to my clients."

"The photos do present a problem," I said.

"I agree, Your Honor," Winnington said. "The prosecutor is bullying those poor troopers. He's using these questionable photographs as clubs to beat them with. Evidence should not be used in that manner. We will introduce expert witnesses who will show that the camera can deceive . . . Foreshortening, perspective, angles—all these can twist the perception of a photograph. What a black-and-white image depicts may be totally at variance with the actual situation."

"Nonsense," Kalt said. "I'm merely asking the defendants to state what these photographs tell them."

He then showed me one of the key pictures, taken, I seem to recall, by the photographer for the *Clarion-Ledger*. Kalt said it had been determined it was snapped two seconds before the shooting. It was eleven-by-fourteen, a glossy print. I must confess it was totally at odds with the troopers' version of events. A sprinkling of students quite close, a few more a hundred feet back, and then a mob three hundred or so feet away. No one was charging. I did not even see an arm raised, as if hurling a missile. The police had their backs against the facade of the administration building and were levelling their weapons. They were helmeted, wearing gas masks, looking like men from a spaceship. I concluded that this photograph was "out of sequence," and not, as the government, as Kalt, claimed, the actual situation seconds before the firing commenced.

Having resolved this dilemma, I seized the bull by the horns and prepared to announce my decision to counsel, confident I would sleep soundly.

I looked at Kalt, then at Winnington, whose eyes were fixed on mine. Was he trying those old bullyboy tactics again? Perhaps trying to remind me how much he knew about my life and my career, including that outrageous incident against my law partner (dismissed, of course) and those things said about me, as though guity by association (how *unfair*)—I cut off the thought and proceeded to do my duty.

"Gentlemen, the court rules that these photographs may be shown once, and once only to defendants, witnesses and jury. However, they may not be used to interrogate or cross-examine anyone. That is forbidden."

"I must object," Kalt spluttered, "Your Honor owes the government an explanation."

So again I spelled out my misgivings about the pictures. Oddly, I sounded like Winnington. *Misinterpretation . . . inaccuracies . . . vagueness . . .*

Kalt made the mistake of quoting the famous writer who'd seen the photos and, he said, almost fainted in astonishment. *Why is there any argument over this?* he'd asked. *No one's being overrun. There is no charging mob. No one is surrounded . . .*

I brought him up short. "This, Mr. Kalt, is a trial, not a literary seminar. You will confine yourself to the evidence and the issues at hand."

"Your Honor, I must respectfully ask that you reconsider. If the FBI has vouched for these photographs—"

Merritt couldn't resist a dig, and I was obliged to suppress a smile. "Since when has Mr. Kalt been such a friend of the FBI? He's always seemed to me one of those who went out of his way to attack the Bureau."

We had wasted, I decided, far too much time on the photographs. I ordered them both to resume.

I could see the faces of the defendants—Kevin Case sweating on the stand; Kazinski, overweight and sickly looking; Hofheimer, Boyle, Trippi, Markland.

And the wounded. The Overstreet girl in her motorized wheelchair, her head braced in a metal contraption. That sneering Mallory creature displaying the target on his T-shirt. Colson, the farmer. Hoch, who was in medical school at the time. Oh, not really a bad bunch of young people. I was sorry for them. They had a right to their day in court. But I could give them only so much . . .

And the parents. I recall the Christopher woman, quite attractive, refined, sitting with the Schlesses. And that cursed dentist, determined to haunt me to my grave, huddling with her, scowling, all but shaking his fist at me.

"I repeat, Your Honor, this is an outrage," Kalt said. He was so angry that the words seemed to hiss from his mouth. Merritt's grin of victory rendered him even more furious, as, no doubt, did my ruling.

"I will decide what is and what is *not* evidence," I said. "You may show the photographs once and once only to the jury, and that is an end of them. No interrogation, no use of them in the summation, no references to them. They are then a dead issue, Mr. Kalt, I warn you not to raise them again."

He showed me another glossy. Three students on the ground. The Christopher boy crumpled, blood issuing from his chest. The Overstreet girl, wounded. The McCandless boy, with a bloody hand to his shoulder. And again, that vast expanse of lawn between them and the police . . .

"Your Honor, this photograph clearly—"

"No, no, no," I said. "Mr. Kalt, I will tolerate no more of this. The photographs will be utilized only in the manner I have indicated. They will not be shown to defendants or witnesses for the purpose of creating misleading and equivocal testimony. They are only reproductions of the event, and subject to question."

Kalt shook his head, sputtering. I could see Merritt's colleague Carter Hudspeth grinning as though he had scored a hole-in-one.

"Thank you, Your Honor," Merritt said. "That is fair. After all, the photographs speak, or don't speak, for themselves. They need no interpretation, nor should they be used to confuse or intimidate defendants."

Now, half-dozing in bed, I know that I did the right thing. I'm sorry those young people died. But sometimes society has to be cruel to survive. Isn't it all a matter of survival? Besides, what I did was what the people . . . eighty percent of them . . . desired. Community standards . . .

My limbs ache. The knees and the ankles don't seem to be functioning, as if they need lubrication. Crazy, but I have visions of Dr. Schless coming after me. The man is unbalanced. He won't rest until he goes to his grave. Or drives me to mine.

## Helen Christopher

As soon as the workshop—I hated the word—began I knew I was out of place. My mind wandered. I was afraid that these civilized, friendly exchanges of ideas didn't amount to much. I've decided that the real power lies somewhere else. I'm not sure where or how it gets its strength, or how ultimate decisions are made. But not in workshops or encounter groups or what they used to call rap sessions. Exercises in futility, Dan calls them. (Although ironically he was forced to attend a week of these seminars at the bidding of his company. Something about corporate responsibilities in a changing world.)

Our workshop was on family roles, for heaven's sake, chaired by a black woman undergraduate named Clovis McDaniel. Reverend Jensen and Tom Finnegan, who'd set up the seminars, wanted Joshua College undergraduates to participate and take a leading role. They hadn't drawn much of a response. Very few students were interested. After all, it was nearing the end of the academic year and they were studying for exams, or playing spring sports, or worrying about jobs.

The other members of our panel were Wilma Overstreet, her fiance Timmy, a sociology instructor whose name I didn't catch—a bushy-haired man who stoked a pipe and said almost nothing—and Mr. and Mrs. Carl Fein, owners of a Joshua hardware store. They seemed shy and confused, and they told me later that the only reason they were there was because Reverend Jensen asked them to. He was short on local people, he told them, and the Feins, as respected local residents —they had a son at Columbia and a daughter at Brandeis—seemed to fill the bill.

"Frankly, Mrs. Christopher," Mr. Fein said to me, "we'd just as soon not be here. For us it's better to forget that whole awful thing. It was a disgrace. All of it."

Nobody seemed to want to speak first. Finally Clovis, who was an articulate young lady, prevailed on Mr. Fein to say a few words.

"Okay, I'll try . . . Look, who can argue about family influence? We all try to teach our kids to do the right thing. Sometimes we succeed. Sometimes we fail. Sometimes other influences work on them. I know plenty of kids from good families who go wrong. Less today than maybe ten years ago. But they still go wrong."

Clovis suggested that television might have something to do with it, the TV set taking the place of parents . . .

The conversation drifted and swirled around me, like those low clouds of artificial fog one sees in old scary movies. I suppose I should have contributed more but I'm viewed as sort of a martyr by association, a role I don't relish.

Mr. Fein was saying, "A terrible accident, the whole thing. A lot of those kids didn't understand how mad people can get. I mean, they weren't bad youngsters. Mrs. Fein and I can tell you, six of them came around to help us clean up broken glass, to get the stock back on the shelves." He sighed. "I don't know what the kids were after. I don't know why they felt they had to curse everyone, burn buildings."

Clovis McDaniel listened politely. I sensed her priorities were elsewhere. She turned to me. "Mrs. Christopher, do you want to add to what Mr. Fein just said?"

"I'm afraid I'm still confused about a lot of things that happened." I hesitated. They were all looking at me, the Feins, the bushy professor, Clovis, Wilma and Tommy.

"God forgives everyone," Wilma offered.

Timmy's Adam's apple did a dance. "Yes, God understands why these things happen. He isn't angry at anyone. If everyone accepted the Lord He would make all things clear."

Wilma clapped her long white hands. "Oh, God is so good. He teaches me every day to love Him more, to love everyone. I have no hate in me, not even for the policemen."

The sociology professor cleared his throat so loudly I thought he'd strangled on his pipe smoke. But he said nothing. One finds it hard to fault (or to agree with) the Wilma Overstreets of the world. They have, after all, all the answers. They are strangers to doubt. There is really nothing to be discussed. Workshops, indeed.

Clovis smiled at me. "You were saying?"

"I'm not sure what. I lost a son. I grieve for him. Maybe at this late date I'm almost willing to accept that it was a dreadful accident, a freakish thing. But, but . . ."

They were all looking at me . . . for what? I hate to be the center of attention. I wished Tom Finnegan were there. Or Dave Schless. Dave would have jumped in with both feet.

"Go on," Clovis said. She'd make a wonderful school principal someday. Maybe a director of a social welfare agency.

"Well," I said, "this isn't original with me. but it seems people reacted to this as though it were a television show. They could hate the students and defend the police and feel it was all right because maybe no one *really* died . . ."

The sociologist blew smoke at the ceiling.

"I don't know. Maybe people were able to work out their own secret emotions. Believe those dreadful lies that Andrea and Lucy were pregnant or had diseases. Or that my son was a dangerous radical. It was a TV program."

The sociologist finally spoke. "The bullets weren't make-believe. They were real, Mrs. Christopher."

"And for that matter," Mr. Fein added quickly, "the curse words, the things thrown, the threats from the students . . . they were real also."

"I think," I said, looking at the sociologist, "I'm aware the bullets were real. As opposed to the rusty gun that was supposed to have been found on my son's body by a state trooper who admitted it was a lie."

To my amazement none of them—including Wilma—remembered that I kept quiet after that. I was too damn angry to trust myself to speak.

## Dr. David Schless

Billy Mallory grabbed hold of me as I came out of the police relations workshop. The session had gone surprisingly well. None of the local cops had participated and none of the state police, naturally. The commissioner of state police, a guy who was not in office five years ago, sent a polite letter, hoping that our meetings would lead to "greater understanding." I kept hearing about *understanding* when what I wanted was justice . . . revenge.

Still, it had been a good session. Lots of interesting information from a police chief named Busby from Massachusetts, a guy with a master's in social work, young, tough, a former naval officer, who told us that it was inconceivable that the cops should have had live rounds in their weapons.

Hubie Colson and Bernie Hoch both recalled seeing two of the troopers ramming magazines into their weapons but couldn't remember an order being shouted. I pointed out they were very far away, and amidst the chanting and cursing it would have been impossible to hear orders.

Harriet Blochman said she'd gone over the trial testimony and it was never explained how some of the troopers ended up with rounds in their weapons. They all had testified that they had heard no order, couldn't recall if any officer had given such an order but vaguely remembered someone—unknown—shouting "Load and lock." The testimony was contradictory and ambiguous and had a strange odor—as if Kazinski and Doyle and the others couldn't get their stories straight. Then good old Gus Frankendorf, Harriet recalled, had jumped in and scotched that line of inquiry.

The Massachusetts cop said it was unthinkable, beyond the range of proper responses for men in such a situation to face a crowd with live ammo. But he couldn't venture a guess as to how they came to do it, who would give such an order and why.

I mentioned that Colonel Offitt had denied that he had ever given the order to load and lock. The two junior officers present, Captain Durham and Lieutenant Mrak, had likewise sworn that no such order was given. It had just happened. *Boom,* weapons were loaded, *boom,* they were fired into the crowd. Kalt, the prosecutor, had tried repeatedly to get Kazinski or Doyle or Case or the other three to say *precisely* why they had loaded up, but he had failed.

Billy Mallory, who'd taken part in the college affairs workshop, stopped me on the steps of Dexter Hall, where I was waiting for Rita and Harriet Blochman. Harriet had invited us to her apartment for lunch, a chance to rest for an hour or so before the afternoon meetings and listen to some of Harriet's classical records. Why is it that mathematicians and physicists are so taken with classical music? I guess the precision, the construction, has something to do with it. A musical score always seems to me to suggest a page of equations.

"How'd it go, doc?" Billy asked.

"Good. We may get a story in the local papers on the visiting police chief's statement. Interesting stuff on riot control. Why the weapons should never have been loaded. Why they didn't use more tear gas."

"I could tell 'em. Me and Pulsifer were tossing the canisters back as fast as they could lob them at us."

"Sure. You're some hero." I like Billy. Harmless, wise to himself. Unlike a few other parents, I've never blamed him, or Lyle Pulsifer, or any of the other crazies for what happened to Andrea. The truth is, Billy and the other presumed agitators were never a match for the powers-that-be, the force of the state. Oh, they could cause an eruption here and there, burn a building, call a student strike, shout obscenities.

But when it got down to cases, they were a tiny minority who aroused hatred and fears among ordinary Americans all out of proportion to their numbers and their significance. Sorry, kids. Well, what about the Vietnam War, you may say. Look, I'm a dentist, not a pundit, but it seems to me that war ended when the *middle* of America came to see that war on television and to ask questions and decide it was a failure and a mistake. And it came to a dead halt when Richard M. Nixon and Kissinger followed suit, even if they did so kicking and screaming. The demonstrations and sit-ins and teach-ins had less to do with it than people would like to think. The conservatives and middle America, ironically, did the trick. After all, Vietnam was a liberals' war. Kennedy and Johnson, and their genius advisers, McNamara, Taylor, the Rostows, the Bundys, et al., were proving to the world that they were a hundred times more anticommunist than the Republicans. No future Joe McCarthy could ever paint them red. It took a conniver like Nixon, an anti-red conservative with no firm belief in anything, to end that awful slaughter, just like it took Ike to end the war in Korea. He could afford to. Who would ever accuse the general of being soft on communism . . .

Rita joined us. We strolled down the sunlit steps of Dexter, saw Harriet Blochman striding purposefully in jogging shoes.

Billy lingered, as if something were on his mind.

"Catch you this afternoon," I said. "There's a report on the seminars scheduled for five, then we break and the evening is free."

"I may split," Billy said.

"Why?" I asked. Rita frowned.

He scratched his neck, tugged at his ponytail. "I dunno. It's getting oppressive."

"I do anything wrong?" I asked. "The memories too much for you?"

"Nah. I can handle them. They're worse for you and the missus."

We walked toward Harriet, who greeted us.

"Billy is thinking of leaving," I said.

"I hate to sound like a rat fink, so I better tell you," he said. "Lyle Pulsifer sent me a letter. My old lady read it to me on the phone this morning. It's sent me up the wall. I mean, it makes me think I'm the wrong guy to have around, that I'm not exactly a hero. Or much of anything else."

Rita said, "What could Lyle possibly have to tell you at this late date?"

"Plenty. Lyle says he was a police stooge. The local cops had busted him for peddling drugs. They were threatening to send him away forever. So when the demonstration began—so Pulsifer says—they came to him and forced him to spy on us or else they'd pull the plug on him."

"Lyle?" Harriet asked. "That starved wretch who never seemed to know the time of day?"

"Zonked out of his noodle half the time, Harriet," Billy said. "But that wasn't the worst of it. He was finking on us to the cops. And more."

"Don't tell me," I said. "He was the sniper?"

"Almost. Lyle says he was ordered to torch the Quonset by unnamed police types. They said to him, go burn it or you'll forget what the sky looks like. So he suckered me to go along with him, the two of us being the only certified radicals around."

I nodded. "And the next thing you know, Cudlipp calls in the state police and then there's shooting the next day."

Mallory nodded. "Lyle says he had to tell somebody, that he's finally ready to face the music if they come after him in Alaska. He's bumming around on fake papers but they'll catch him if they want him. He says he's sorry, but they could have thrown the book at him."

"They still can," Rita said.

"So?" Billy asked. "You see why I want to get out of town? I'm not so brave or cocky any more. Jesus! Euchred into starting this mess by my best buddy. I'm sick of it, doc."

"You're staying," I said. "And you'll tell this at a press conference this afternoon."

"Do I have to, doc?"

"You have to, Billy. I realize there's no chance we can get Pulsifer here before the weekend, but by God, he will come back to Joshua soon and he will spill his guts."

"What if he doesn't?" Mallory asked. "Maybe he'll hide out with the Eskimos."

I confess I sounded stronger than I felt. For all I knew Pulsifer could be lying.

"He'll come back," I said, "if I have to drag him back by his hair."

Rita shook her head. "Old Mountie Schless. He'll get his man, come glacier or grizzly."

Mallory brushed his hair back. "I guess you're right, doc. I'm not proud of myself. Dirty words and empty threats. I'll hang around.

I'll try to get Lyle to say publicly what he said to me, maybe soon."

"In public and under oath," I added. I hoped.

## Helen Christopher

The Finnegans invited me to have lunch with them and with two reporters, one from the Flagg City newspaper and one from a television network. But suddenly I was terribly tired, drained. I began to wonder if Dan had been right and that I had done myself no good coming back to Joshua.

I pleaded fatigue and went back to the motel, where I found that Dan had phoned me twice. It was Saturday, his day for golf or working in the garden, and I felt vaguely ashamed of myself for leaving him. I knew he didn't like to be alone. Dan was always a social man, a friendly man. His loud, emphatic voice dominated parties, echoed through the bar car, resonated in locker rooms. People didn't object. Dan's gregariousness was rarely resented. He needed an audience (no matter how small). So in spite of the argument we'd had about my running off, I understood why he felt the need to call me. Perhaps he'd played an early-morning eighteen holes and was now home preparing a cold lunch, looking at the dogwoods that needed pruning. He wasn't too keen on trees.

He sounded subdued, no hint of drunkenness—his voice tended to get thick after two drinks.

"I miss you, hon," he said. "I'm sorry we had the scrap."

"I miss you too, Dan."

"Then come on home. You showed up, you met the press. Whit Bundy said he caught a shot of you on CBS sitting on a dais or something. Enough, Helen. Grab the next plane back."

"Just one more day, Dan. I'll be home Monday."

"Well, I'll respect your choice. But I don't agree with it. How are you handling it? I mean, walking around that campus, seeing all those places . . ."

166

"I guess well enough. As well as the others, the Schlesses, the Terragnis."

"Well, don't let anyone use you."

"Use me?"

"I saw an article in the paper today. Column by that writer Arnold Shreck. He says the Joshua memorial is a commie operation—"

"That's absurd. He made the same sort of idiotic statement at a press conference here. Dave Schless challenged him to produce a shred of evidence, and of course he didn't . . . Dan, is that why you called me?"

"I just felt you should know. I hoped it would help persuade you to come home."

"To get away from the KGB agents? Really, Dan. Who? Tom Finnegan, who has a chestful of medals from the marines? Or Dave? Or the Terragnis?"

"He named some guy, an informant, an expert on subversion . . ." He paused. "Anyway, I *really* called you because I miss you, honey. I don't want us scrapping over Jack or anything else."

"I agree with that, Dan. I'll be back Monday." Back to dutiful wife, tennis player, garden club lady, hospital volunteer . . .

"I was looking at our wedding pictures . . . I needed to talk to you. You know I love you, Helen. You're a so much better person than I could ever be—"

"Nonsense. I'm hardly perfect, and I didn't marry you because you weren't a good and decent man—"

"Well, anyway, I went sort of crazy when I saw those photographs. You're so beautiful. Then and now. That white satin and lace dress with the low-cut shoulders. I could smell the lily of the valley. God, I wanted you. Couldn't wait to lift that satin skirt, all that trailing stuff . . . I'd like you right now, if possible, in your bridal gown with all the lace and elastic and stockings and garters . . . honey, I've never loved anyone so much, I'm sorry our lives have taken this lousy turn. I'm sorry about that letter, the things I said about Jack. Come home, honey, I *need* you."

"Dan, I promise you we'll try. But I think I owe it to Jack to be here. To the end."

"Helen, will it ever end with them? Dammit, I want Jack out of our lives. Yes, I do. He's dead. Helen, you know that for five years now we've had lousy sex. We can't wait to get it over and done with—"

"Dan, don't—"

"Yes, you know it's true. Something went out of us after he died. He messed up his life and the truth is, he messed up ours."

I tried not to cry. "I can't hear any more of this, Dan. You have to respect my feelings, too. I've always tried to respect yours—"

"Maybe it's the way it had to be. I know my limitations. I'm not as strong as you are. You do things right. Me, I blunder, I fake, I'm full of locker-room baloney and bad jokes. But I need you. All of you. Including the part my son took with him when he—"

"What do you need, Dan?"

"You. Helen, can't you understand? My life is checking up on other people's reports, pushing papers, nodding my head at meetings, trying to break ninety. There's got to be more than that. You were always the *more,* Helen. If the office was a pain in the neck, or my friends didn't measure up, or if Jack and I had a fight, you were there."

"Dan, did it ever occur to you that I should be more than just a prop for you? Someone to keep your ego afloat? Or satisfy your sexual needs?"

"Hell, yes. I understand your needs. I never objected to your career. Teaching, tutoring. I encouraged you, didn't I?"

Well, he hadn't been exactly enthusiastic, but what was to be gained by raking up the past? He'd always chosen our vacations, what movies we saw, who our friends were. I accepted and maybe I deserved what I'd come to be . . .

He insisted on reading me a few lines from the newspaper article charging that we were KGB dupes, and then his voice rose and he said again he loved me but that I made things difficult for him. We ended the conversation on a strained, uneasy note.

I took off my dress and my slip, lay on the bed in my underclothing, a cold compress on my forehead, and thought about our picture-book wedding in picture-book Old Surrey. It was October. The Connecticut foliage was riotous with oranges and dark reds and bright greens, almost too bright and beautiful to be taken in. A small wedding, an old white church, our families and friends. Dan was handsome. I was pretty. We were both young and very much in love.

And I recalled how he had managed later at the country inn upstate —it was quite a feat—to make love to me in my wedding gown. I would be lying if I said I didn't enjoy it. He'd been a vigorous, attentive lover.

And he was right about our sex lives having deteriorated after Jack's death. I sympathized with him, and was as sorry about it as he was.

Once, after an evening of trying to arouse one another, he said, "You never stroke the back of my neck anymore. You don't run your hand against the grain of my hair the way you used to."

I mumbled that I was sorry. I began to caress his head. But it didn't excite him. My mind was on Jack, wondering what he was thinking, how much pain he was feeling when he was struck by the bullet. I wanted to ask Dan—as I did months later—how in God's name he could have written that letter? He was kissing my breasts, saying that they were like the breasts of a twenty-year-old girl and that no other woman had ever excited him the way I did, but I just lay there, unfeeling, barely responding to him.

It was a warm sticky night. We were tired after tennis and had bathed. In the old days, before Jack died, we would have devoured each other. (How little people know about us WASPs, Dan would scoff, how all the surface blandness hides an ocean of passion, and he'd kiss me all over, clutch at me, probe me, almost in tears . . .)

And when he entered me—after a lot of fumbling and missing and grunting—I couldn't join him and I felt sad for both of us. The intervals between grew longer, the sessions shorter, the joy diminished, and I knew much of it was my fault . . .

"I want you back here," he was saying again. "Dammit, you're all I have, you know you mean more to me than anyone in the world."

I told him I'd be back on Monday, if the KGB would let me go. He didn't laugh.

## Billy Mallory

I'm getting paranoid. If I didn't like Doc Schless so much I'd split. That's one thing about us burned-out cases, we really don't like getting hit, taking the fire. Forget all that stuff about demonstrations, sit-ins, nonnegotiable demands. Most of us couldn't stand the heat. Not just the clubs and tear gas, but we didn't like the bad press, the ugly publicity, the hatred. Fact is, we were mostly spoiled middle-class kids with big mouths. Me included.

Doc Schless had every intention of grabbing me by the ass and shoving me in front of a microphone to tell the conference what Lyle Pulsifer had said in his letters. Some radical, some revolutionary. I always suspected we couldn't have staged a revolution in a raw-sewage treatment plant in North Dakota. Doc had this obsession with the Joshua College thing. It dominated his life. I wonder how the poor guy ever had time to fill a bicuspid or yank a molar. And his long-suffering wife, Rita. People used to call her "Poorrita," like it was one name. A nice-looking, tall woman with dark brown eyes and prematurely gray hair. She was a social worker. But I could see that the anger inside her husband for what the bastards had done to Andrea was grinding her down.

So I decided to stay. I'd known Andrea Schless slightly and I liked her. Kind of dreamy girl, with a long pale face like her mother, the same eyes. She'd had a few boy friends. One was a guy I knew slightly named Eddie Galanter. A terrific bridge player. She never impressed me as much of a radical. She was just out there, like most of us, pissed off at the sight of so many helmeted, masked, armed cops on campus. I don't even know if she was angry about the tuition increase.

You know about the crazy stories that went around about Andrea. I wonder about the depths of hate and meanness in people. They cheered the murders, lied to cover them up, and had to drag the dead and the wounded through garbage . . .

So there we sat in a green plastic booth in Meyerhof's Luncheonette, Harriet, cool and unemotional, the Schlesses and me. Nobody paid any attention to us. When Wilma came in, pushed by Timmy, a nifty wheelchair driver in spite of his rambling Adam's apple, she drew a few stares but that was all.

I could see Wilma and Timmy bending and praying before eating their tuna-fish sandwiches (they'd brown-bagged it and ordered lemonade to go with their lunch) and it made me feel vaguely optimistic and a little ashamed of myself. Normally I can't abide Christers and Bible-bashers. But maybe Wilma had the answer. Shoot me in the spine and cripple me, but I will still pray for you, I will still love you.

At least nobody went around saying Wilma was gay or pregnant or

170

had VD, like they did about Andrea. You can't pull that crap on a devout Christian. Every few years some fundamentalist born-again, evangelizing, antiabortion proprayer clergyman surfaces who, it seems, has been screwing the girls of his flock or buggering boys who share his faith. Amazingly the charges never stick. No one gets hurt. Nobody does time. It seems that if you are holy enough you are excused anything at all. Old Samuel Johnson—it's all I remember from English Literature Survey, 101–102—said that patriotism was the last refuge of a scoundrel. But I sometimes think it's religion.

We munched hamburgers, sipped drinks, listened to the whirr of the air-conditioning and wondered where we were headed. Doc Schless noticed that a truck had delivered the afternoon paper from Flagg City. The driver had barely loaded the newspaper paybox outside than Doc was up, out of the luncheonette and back with a copy.

"Shreck is after us," he said after sitting down. He showed us an eight-column banner headline on top of the logo:

### HOW THE KGB TOOK OVER THE JOSHUA WEEKEND

The story carried Shreck's by-line and his title "Columnist, Global News Service."

To his wife's distress, Doc started to read Arnold Shreck's exposé. Much of it was the same junk Shreck had spouted at the assembly that morning. Reverend Al Jensen was quoted as saying the charge was nonsense. Tom Finnegan and Harriet Blochman were identified as "leaders of left-wing causes." But Shreck was careful not to say they were getting Moscow gold to organize the three-day conference. Nor did he name anyone as a dupe or an agent.

"Nothing new in it," Rita said. "He doesn't give a single name. He didn't at the meeting, and he doesn't now. Because he doesn't have any."

Schless pushed away his cheeseburger, gulped his coffee down and was scowling at Shreck's article as if he wanted to eat the paper. He riffled the pages, turning to the news report on our conference was brief —and scanned the rest of Shreck's attempt to cut out legs off.

"Ah, a *name,"* Doc said. "Listen to this. 'Much of the information in this report comes from the files of Mr. Miles Pendragon, a respected Washington consultant to government and business, and the head of the Manifest Destiny Group, which keeps files on communist activities, espionage and disinformation. Mr. Pendragon, in conjunction with this writer, will soon produce documentation and other evidence establishing the extent of KGB infiltration into the Joshua case."

"That's a nifty handle. Miles Pendragon." I laughed. "Who he?"

Doc handed the newspaper to Rita. "I don't know. But I'm sure as hell going to find out." He got up. "Got a friend at the AP bureau in Washington. We'll run a check on Miles Pendragon, maybe know more about Shreck's source. Maybe Arnie will earn himself another belt on the chops."

"Dave, no," Rita said.

"One phone call, Rita, that's all." He lumbered to the pay phones at the rear.

Doc had gotten to know a lot of important journalists after the massacre. He was an honest source, always ready for quotes and TV statements, afraid of no one, and I mean no one, not the state cops or the governor or a roomful of right-wing loonies.

Doc came back grinning and rubbing his hands. "My friend at the AP is going to do a little digging. He saw the Shreck piece too and he says it smells like a dead bluefish."

Rita asked, "Suppose you prove that Shreck's accusation is a bunch of lies? Will it make a difference? Does anyone care anymore? People can say anything they want about us. Just the way they said those things about Andrea . . ."

Doc Schless's face turned gray. "It'll matter to me. I hate these bastards. I hate their lies and their vicious tactics. If I can nail them I will."

Lunch didn't go too well. I glanced at Wilma and Timmy, eating their homemade sandwiches, and thought once again that maybe they'd found the best response to the horror. For them, anyway, the Lord had all the answers, and He didn't care doodly about lies, fakery or smears.

## Sally Terragni

I bought an Italian bread, some ham and provolone and black olives in Mangara's Deli, and Joe and I sat and ate with Hubie Colson and the Hochs under a beautiful big oak tree about fifty yards from the fountain where Lucy was killed.

All of us fussed over the Hochs' baby Jonathan. He was only ten months old but was darn near walking, an active, happy infant. Bernie Hoch—hard for me to think of him as Dr. Hoch—would let the baby hold his index fingers, and little Jonathan would walk up Bernie's stomach, his chest, right on to his face and forehead, giggling and gurgling all the way up. It was amazing the way the baby was able to climb almost straight up, digging his curling feet right into Bernie's body, never tottering.

Sandra Hoch kept telling Bernie not to be so rough with the baby, not to raise him so high, but Bernie laughed and said the child had wonderful coordination and muscle tone and would probably be a gymnast or a track star. We all laughed at the way the baby refused to stop, bawling when he reached Bernie's bald head, demanding another climb up his daddy.

Then I saw Joe blinking behind his sunglasses. He put down the poorboy I'd made for him and stared at the infant. I knew why. Lucy had been the same kind of active, well-coordinated baby. She'd walked at ten months, talked a few months later, amazed us with her smartness. Two of our boys are terrific athletes. Ron is a Little League pitcher and Vincent is a basketball star at Flagg City High. But when they were tots they couldn't compare with Lucy in acrobatics and running. I remembered that Lucy used to walk up Joe's hard body the same way when we'd be fooling around in the backyard, and how just like Jonathan Hoch, she'd holler for more, another swing through the air, another bear hug from her daddy . . .

Joe looked away. He keeps his thoughts to himself. He was a man who thought he'd figured the world out as best he could. At least our world. We are working-class people. Joe had spent most of his life in the foundry. He became a shop steward, served on union-management boards, ran for local office—board of finance—and was a member of St.

Leo's Church and the American Legion. He bowled, he fished, he kept a gun in the house (never fired it, even in practice), voted the Democratic ticket but opposed school busing. A real American, he called himself.

But somehow he'd lost faith in all the things he believed in and all the organizations he supported after Lucy was killed. At first we accepted it as an accident. But it was *not.* Someone fired those guns. Someone made excuses. A lot of people lied. *And that trial!* They were all against us. For a long time, no one would sit near us at mass. The Legion voted to expel Joe after he began collecting signatures for a new trial. The union voted Joe off their governing board. Men at the factory who'd been his best buddies, bowling and fishing pals, they snubbed him.

It changed him. He was so solemn now, sitting there silent for hours, wondering how this had happened to him. Trying to find answers. I wish I could have helped him. I wished I could help him now. He isn't an educated person like Dr. Schless or Helen Christopher, but I don't think there's any education that would help him figure out why he lost a daughter and his faith in a lot of things he once believed in.

My poor Joey.

Hubie Colson picked up a copy of the campus newspaper, the Joshua *Trumpet,* and was reading a story about the weekend observances. The paper was sympathetic to us. It had run an editorial welcoming the three-day event as a chance, it said, to improve "student-community relations, a chance to learn something from the awful events five years ago."

"Like what?" Joe asked.

"It doesn't say," Hubie said.

Bernie Hoch offered a bit of cheese to the baby, who chomped it, bubbled, spit it out. "Don't like provolone, Jonny?" he asked. "Try some ham, kid."

Sandra clucked her disapproval. He'd ruin the baby's feeding schedule, she said. Not to mention his standing with the rabbi.

Hubie read on. The newspaper report had nothing new in it except for one thing. We all perked up our ears when Hubie read it.

"Hey, get this," he said. " 'A college trustee who refused to be identified told the *Trumpet* that plans are afoot to construct a new computer center halfway between the administration building and Dexter Hall, at the site of the Florentine fountain." He didn't say this would wipe out where the killings took place. He didn't have to. He finished reading the quote. " 'This expanse of empty campus would be an excellent site for the new building.' "

All of us were stunned. There'd been talk about a statue, or a plaque on an archway, something of that sort, so that future students would know about the massacre. But it seemed the powers-that-be had decided that a computer complex could better fill the space and erase forever the bloody ground where Lucy and the others died.

"Sounds like higher-ups, politicians," Bernie said. "I never thought the idea for a statue would get very far. Anyway, I'm not so sure it would help."

"Maybe not," Sandra said. She gave the baby the bottle. He jammed two tiny fists against its plastic sides and sucked hard. "But at least the ground should be left alone. Nothing should be built there."

"Says here," Hubie read, "the college doesn't have any more available grounds and can't afford to buy new land."

It didn't seem right. A gray building, all stone and metal and glass, filled with blinking lights and machines, all that computer noise and gadgetry, right over the green grass . . .

Joey hadn't said anything when Hubie read the article. Then he coughed, raised his head and said, "By God, if they try, if they just try, I'll be the first one to lay down in front of the bulldozer. Nobody puts up a building where my daughter died."

We said nothing. The baby gurgled. Across the campus some young boys in T-shirts and shorts tossed a Frisbee.

"You wouldn't, Joe," Colson said. "What good would it do?"

"It would do me good."

I took his hand and kissed it. Ten years ago he cheered when the police dragged away some long-haired kids who'd squatted at the gates of a nuclear power plant. Now he was ready to lie down in front of a bulldozer.

"I'll get on the grass with you, Joe," I said.

I must see Helen again. Marge is gone. I'm restless, filled with tensions I can't stand.

Twice I've gone back to the footlocker in the attic, taken out the blood-red envelope. The last time I didn't put it back. It's setting on my desk here in my study, and it almost seems to be alive, or possessed of some inanimate power, like a radioactive chunk of metal, or a triggered booby trap. What shall I do with it?

I keep feeling that this pack of papers—notations to myself, transcripts, bits and pieces I've saved—can bear on my feelings about Helen Christopher.

I telephoned the motel. At the sound of her soft, somewhat breathy voice, I began to sweat, like a damned amorous schoolboy.

"Helen. I must see you again."

"Why?" she sounded distant.

"I . . . I'm fond of you." I felt like an ass but I couldn't stop. "Are you busy this afternoon?"

"Please, colonel, it isn't right"—even though, she thought, it might be helpful to Dr. Schless's cause—"I'm not interested, not in the slightest."

Did she protest too much? Wishful thinking? "Helen, you've suggested your marriage is unhappy. That letter your husband wrote, things haven't been the same—"

"Stop it. Such things are none of your business—"

"I apologize. It was stupid. Don't think in terms of anything physical . . ." Saying so, I realized I was lying, like a drunken soldier caught sleeping on guard duty.

"I'm exhausted," she said. "This weekend . . . It seems we have too much justice on our side. Too much evidence. Facts are irrelevant. Testimony can be thrown out. Oaths are broken. Why? It seems my son deserved to be killed and that your people had a right to do it. It came too clear when that terrible writer Shreck made his speech and printed that column. We are part of the great conspiracy. Such idiocies. Maybe my husband was right and I should have stayed home—"

"But then we wouldn't have met."

She paused. I had the feeling she was shaking her head at my naivete, maybe suppressing a laugh.

"Helen?"

"Yes . . . I'm willing to believe you personally had nothing to do with Jack's death. But I can't have any relationship with you, on any level—"

"I offer my friendship, that's all." What else could I say?

"I'm too tired to talk anymore. What do you want? My forgiveness?"

"There's nothing that would mean more to me. I wish we could be friends . . . Can't I visit you this afternoon?"

My legs were unsteady. I thought vaguely of my undergraduate days, courting Marge, when she was slender, blonde, a wispy girl from an upstate New York town. All flowery in a pale blue chiffon gown at my graduation day at the Point.

The images were vague. Our first night of love . . . a hotel in the Adirondacks near Schroon Lake. A stone and log place with bearskin rugs, high ceilings, blazing fireplaces, and her tears. From the start they inhibited me . . . I recalled Marvell . . . *Had we but world enough and time,/This coyness, Lady, were no crime* . . . Except there was not enough time. I was, after all, sixty-five . . .

"Colonel, I'll be resting for the vigil. I promised the others I'd be there, holding my candle through the night, singing and praying. The Schlesses are counting on me."

"Maybe I am too."

"You mean you're for us? This sinister mob of Soviet dupes lamenting their lost children who got what they deserved . . . ?"

I knew she was avoiding my real meaning but I had to answer her. "No, I sympathize with you. I've said so. I said so at the trial and afterward—"

"You also said the system still works."

"I meant that the matter needed to end, to be laid to rest. Helen, we both know there is no such thing as perfect justice. Never has been. I'm afraid you must accept the terrible turn of fate that singled out your son."

Was she breathing heavily? Did I imagine it . . . as I imagined her bobbed light-brown hair, serene forehead, clear blue eyes. Was she undressed? She'd said something about trying to nap . . .

"I want to see you again," I said. "Learn more about you. Try to console you. I can't manage a lifelong burden of guilt. Not where you're concerned."

"What about the others? Can you bear the guilt of Andrea or Lucy any easier? Are you without any burdens over what happened to the Overstreet girl?"

"You're the only one I've ever admitted to how I felt."

"Interesting. You've never been indicted, the grand juries didn't touch you. The governor even praised you. The judge congratulated you."

"Guilt isn't always settled in court," I said rashly.

We went on like this a bit more. I was grateful for every moment of it . . . "I have an idea," I said. "There's a concert on campus tonight. A string trio. I'd like to take you."

"Ridiculous. My friends—the Finnegans, the Schlesses—they'd be convinced I'd lost my mind." She hesitated. "What would they think of my sitting on the lawn with the man in charge of the troopers . . . a man some think may have more to tell than has come out—"

"I have suppressed nothing, I've nothing to hide." At that moment I think I believed it. "Look, we can sit in my car and hear the music."

"It sounds like a drive-in movie."

Was she weakening? "I'll be a gentleman, I guarantee. Please, I'll pick you up at seven-thirty."

She waited. Then . . . "Well . . . all right. I could use some relief from worships and press conferences."

Her voice sounded cool. No matter. I would take her on any terms, in any mood. Humiliating? I didn't care.

## Dr. David Schless

Tom Finnegan heard a rumor this afternoon. A lousy one. Counter-demonstration. Strong possibility that the local lumpenproletariat and their friends, hardhats, angry patriots and so forth, will stage their own demonstration tomorrow night when we begin the vigil.

Tom learned about it from a bartender who was in his old marine division, a guy named Sal Valenti. Valenti—I'd met him once—is not especially sympathetic to us but he's not the type who thinks the cops should have killed three hundred instead of three.

Anyway, he told Tom that a bunch of local toughs, millworkers, unemployables, jocks were being encouraged by some shadowy older guys—I never learned who they were—to stage their own rally for God, flag and country just off campus near the main gates. Finnegan asked him if they were looking for a fight. Sal said, no, just a lot of noise. Loudspeakers, flags, songs and so on. They were inviting State Senator Anders Foxwood to speak. He was the most conservative member of the legislature, the guy who started impeachment proceedings against the governor when the latter agreed that the federal grand jury should take over. Foxwood was a buddy of Merritt Winnington, the troopers' lawyer, and had been close to Bates Woffler, *alev hasholem.*

Rita overheard my conversation with Tom. We were sitting on campus waiting for the afternoon workshops to start. I was sorry Finnegan blurted it out in front of her. She wanted the weekend to end. The memories of Andrea were getting to be too much for her. She looked worn. Every now and then I saw her dab at her eyes with a handkerchief. Oh, my friends, it is no small thing to lose a child. At least I have my rage to keep me going. Rita is too gentle to live on anger.

"What if they pick a fight?" she asked.

"Unlikely," Finnegan said. "A lot of noise, tributes to John Wayne and George Patton, military marches. President Cudlipp doesn't like the whole idea and they've been banned from campus. He's also getting out all the local cops and a platoon of state troopers."

"Oh, yeah," I said. "We know how friendly they are to us."

Finnegan tugged at his red beard. "They've changed, Dave. Really, they have. If any good came out of the five years ago it's that they now give these guys special training in riot control. Loaded weapons are *verboten.* They even hired a psychologist from the state university to brief them on riot situations. They seem to be a pretty decent bunch. Maybe the powers learned a lesson."

"At our expense."

The Terragnis came up to us. We were sitting on a stone bench not far from the Florentine fountain. It had been turned off. I don't know why.

Joe Terragni, like Tom, had heard about the counterdemonstration and he was sore.

"It's a free country, I told Joey," Sally Terragni said. "If we stand around with candles and pray, I guess they can do their thing too, right?"

"I know half those guys who'll show up," Terragni said. "Wife beaters and drunks. The kind of bums who goof off on the job and spend their overtime pay on boilermakers. I mean, if you're gonna counterdemonstrate against me, at least send something better than that."

Joe knew those people, he was one of them, and all they would need was to get sufficiently beered up, stirred up by State Senator Foxwood, and there might be some bad moments.

I tried to sound confident about the news, mainly for Rita's sake—but I was upset. Maybe I'd run into one fat bum I'd met five years ago outside the Flagg City Hospital . . .

*Who ya lookin' for, Skippy?*

*Andrea Schless. My daughter.*

*Oh, she's dead. Got caught in a crossfire. The students were shooting at the police. One of the students' bullets killed her . . .*

And the fat bastard *grinning* at me. The louts behind him under the bright fluorescent lights of the hospital entrance snickering and winking, cradling shotguns and patting sidearms. Did one of them call me a Jew fuck? Rita says I imagined it. I always am imagining things, she said.

And this big turd, pale white face, black sideburns and droopy mustache, a belly like a bass drum, and an inner tube of fat bulging a blue T-shirt. I wanted so badly to punch the living shit out of him. Maybe, maybe dear God, he'll show up with his concerned patriots at the college gates, and maybe God, you'll give me the chance I missed, the offer he refused. Of course I would have to do it without Rita's knowledge. She'd never know. Oh, Lord, grant this to your humble servant, your devoted petitioner David Arnold Schless, D.D.S. . . .

Finnegan had set up an office for the memorial directors in the basement of Dexter Hall, where most of the meetings were being held. The reporters were invited to use it, and people like Tom, Al Jensen, Harriet and myself utilized it to make phone calls, catch our breath and so forth.

I stopped off there to see if there were any messages and was delighted to learn that my friend at the Associated Press, Ben Millhouse, had called back. Quite a guy. Smokes a pipe, is given to long silences, and has won two Pulitzer Prizes. Also, he is a registered Republican, a Presbyterian and a teetotaler. But the man is ferociously honest and always gave me a fair shake.

I returned the call immediately and got through to Millhouse. He had a tendency to whisper, to muffle his voice. He told me once that it was one of his greatest weapons in covering Congress. The lawmakers imagined that a man so quiet, mannerly and self-effacing couldn't possibly be a threat, and consequently talked their heads off to him.

"News about Miles Pendragon?" I asked.

"Arnold Shreck's source for the story on KGB infiltration of the Joshua Memorial movement is an interesting fellow, David."

Only Ben Millhouse and my mother call me David. "Such as?" I asked.

"Mr. Pendragon has been a professional informant for about eight years. Witness for committees, publisher of a newsletter called "Fight We Must," lecturer and panelist on such topics as How to Destroy Secular Humanism and The War that Must Be Won.

"Is he for real?"

"Pendragon is described by my sources as an habitual liar, a con man, a perjurer. He's been indicted for mail fraud."

"You're making this up."

"No, it's real."

"Who's your source, Ben? Some lefty sorehead?"

"Nope."

"Who? Some anonymous spook? Informed source?"

"Goodness, no."

"Who, Ben?"

"The FBI."

I whistled loud enough to draw a startled look from Rita. I heard Finnegan say to her, "Doc's on the warpath again, must be good smoke signals . . ."

"This for attribution, Ben?"

"No names, please. But the FBI didn't hesitate to release the text of a report they issued to a congressional committee on Pendragon. Quote: 'Pendragon is viewed as an unreliable source whom the FBI refuses to use and whose statements and publications must be regarded with suspicion,' Unquote. There's more. All here from the Bureau. I've got friends there."

"And a dear friend here, Editor Millhouse."

Well, we were getting somewhere. I couldn't wait for my next *mano à mano* with Arnold Shreck. All those flaming conservative ex-liberal intellectuals . . . sooner or later they'll have to learn whom they've crawled into bed with.

Finnegan and Rita were in the office with me. "Doesn't surprise me that Shreck's swallowed Pendragon's slaverings," Finnegan said. "Those guys have the notion that *anything* they disagree with has to be the work of red Russian godless atheism. You'd think Shreck would know better. He *used* to be a liberal until someone pointed him the other way."

"There's nothing wrong with being against communists," my wife said. "Dave and I are. We don't like what they're doing in the Middle East and Africa. Or at home, for that matter. But this compulsion to label everything you don't like—our weekend, for example—as being part of a Soviet conspiracy, that's too much."

I rubbed my right fist with my left hand—as if getting ready to belt Shreck again as punishment for his failure to check sources.

"Cut that out, Dave," Rita said. "I know what you're thinking."

"He'd goddamn well better retract that trash he published about us or he may have to bandage the other side of his jaw."

"Dave, stop," Rita said, but she was smiling.

## Helen Christopher

Three times I've been tempted to pick up the phone and call Colonel Offitt. Why did I agree to see him? I need to try to be honest about that.

Here I am, watching the evening news, waiting for him to come to take me to that concert. The man who made excuses for the police who killed my son! And I'll be sitting in his car, turning away his advances . . .

Why? Some perverse attraction? Wanting to understand the mind of a man like that, to better understand my son's death? To encourage him to tell something to help Dave's case?

Maybe I'll call him in fifteen minutes and I'll plead a headache or a bad stomach . . . I was barely aware that the local news program was presenting a mini-debate between our friend, Assemblywoman Peggy Sharpless and the so-called journalist Mr. Shreck, who said we were unwitting dupes of the Russians . . .

I'd gone to a legal issues workshop chaired by Alvord Jensen and I had found it confusing. A lot of smart lawyers and legislators, a professor of criminal law, but all their talk about laws, protection, rights to a trial, the Bill of Rights rang a bit hollow. What's the good of such things if most of the public favors awful miscarriages of justice? No one confronted that. In a way the armed vigilantes who'd faced Dave Schless at the hospital seemed to be calling the tune. *Their* notions of justice appear to be society's response to the killings . . . as if that damned effete Judge Frankendorf, that gentle, cultured bachelor, were taking orders from fat men in leather coats, swilling beer from the can and carrying guns. God . . . it can't be so, I don't want it to be so. But there it is . . .

At least Colonel Offitt is a cut above those people, except I can't forget he supported his police. He was an important witness for the defense—his character, combat record, appearance did much to sway the jurors . . .

Watching the debate between Peggy Sharpless and Shreck did nothing to make me feel better. It seemed the opposition had everything on their side. To use an expression of Jack's when he was in elementary school, Shreck "wiped the floor up" with the state legislator—one of our few friends in an official position. The Shrecks of the world (left or right) seem to win arguments. Those of us in the center take on a heavy burden. We try to listen, admit mistakes, aren't always sure. But if you're a Shreck you have all the answers, you're right, the other guy is wrong.

"The police were well within their rights," Shreck was telling Peggy Sharpless and the moderator, a TV newswoman. "No one wanted anyone killed or wounded. The students invited the firing by their arrogant refusal to disband and remain behind the line between Dexter Hall and the administration building."

"But *live ammunition,* Mr. Shreck?" she asked. "Loaded weapons for a crowd of unarmed students?"

"They were not unarmed. Stones can kill. Sticks can maim. Three troopers suffered serious contusions. One was hyperventilating. The police later collected knives and clubs and other lethal weapons including a homemade grenade."

I was bursting to cue Ms. Sharpless. *Ask him about the rusty gun they claimed to have found on Jack's body.* But either she didn't know or didn't want to raise the issue. Shreck had ridden roughshod over her, made her look rather foolish or at least naive. He defended the police actions. In the chaotic situation it was natural for the troopers to feel threatened, to load their rifles and to fire back.

"*Back?* Did anyone shoot at the police?"

"Missiles, sticks, stones, canisters—language that no man could tolerate for long."

"This justifies killing?"

"It *explains* it and the courts have upheld it. Ms. Sharpless, this entire weekend is an exercise in futility. It is being exploited by those who seek to undermine our system. It is not a memorial observance. It is a dangerous political act coming at a time when our country needs healing, not new wounds . . ."

And so it went. Viewers were invited to phone in to ask questions. The first caller was a deep-voiced woman who congratulated Mr. Shreck for "putting the record straight," then said, "You know, of course, that there were two snipers on the rooftops who opened fire on the police before they fired back. It's a well-known fact. These two communist gunmen came down from Chicago and started it and then were sneaked off campus. Why is the media suppressing this?"

Shreck agreed this was valuable information and said he would pursue it. All this five years after the FBI, the district attorney and two grand juries had dismissed any possibility of a single shot being fired from the student ranks. It made me dizzy, nauseated.

Another caller blamed the riot on something called "the Tri-Lateral Commission." No one understood him.

I couldn't take any more, turned the TV off. Yes . . . Jack did a foolish thing joining that mob, shouting obscene words, throwing stones at the police. Who would have thought that our bland, unfocused boy could end up that way? Or explain it?

Once a psychiatrist told me that Jack's was an act of defiance aimed at his father. The man was prissy, with a mustache. He had a didactic manner. We were at a pool party at the Wallings' estate down the street from us. The psychiatrist (so Dan made sure to advise me) had his eye on me all afternoon, touching my elbow and my knee as we sipped gin-and-tonics at poolside, letting his eyes linger on my thighs. He knew all about Jack's death and the way Dan and I had disagreed over that letter.

"Rebellion against authority," he'd pontificated. He looked a bit like a bald chicken and moved like one with jerky movements of winglike arms. "Urge to kill the father."

"I beg your pardon?"

"Those kids. They see the cops and the university officials as their fathers. And every male has that need—"

"That's ridiculous. Jack and Dan had their problems but they loved each other."

"No matter how loving the father, all sons want to kill him and possess the mother."

"The Oedipus complex? I don't take it as gospel, sorry. Of course there's a glimmer of it in children. The mother gives love, affection and warmth. The father is big, loud, strong, maybe a threat at times. But murder—"

"It's there, Helen. In the hominoid band—the old ape men who preceded us, and from whom we haven't progressed very far—it assuredly took place. At a certain point the sons decided they'd had enough of the father's bullying, so they clawed and bit him to death and mounted the mother. There's no taboo against incest except in humans."

I tried to get away, but Dr. Arenas held me with a talonlike hand.

"I realize you've been wounded. What I tell you should be part of your psychological preparation to confront the loss of your son . . ." God, what a terrible pompous pedant . . . "Let's get back to the hominoid troop. They not only killed the father, but they ate him. Why waste meat? This primeval racial memory is with us. *All* of us. Part of our heritage, whether we like it or not. Kill and devour the father, couple with the mother. It's so basic, face up to it."

"*People* aren't apes."

"Apes and worse. Your son, from what I've read, was a gentle type. The kind who repressed his feelings. Oh, he loved Dan. Daddy, what'd you bring me from New York today? Daddy, you got a present for me? Can we go fishing? Can you teach me to ice skate?"

He said this in a child's sing-song, and for a blurred moment I saw Jack standing there (overweight even as a nine-year-old), lank blond hair falling over his pale brow, his chubby hands hooked in the belt around his baggy shorts. Nothing ever seemed to fit him right—broad in the beam, paunchy, thick-legged. Jack . . .

"You're saying that my son exposed himself to loaded weapons, taunted the police and invited the bullets because he saw his father on the portico?"

"Of course. He was getting back at the old bull-ape. The Oedipal dream. Kill the father. Know the mother."

"And the girls? The Schless girl? Lucy Terragni? Wilma Overstreet?"

"More complex. But if they were actively engaged in throwing rocks and cursing, then they viewed the police, deep in their ids, as their mothers. It's the mirror image of the same thing. Destroy the mother, cohabit with the father. Probably a less strong drive but it's there—"

"Nonsense. Half the kids who were shot were shot by accident. They weren't even part of the demonstration. Lucy Terragni was crossing the campus to go to a class."

"Accidents, yes. Doesn't invalidate the basic truth. I'm just trying to explain Jack to you. He was responding to a primordial urge. Cops/father. Guns/his father's penis—"

"I won't listen to any more of this."

When Dr. Arenas finally left to ply his trade with a blonde TV actress —at least at the moment he wasn't charging a hundred dollars an hour for dispensing his gems—I closed my eyes and absorbed the summer sun, listening to the *pop-pop* of a tennis game, hearing people splash and laugh in the Wallings' Scott pool, which with landscaping, deck and other accessories had cost them one hundred and ten thousand dollars, we'd been told. There was even a waterfall rushing over native stone.

With the sun heating my face, creating splotchy patterns of reds and oranges inside my lids, I had the upsetting notion that maybe there was *some* truth in the psychiatrist's attempts to "explain" my son's actions that day . . .

Jack did always seem to be hanging around my bedroom when I was getting dressed. Peeking from behind half-open doors, even bursting in at times and, I suspect, looking through keyholes while I gartered my stockings or put on cosmetics. Even as a small boy he'd be around, staring at me, his eyes fixed on my half-clothed body, my stockinged legs, my high-heeled shoes . . .

Yes, he must have had some compulsion to gaze at me, to wonder about my body, to entertain a child's obsession and curiosity with those normally unseen lace-and-elastic-and-satin garments that his mother wore. Once he stole panties and a bra from my dresser. I never did find the missing panties. Pale green, I think they were. Did Jack use them for . . . ?

And once I discovered him—he could not have been more than six —crouching in my closet, pressing the hem of my black evening gown to his face. He said he was hiding from "bad guys."

But so what? The mother is of course a male child's first sexual object. How can it be otherwise? But there was nothing abnormal or dangerous in Jack's childish infatuation with me, his harmless voyeurism. To make the leap from this to his participation in a student mob, inviting the punishment of police guns, made little sense. A student riot is a student riot. Male and female students, jocks, radicals, grinds and a lot of neutral types like my son were swept along, just to be part of the crowd, to see how far they could go in baiting the authorities, daring the police to act.

What did any of that have to do with Jack's fear of his father or his infantile attraction to his mother? Nonsense. Just as I'd told Dr. Arenas.

He'd come back now, wet after his swim, and was taking a survey course in my extended legs, peering obviously at my crotch. Such subtlety.

I could see Dan on the other side of the pool, arguing with some men about computer chips, glancing at me now and then, even winking as he noticed Dr. Arenas's attentions to me. I think perhaps it reinforced Dan's pride or something when other men were attracted to me. Or maybe it was a way of handling jealousy.

"You see, Helen," the psychiatrist was going on, "you're a discreet, reserved woman. Discerning men understand that beneath that veneer of propriety there's an erotic woman."

"Oh, dear." Lord, he was so corny, and obvious. Hard to believe he had the reputation as a good therapist. He must leave himself at the office door.

"I hope I won't be charged for this analysis." After that he drifted away, gave me up as a hopeless case, I hoped. Still, it's true I wanted men to be attracted to me. And it's true something . . . some lack . . . some failure in our marriage gnawed at me. Not a failure in bed. There were missing parts, a picture that was incomplete. Neither Dan nor I were strong or candid enough to face up to it. Much of it was my fault. I guess I felt sorry for him. I knew that his moodiness and his drinking and his impatience with Jack (less so with our daughter) reflected his sense of an unfulfilled life.

These random thoughts about my marriage passed through my mind as I rested, half-clothed, in the cold motel room, watching the sun set over the green fields outside. (Joshua is rich farming country. One tends to forget that, probably because the name has become so closely associated with the college and the rioting.)

Again I was tempted to call Offitt and beg off. Once I actually dialed his number, then hung up after the first ring. It had been stupid and weak to agree to see him, no matter how I rationalized it.

Rita Schless phoned to see how I was holding up. All the afternoon workshops had gone quite well, she said. There was a good national TV coverage. A news magazine was interested in a wrap-up article, a look at Joshua and the people involved five years later. Again, would I be willing to be interviewed?

I said yes. It was the least I could do for Jack, and for Andrea and Lucy. Especially since I was about, for whatever reasons, to consort with the enemy.

# August Karl Frankendorf

Merritt and young George Dempsey had me out to the club for dinner. The usual polite, almost deferential reception from members and employees pleased me. I've earned it. In a sense, I am an adornment. Not just the judge who presided honestly and fairly at the Joshua police trial, but the man who almost singlehandedly has tried to preserve culture here.

The concert tonight, which I'll attend later, is partially the doing of my little group, working in conjunction with the college. The Kirinskis are in residence at the state university. Absolutely marvelous, brave, talented people. One would think that their courageous escape from the Soviet Union would tell a lot of people about the vileness of the Russian system. It certainly tells me a great deal. The Flagg City newspaper says that communist agents are manipulating the weekend events. If they are, how stupid can people like Dr. Schless and Professor Finnegan and the others be?

Merritt Winnington's wife, "the Duchess"—a formidable creature built, it seems, of slabs of concrete, although local wags say gold bricks are more likely—had gone to Chicago to shop and see a play. George Dempsey was newly married and had a tolerant wife.

So I was glad to bach it with two professional colleagues, even though Merritt had a way of being presumptuous, insinuating, more or less forcing me to come to dinner. He'd snorted at my desire to attend the concert. "Long-hair stuff," he grumbled. "Puts me to sleep." He loves to play the philistine. Many men do, suppressing the sensitive and artistic. I never have. I am not ashamed to say that, like Tolstoy, I weep when I hear Beethoven, and I can be stunned into a holy silence by a Rembrandt. The first time I saw *The Night Watch* in Amsterdam I had to sit down and catch my breath for a few minutes. In my youth I almost fainted when I first laid eyes upon Michelangelo's *David* in Florence . . .

We sat on the veranda under the striped awning watching friends come in from the eighteenth green. We sipped cold drinks—I had only iced tea, since I want my perceptions fine-tuned when I listen to music —and ate roast beef. Ernest, our Negro maître d', and one of the finest men I know, orders the beef from a secret butcher, and there's much joshing over his close-mouthed attitude about his source.

It was peaceful and private, and I was glad that younger men like Merritt and Dempsey were interested in an old fogey like me. We chatted about local politics, and then George Dempsey asked me about Colonel Offitt.

"What about him? A fine fellow."

"Merritt, take over," Dempsey said. "I'm supposed to be impartial, I have official status."

Winnington grinned. I wish the man would stop. And stop acting as if he had some . . . edge on me. He doesn't, damn it. I tossed those photographs into the trash bin because I, and I alone, determined what was evidence and what was not. I didn't need him, or Kalt, to tell me how to run my courtroom. No, *indeed* . . .

"Be glad to, George." Merritt worked on a chunk of pink beef and went on. "I had a chat with Dennis Boyle last night."

"Ah. One of the six."

"Brightest of the lot. I love that kid. He and Markland and Kazinski had a private talk with their former commandant."

I had no idea where this was leading or why it concerned me. But suddenly I had lost my taste for Ernest's roast beef, and only toyed with the great pink slab on my plate.

"Denny is a sharp kid. He's the one who convinced Kazinski to come clean on the rusty gun deal. He also got the guys to agree that the sniper angle was horseshit and they'd do well to drop it. Denny may take a leave to go to law school."

I commented that I'd heard from the young man and would be glad to write a letter of recommendation for him.

"Well," Merritt went on, "Boyle is a bright one. He claims that Offitt isn't exactly kosher."

"In what way?"

"He knows things. Could just be he's hiding something."

Dempsey inhaled. "We thought you should know this, Gus."

Merritt added, "Or maybe you know more about Offitt than we do?"

"Not at all. Everything came out at the grand jury hearings. The trial covered all those bases. None of Offitt's testimony was ever challenged or disproved."

Merritt quaffed his Heineken. "It's what he didn't say that bothers us."

"I don't follow you, Merritt."

Dempsey's eyes wandered to the green-and-white awning, stayed fixed on it. He was glad to let Merritt carry the ball. But what did any of this have to do with me?

"Before Bates Woffler died, Gus, when Bates was in the hospital, he told me some bothersome things," Merritt said.

I asked why he had never informed me of this before.

"No reason to. It was confidential."

"Then why bring it up now?"

George and Merritt exchanged looks—as if to comment on my naivete. The old judge. A little senile. Humor him along. Lead him by the hand.

"That bastard Schless is on to something, is what I think," Merritt said. "Can't take his medicine. Yes, his kid got shot, but if she'd been back in her dorm instead of throwing rocks at the police or calling them cocksuckers, she'd be alive today."

"I wish you fellows would stop treating me as if I were a child," I said. "George, I knew you when you used to deliver the *Clarion-Ledger* to my front porch. Merritt, you and I have gone 'round and 'round many times. What are you talking about?"

Merritt clasped his huge spotted hands and squinted. He did this in court often. It meant he was searching for the right words. "Gus, Colonel Offitt may have told Bates Woffler some things that could prove to be a pain in the butt to all concerned. I never trusted Offitt. A by-the-book guy. Not one of us. He wasn't from Joshua, took graduate courses at Columbia or MIT. I'm not sure he's trustworthy."

Dempsey nodded. "Oh, the colonel is okay, I guess. But Woffler told Merritt that Offitt had serious doubts about the troopers' story. About the defense they were going to put up. About their version of the shooting."

"He didn't talk that way in court."

"Yeah," Winnington said, "but that was after Bates explained to him what was at stake."

"What's the difference? The case can't be retried. The colonel has said nothing. And that civil suit Dr. Schless keeps threatening will never come to pass."

Dempsey stroked his chin. We were silent. I could hear a foursome of club members laughing as they came in. Ed Kettleman was bragging how he'd just broken the course record for "divorced men with hernias."

"Gus," Dempsey said in a low voice. "Offitt had lunch with Blochman and Schless and the Christopher woman. Don't look shocked. Then he postponed his trip to Tucson and sent his wife off alone."

"It does sound odd," I said. "I would think he'd be happy to get away from this unseemly turmoil. Actually I thought of going up to the lake myself. I'm nonplussed. Offitt sitting down with Dr. Schless? Why?"

Merritt laughed. "Maybe he's got the hots for Mrs. Christopher. She is one elegant head, I kid you not. That pickled lady he's married to, that alone would send a virile old combat officer out on a reconnaissance patrol. Well, whatever the reason for his fraternizing with the enemy, it's got George and me worried."

"But what can he say? And why would he do anything now that would open the whole ugly can of worms and make him look bad?"

Merritt said that Boyle and the others were wondering the same thing. Which brought him back to what Bates Woffler told him while he was dying of a massive coronary occlusion.

Parenthetically let me mention that Bates Woffler . . . most tragically . . . died very young. Not even forty, the poor fellow. A bachelor like myself. Evidently he had a history of a weak heart and did not want the burden of a wife and children. He was supposed to have open heart surgery, but he became sicker and sicker, suffered several cardiac incidents and, as I seem to recall, developed a severe insufficiency of the carotid artery. (When one is my age one develops a working knowledge of medical terms, ailments, cures, procedures.)

Bates was an odd duck. Young, lean, sinuous as an eel. With a great curling mop of handsome brown hair . . . and dark silky skin. He had doelike slanted brown eyes and a soft manner. He could be most persuasive. He was extremely conservative, had strong views on society and was much in demand as a speaker. He believed, he said, in a "new kind of American society" based on virtue, honor and obedience. After that he left me . . . I confess I never fully understood him, or felt altogether comfortable with him . . .

"Bates didn't trust our colonel," Winnington was saying. "He felt the way I did, that he'd been exposed to too many influences, had picked up too many peculiar ideas, taking graduate courses at eastern colleges. They can louse up a man's sense of what's really important."

"Woffler actually said he didn't trust Colonel Offitt? I'd like to hear specifics," I said.

"Before he died, Bates told Merritt he suspected Offitt was taping their conversations," Dempsey said.

"Taping?"

Merritt shut his eyes. "Yup. Bates said he thought he heard something humming under Offitt's uniform."

I mulled this for a moment. "Did Woffler say what was discussed?"

"These were conversations just before the trial in your court, Gus. The usual review. Bates was out of the case by now, since the feds had taken over. But he wanted to make sure that everything was covered, and that Offitt knew the drill."

"The drill?"

"You know what I mean," Merritt said. "To keep the right testimony fresh in Offitt's mind. Woffler knew he was dying, and I guess he wanted to warn us. He said that Offitt had started getting antsy before the trial. What about I don't know and Bates didn't say. But he wanted to alert us that there might be recordings of their little chats and we might do well to try to find them."

"But the colonel didn't alter his testimony, and he supported the defense's view of the events in every detail."

"So he did, so he did," Merritt said. "I think Bates wanted to make *sure* he never changed his mind."

"Why should he?" I asked. "The trial is over. The police were acquitted. Experts have reviewed the trial and deemed it fair. The federal government has laid the case to rest forever."

Dempsey said, "We just wondered if you'd heard any of this. From Woffler, or Offitt, anyone. About secret tapes."

"Of course not. I doubt they exist. A dying man's disjointed comments are highly suspect . . . By the way, who else knows about Woffler's deathbed statements?"

Dempsey said there was a suspicion that my fellow jurist Judge Herman Althouse may have heard about Woffler's concerns over Offitt.

"Which may explain," Merritt said, "why Althouse came down so hard on the state grand jury . . . Jesus, the shredding, the burning and the burial of the indictments . . . I think Althouse went overboard."

Things are never quite as we imagine them, are they? I had a great deal of respect for Brother Althouse, though we had differing views on the Joshua matter, and I could appreciate, or at least understand, his displeasure at the way Woffler had handled the state grand jury. Althouse had called the indictments of students and teachers "a stench in the nose of justice."

"How would he know?" I asked.

"Offitt may have talked to him," Merritt said.

"Most unlikely," I said, my palms feeling moist.

"Then maybe he's getting ready to talk *now*. Who knows what that Schless will try? Blackmail, threats, getting the Christopher woman to tickle his balls. I tell you, Gus, Bates may have been a strange young man, but he was no dummy, and if he thought Offitt was a weak link, a source of worry to us, I'd believe him."

"But the colonel applauded the verdict," I said. "He said the system works. His very words. The man is honorable and decent and stood by his troopers. It is inconceivable to me that he would suddenly come up with a story that would make him out to be a perjurer. And what would it accomplish?"

"It would get their damn civil suit off the dime," Dempsey said. I didn't like his patronizing tone of voice.

## Billy Mallory

Doc Schless is still on my case.

I wanted to go beering with Bernie and Hubie and a couple of local potheads who knew me five years ago, dropout types who have settled into middle-class niches such as spot welding and insurance but who long for the old days when we didn't care whether school kept or not.

But Dave had this strategy session scheduled in Finnegan's office, and I had to be there. He was going to have another press conference tomorrow. The reports from the workshops would get a fast shuffle—double-talk, file-and-forget, kiss-and-make-up, come-to-Jesus stuff. It would all, Dave said, be published in handy book form in a few months.

What really intrigued him, he told the subcommittee on publicity—Finnegan, Jensen, Peggy Sharpless and Bernie Hoch—were two breaking stories, headline stuff that would surely make the evening TV news tomorrow. And maybe a few headlines. Schless had already alerted the networks, the AP and UPI.

"Billy is going to make his speech about how Lyle Pulsifer was a police fink and how they forced him to torch the Quonset. Right, Billy?"

"If you say so, Dave."

"I guess I didn't sound enthusiastic. Reverend Alvord Jensen assured me I'd be doing the right thing for God and country.

Schless said he also intended to confront Arnold Shreck with the information on Shreck's informant, some asshole named Pendragon, a wrongo even the FBI tabbed as a con man. Pendragon was the "Soviet expert" who had given Shreck the straight dope: the Joshua Memorial observance was being orchestrated and financed by Moscow gold.

Neither idea seemed to me of much value and I said so.

Doc got pissed. He said that I had better do well and tell everything Lyle Pulsifer had said in the letter. In fact, he intended to get Lyle back to Joshua as soon as he could find him and make him tell his story to the D.A., the FBI and like that. As for the Pendragon story, if nothing else it would give Arnold Shreck a few uneasy moments.

"Yeah, yeah, Dave," I said, "but how long can we go on noodling like this? The country likes to bury this kind of mess. Put it away. Forget it. So three kids got killed. Too bad they were white middle-class kids. But, Jesus, blacks have been getting knocked off down south for a century and no one really cares. There's no retroactive justice."

"This case is not over," Schless said. "The story of what you and Pulsifer did may not get us back in court, but on the other hand, who's to say it won't, that at least it won't make a dent in the wall so that something else will surface that will give us one more crack at those people . . . ?"

There is one tape, that's all. It's eight millimeter, pale brown, tightly coiled around a white plastic reel. It was specially designed for surveillance, secret tapings, wire jobs. I had no trouble borrowing the recorder —about the size of a playing card and a quarter of an inch thick—from the police communications unit in Flagg City. No questions are ever asked of a commandant. I have the feeling that my aide, Sergeant Trump, has long forgotten my asking him to get the item for me.

*Why did I do it?*

Hard to say. A man spends all his life believing in honor, truth and duty. Then something happens to fill him with doubts, questions about what his life has been worth, and how he may have compromised his ideals, his most profoundly held beliefs, through one misguided act, words he cannot call back, amend, retract.

I sat in my living room—not much to show for a life of military service—amid awards, diplomas, the Meissen china my men gave me when I left the ETO, antique Korean pottery, old photographs, a Berber rug that Marge and I bought in Fez—and stared at the tape.

Woffler had no notion that I was taping our conversations. A hateful man, if deceptively plausible. When he started his snide comments about General Eisenhower I was glad I had decided to get his voice on record. Let him speak for himself. *Someday, someday . . .*

But the day never came. I recorded him. What we said to each other. The anger, the threats. Things he would never admit to. And yes, things I would never admit to . . . there in the privacy of his office beneath the autographed life-sized head of J. Edgar Hoover.

"I'm not an admirer of your hero Ike. A naive man who unwittingly, perhaps, aided and abetted subversives. He's the one brought down Joe McCarthy, you'll recall. McCarthy was correct, if crude—"

"McCarthy was a drunken liar, sir. He uncovered not one communist in all his hearings. And I really don't think I need any lecture on communism from you. I fought in Korea and Vietnam . . ."

It wasn't much of a conversation. Woffler didn't want to talk politics. His concern was for the coming grand jury hearings. He said that he'd run them, make the jurors dance to his tune. State grand juries aren't all that independent, I've learned. Local politics, prosecutors, police all work magic on them. And Bates had his set notions about what the grand jury was going to find in the matter of the Joshua Massacre.

"I intend, colonel," he said, "to turn this shameful mess on its head. I know exactly how to do it. There will not be a dirty finger laid on your police, on you, on the college administration. The blame will be placed on those who deserve it."

"Namely?"

"Those who started the riot. And the faculty members who goaded them on. And any agitator, out of state or in state, who descended on our town with the intent to disrupt the orderly processes of life. Clear?"

I was getting all of this on the recorder. He had a resounding voice, and he enunciated carefully. In the courtroom he was terrifyingly effective. Not only did opposing counsel, defendants and witnesses fear him, but he seemed to strike cold terror in the hearts of some judges.

It was as if Bates Woffler possessed some arcane unearthly power, some preternatural ability to cross boundaries and enter forbidden places. Others in the legal process steered clear of these miasmic corridors. Bates Woffler sought them out.

He knew in me he had a willing audience, and could be far less beguiling or subtle than in an open courtroom. My career and my reputation were indeed on the line. I wasn't just another witness. I was a potential *defendant* if the federal government ever invoked the Civil Rights Act. Moreover, I was in the eye of the hurricane. Men under my command had pulled the triggers and killed three students. The buck had to stop somewhere.

The reels spun noiselessly in the mini-recorder that was taped to my chest under the khaki shirt. (I was in uniform that day.) The microphone was cunningly designed to look like the head of a fountain pen. It protruded from my shirt pocket, peeking out of that little eyelet they sew into military flap pockets. I could not hear the battery-powered spinning of the reels, but I felt a faint vibration, a rhythmic sensation, almost as if a pacemaker were humming beneath my skin.

"You've been terrific so far, colonel," Woffler said. "You've said the right things."

"Very few things."

"Even better. The less we talk to those biased liberal reporters and TV people, the better we'll be. Now that those unfortunate photographs are turning up everywhere—I'd like to burn all of them, get the negatives and destroy them—it's best we keep our mouths tight shut. I'll have a few surprises for those people when we get before the grand jury. They'll regret they ever started whining over those students."

"Bates," I said, "doesn't the publicity over the photographs change things?"

"How?"

"Life magazine ran twelve pages on them. Some writer is putting a book out with *all* of them. A *book.* They're shown on television, people are asked about them, questions are raised. It can't be that all those photos were faked. I mean, three hundred feet away isn't the same as thirty feet away. No one can seem to find that onrushing mob, that horde that was about to overrun the troopers. I don't for a moment doubt the police *perceived* it that way . . ." My voice trailed off.

The path not taken. The bridge not crossed. The almost pleasurable toying with shame, with a loss of courage and decency. The death of honor.

"Stop right there, colonel. You and I have to talk to each other like brothers. *We* are on the side of the law. Of the flag. Of the family. Of God. We can't and we won't be sidetracked by deceptive photographs. *Or* anything else."

"They'll be introduced as evidence."

"Not in my presentation."

"It may go to other jurisdictions."

"We'll handle them as well."

And so he asked me to review my recollection of the sequence of events. I'll have to hear the tape—I typed parts of it myself, laboriously, trusting no one—to find the exact moment when I lost my head and we went at each other.

I can imagine what Dr. Schless would give to have his hands on it. Or Helen, for that matter. Yes, Helen . . .

Quite candidly, I'm glad Marge isn't here. She isn't able to share my dilemmas any more. She'd be of no help. It would be impossible to discuss this troublesome matter with her. "Whatever you think is right, dear," she'd most likely say.

*But what is right?* And then I wonder: what if my release of these materials makes no difference at all? Is it possible we . . . the world, the public . . . have come to accept and even welcome deceptions, nurture falsehoods?

What if, in some foolish burst of remorse, a knight-errant act of valor to win favor with Helen, I gave this information to the press via the Joshua committee?

*Nothing at all may happen.*

Only my own ruin and ostracization. Possibly an indictment for perjury!

I won't play the tape. It's fragile. I don't want to take the chance of ripping it or erasing it. Funny. I never did return the mini-recorder. No one seemed to miss it.

But I read the transcript again. There was no mistaking what we said to each other. None.

## Sally Terragni

I felt sorry for Dr. Schless afterward. And for his wife and some of the others. My Joey shrugged and said it didn't bother him. You never knew when people like that—Wilma and her young man—would go into one of their routines.

Joey's not intolerant. We're good Catholics, and Father Schmidt teaches us to accept all people, to respect their faiths. We do the "kiss of peace" in church. It's just Joey gets itchy around what he calls these fanatics.

A group of us were sitting in the lobby of the motel before dinner. Dr. Schless and his wife, Bernie Hoch, Reverend Jensen, Harriet Blochman.

It was sort of a free night. Some of our group were going to the concert—the Russian refugee musicians—and there was a free movie at the student center, a Japanese film. But most of the people were tired from the workshops, wanted to get an early dinner and go to bed.

Reverend Jensen was saying he was pleased that the community was accepting the observances in such good spirit. Five years after the shootings, he said, many people, merchants, businessmen, even some police, seemed ready to give up their sides, to say, yes, it was terrible and should not have happened.

Dr. Schless and Joey didn't think this was a big deal. Dr. Schless said it meant they figured they'd gotten away with murder, that no one could touch their policemen any more, so we could go ahead with our harmless demonstrations, and our meetings, and what difference would it make?

"Not quite, Dave," Reverend Jensen said. "To get the average Joshua residents to admit that it was a tragedy is something. Five years ago a majority was saying that hundreds of students should have been shot, almost cheering what happened. I'm convinced they have some real doubts now."

Dr. Schless cleared his throat, but Rita touched his hand, warning him not to get excited, that maybe Al Jensen had a point.

Bernie Hoch seemed to agree with Al Jensen. He said he'd talked to people in town. Many were ashamed of what had happened. Bernie said it was especially so among younger people. He kept hearing that there should have been a better way of handling the students, that guns needn't have been fired and so on.

"Yeah, but they got away with murder," Dr. Schless said.

Harriet Blochman agreed. She said that like Dr. Schless she was now more eager to see the civil suit come to pass, and hoped we'd be back in court.

While we were talking Helen Christopher came down from her room. She's really a lovely-looking woman. I wish I could have kept my figure the way she has. But nothing flashy. She was wearing a checked brown suit, a white blouse and pearls. Her hair was done up and she looked terrific. I wasn't jealous, I just knew that she was, well, different from us. That little place in Connecticut where she came from, and tennis and golf, and Ivy League schools . . . Still, our children were both killed. It didn't help Jack Christopher that he came from a classy family when the bullets hit. That's a rotten thought.

"Going someplace special, Helen?" asked Dr. Schless.

She seemed nervous. Especially for her. She said, no, she was meeting friends.

She wished us a pleasant evening and walked out. From the rear, she looked about twenty-eight. I wondered why her husband Dan hadn't come to Joshua. Oh, I know he wrote that letter, but you'd think he'd be over it by now. I mentioned this to Joey.

"Hell," Joey whispered, staring at Helen, as she left, "if I were her husband, I'd be here to keep an eye on her."

There was a big, big, distance between people like the Christophers and us. I knew it. I wasn't ashamed of it. Not that Helen was a snob, or ever looked down on us. She was just different. It was funny. Dr. Schless and his wife were just as well-educated as she was, and probably richer, but I never felt any gap between the Schlesses and the Terragnis. Maybe it was because they were Jewish. Does that make sense?

A few minutes after Helen had left, and it was getting dark outside, a warm dry night, we saw Wilma Overstreet and her beau Timmy approaching. Wilma's head was in that metal brace. How smooth and unlined her face was, almost like plastic. Her eyes were magnified by rimless glasses. She wore a long-sleeved gray cotton dress that covered most of her legs. Her large feet looked stuffed, like dummy's feet. I felt sad for her. She had wanted to be a physical therapist. Bernie Hoch told me she'd lost interest in that career and had decided to devote her life to working for the Lord. Timmy was a computer programmer.

"Join us, kids," Joey said.

"How about dinner on the committee?" Dr. Schless asked. "We're all going inside in a few minutes."

"I don't think so, Dr. Schless," Wilma said. She smiled.

Sandra Hoch came out of the elevator, carrying her baby. He looked fat and happy. A pacifier was stuck between his lips. She sat down next to Bernie and gave him the baby.

"No problem, Wilma," Schless said. "The committee has a fund for dinner meetings. How about it?"

"No, I don't think so."

"You've got to have dinner," Rita said.

Timmy coughed nervously. He seemed ready to say something but instead bent down and whispered in Wilma's ear.

"Timmy and I are leaving tonight," Wilma said. "We can't stay any longer."

For a moment no one knew what to say.

"Anything wrong, Wilma?" Joes asked.

"No, everything is wonderful," she said. Her eyes widened, like two blue flowers opening. "Wonderful. Isn't everything wonderful, Timmy?"

"It sure is, Wilma. God is wonderful."

"We're leaving," Wilma said. "We're driving home tonight."

There was silence. Someone dropped a plate in the motel dining room. An elevator clanked its way down.

"Leaving? Why?" Bernie asked.

"I don't want to hurt anyone's feelings," Wilma said. "So maybe we shouldn't say what's on our mind."

Reverend Jensen leaned forward. "Wilma, we're all family here. Sure, we have differences of opinions among us. Dr. Schless and I have had some right here in this lobby. If something displeases you about the way we're conducting the weekend, tell us."

"Al's right, Wilma," Dr. Schless said. "Have I done anything to offend you? Maybe some of the other kids?"

Joey nudged me. "He's talking about Mallory. Billy gets on people's nerves."

I found my voice. "Wilma, we all love you. You know that. We want you to stay."

"I'm sorry, Mrs. Terragni. But Timmy and I have made up our mind. We're leaving as soon as we load up the car."

"We hoped you'd stay for the vigil," Rita Schless said.

"No, Mrs. Schless, we can't."

Reverend Jensen said, "That isn't quite fair to us, Wilma. Of course you're free to leave. We respect your wishes. But you did come back to Joshua. Why have you decided to go?"

"Oh, dear," Wilma said. She stared at Timmy. I saw him nod. Her eyes turned cold behind the glasses. "Timmy and I have decided that this weekend is being run by secular humanists."

"And we are against secular humanists," Timmy added. He sounded angry.

"What's a secular . . . what d'you call it?" Joey asked.

"Secular humanists," Wilma said. "They're worse in a way than communists even, or atheists."

Timmy said, "They're so clever, they pretend they're on the right side but they believe in evolution and abortion and birth control and homosexuals. We just can't be part of any group that's run by secular humanists."

"Wait a minute," Dr. Schless said. "I'm Jewish. So's my wife. So's Bernie. The Terragnis are Catholics. So's Billy Mallory. Lots of us are Protestants, like Al Jensen. Not a secular humanist in the house."

Timmy smiled, as if amused by Dr. Schless's innocence. "People can be secular humanists and don't even know they are. They're in favor of sinful things. They defy God. They're antilife. Wilma and I have sensed this all along, things have been said and done. We *can't* be a part of it."

"Yes," Wilma said. "We really hate secular humanists."

"Do you hate me?" Schless asked. "Or my wife? Or Bernie and Sandra? And Reverend Jensen?"

"You don't understand, doctor," Timmy said firmly. "It isn't the people we hate. We love all of you. God tells us to."

"Oh, God is so good," Wilma said.

The young lady, who was a reporter for the local newspaper—I forget her name—overheard the conversation and came by, standing to one side while the rest of us listened to Wilma and Timmy go on how they hated "secular humanists."

"Yes, Timmy has it right," Wilma said. She was clenching her fists, unclenching them, her eyes locked, as if struggling with something.

"What, Wilma?" Rita asked.

"We don't really hate *you*. It's . . . what you stand for. That awful secular humanism. Yes, it's against the Lord. Timmy and I are going home, and we'll dedicate ourselves to love—"

"And against the teaching of evolution," Timmy said. "That's where it all started. That's why Wilma got shot and that's why she is the way she is."

Wilma was sobbing. "But I'm not sad. I'm not afraid of anyone or anything. God is good and kind to me. Timmy, I want to go home and just love God."

There wasn't much else to say. Everyone was stunned. These people, Joey says, they have a way of doing that to you. You can't say anything to them, you can't argue with them. It's even hard to feel sorry for them, and God knows we all felt sorry for Wilma.

The reporter followed them to the door. She was taking notes. Oh, the papers would have a time with this. The poor paralyzed girl, one of the Joshua victims, who deserted the memorial services because we were a bunch of "secular humanists."

I don't even know what they are. I still don't. And what does teaching evolution have to do with anything?

## Dr. David Schless

No one had any appetite for dinner. We sacked in early. We needed each other after the act that Wilma Overstreet and her young man put on. No, it wasn't an act. They *believed*. Believed deeply. Why were we secular humanists? What had we done? Maybe because we hadn't accepted the killing of our children as God's will.

There's something about these mystics that sets you back on your heels. There's no arguing with them. You can't win. They have the true faith, the revealed religion. It's as if, long after the Almighty has dealt out the fifty-two cards in the deck of miracles, He's got a few more up His sleeve for them.

I have no time for true believers, whatever their faith—including members of my own persuasion. I'm a pretty good Jew, not observant, but knowing where I came from and what Judaism at its best means. But these fellows who are full of signs and portents and numbers and revelations, they lose me. *Trust in us, it's all God's way, it has mystical significance . . .* And, of course, there's no way of disputing them. You're either moved to pity or frustration or fury.

Who knew what a secular humanist was? I could see the confusion on the Terragnis' faces, the perplexity on Jensen's big round face, the way Bernie and Sandra Hoch looked as if they were confronting someone speaking Choctaw. The senselessness of it all made debate impossible. Besides, we all had a special place in our hearts for Wilma . . .

"You feel lousy, right?" Rita asked.

"Hold me, baby. It's as if we got a curse on us. Nothing seems to work."

"That's not my fighting dentist. Why did Wilma upset you so?"

I kissed Rita's neck. She smelled sweet and clean. "Because she's a lot of the country. Moral, kind, religious—and she's decided we're wrong. She forgives the people who made her a paralytic. We're the guilty party. Maybe that's what most people want us to be. Not just Andrea, or Jack Christopher, or Lucy Terragni. They were guilty all the time. But *us*. Anyone who stirs the pot, doesn't go along . . . we're commies, reds, agitators, enemies of the state, of religion, of God, and now we're secular humanists. It would be funny if my guts weren't being torn apart."

"We'll survive, Dave. We'll manage." She began to cry softly. "I have the feeling this won't ever end for us. It brings on more agony. How can we ever do the right thing for Andrea?"

"Honey, I'll die trying."

"I won't let you. It'll ruin our life, what's left of it. We can't carry that burden forever."

"No choice," I said. I stroked her thigh, kissed the small of her back. I wished I could love her more. We were once so deeply involved with each other's bodies. Two strong passionate people. It got better as we got older. But I know what happened. The knowledge that our murdered daughter would never share this wonderful passion, never enjoy the wonderful feeling that comes with maturity and affection and two people needing one another, the knowledge that Andrea would never know this made us reluctant, tentative with each other.

Guilt, you old Jewish mother. It denied us our flesh. Andrea was obliterated, terminated. So our love could never be the same. Homage to death. Impotence brought on by loss. Damn them, all of them . . .

"Maybe you'll be better after the vigil," Rita said. She turned and hugged me. "You're a bear, Schless. The old linebacker, the light heavyweight."

"Yeah, the battling Jew. I don't weep, kid. I may complain to you, and get down in the dumps in the privacy of our bedroom—"

"I have space for it, bear."

"Bless you. Outside I'll be the same angry Dave Schless. Maybe we won't get those bastards into court, Rita, but it'll be worth it to see them sweat and squirm and mumble their excuses."

"Ssshh. Love me. Just a little."

"Easy."

Later I sat on the edge of the bed and wondered where Helen Christopher had gone all dolled up. She looked sensational.

*Offitt?* I wondered. Why not? Ironpants had made no attempt to hide his severe case for Helen. And who could blame him? It couldn't be. Not Helen . . .

I began mulling possibilities. Was Offitt going to turn out to be the soft underbelly of the opposition? Could he be the crack in that wall of lies, of deceit, conspiracy and fraud that had denied us justice . . . ?

Consoled with the old (false) notion that you win a few and lose a few, I slept for a while, then paced the room, then made notes on a yellow pad. First thing in the morning—it was Sunday, but what the hell—I'd get our lawyer Brian Dooley on the phone. In his posttrial investigation (I seemed to recall) he'd said something about Offitt refusing to talk to him, yet indicating he wasn't altogether unsympathetic to our cause. Dooley had also said that some of the troopers—maybe Markland and Kazinski—had gotten bombed one night and were overheard to say some nasty things about their old C.O.

Could this lead anywhere? Was the colonel a weak link, someone who might open up? I would have to talk to Helen, seriously this time. She was hardly the sort to play the vamp or the spy, but any man who didn't want her approval, who was reluctant to hold her hand or sneak a kiss was less than a man. Maybe I was on to something.

## *Helen Christopher*

Twice I halted and thought seriously about not showing up. I'd never done such a thing in my life, never even came *late* to an appointment. Dan says I can't bear to offend anyone or the thought that someone thinks ill of me . . .

I remember agreeing to go to Amherst for a prom weekend with a boy I didn't like. Short, bespectacled, prematurely bald Harry Miller. Pity triumphed over distaste. He could barely dance, chewed gum and talked nonstop about his future career as a physicist. How could I hurt him? Maybe by keeping him at arm's length. (I suppose he had the last laugh; he grew up to become the head of nuclear research at some big corporation in California, rich and famous . . . )

It was a fine evening. I just couldn't allow myself to turn around and avoid the painful meeting with the colonel and leave him waiting like a pining schoolboy.

At the corner, fifty feet from the iron gate leading to the campus, I waited, drew whistles from two young men in a pickup truck, and saw his black Chevrolet approach.

He got out and opened the door for me. His eyes, without the dark aviator glasses, took in my suit, my blouse, the pearls. "You look stunning."

I arranged my skirt, tucked my feet beneath the seat. "I think the conversation has to move in other directions. A moratorium on personal comments."

"What can we talk about then?"

"Why don't we just listen to the music?"

He drove slowly through the stone pillars.

In the purplish dusk the campus lights suddenly went on—bright yellow globes, those marvelous old-fashioned lights mounted on elaborate wrought-iron poles. During the rioting, they said, the students had smashed almost every light on the campus. "Trashing" was the word used.

Offitt asked me about the workshops. He actually seemed interested. I told him about the police chief from Massachusetts who had been critical of the handling of the riot. The business of loaded weapons; the failure to communicate with student leaders; the failure to make mass arrests the night before; the failure to use tear gas more efficiently.

"A critique of me. Did you agree?"

"I'm not a police expert, but a great deal of what he said made sense."

"Did you learn anything? Are these so-called workshops making you feel any better?"

"I'm afraid not. I'm getting the notion that beneath our veneer of civility there's a good deal of hate and fear and brutality. I never felt this way until Jack was killed."

"It was an aberration, a product of the times—"

"Perhaps not, perhaps it filled some public need for blood sacrifice."

"I'm pained to hear you talk that way, Helen. I must believe you don't feel that way about me. As you know, I never condoned the shootings, just tried to explain them—"

"Explain them away?"

He parked the car on a rise from where we had a distant but clear view of the graded seats and the curving band-shell and stage.

"That is not so."

I turned to him. "I think I should go, colonel. It was wrong of me to agree to come. We're on the opposite sides of the fence. There's nothing more to—"

"Please don't leave."

"Why? What do I owe you? It's you who owes me, and more than apology. You at least owe me an *admission* that you were wrong. The system does *not* work. Justice was *not* served. Murder was condoned. People went about bragging that next time they'd get more, that more should have been shot down."

"I've *told* you. I was never party to any of that—"

"It doesn't matter. You were one of their heroes. I'm going."

Offitt touched my shoulder gently. "You owe me nothing. I'm not certain what I owe you, but I respect you. I share your sorrow. Believe it or not, I feel wounded by what happened. I beg of you to stay . . ."

I looked at the peaceful campus. Couples strolled by holding hands. Students sat on the grass and on the benches, chatting, necking. Some boys tossed a Frisbee in the fading light. A stream of people were heading toward the open amphitheater where the concert was to take place. Their voices were low, joyful.

"I've lived with this for five years. It frightens me that so many Americans could nod their heads and say, yes, they *deserved* to die. Including, sad to say, my own husband."

"Does he still feel that way?"

"I don't think so, but there's no retracting that letter."

"It can't be easy for you sitting here with me. Not after what you've been through. May I tell you something?"

I managed a smile and nodded.

"I want to tell you that I deeply regret having made that statement about justice having been served. I never should have said it."

"Would you retract the statement publicly?"

208

"How can I?"

"You could come to Dr. Schless's press conference tomorrow."

"But I couldn't. It would . . . make me out a dolt. Worse, a liar."

"But if you truly believe that the acquittal of your policemen was not just, and that they were guilty, why not say so?"

"I can say things to you. To no one else." He stared at me. "Your respect means a great deal to me. I want you to know that I have long entertained serious doubts about the trial, the part played by the judge, the defense lawyer, the whole apparatus of the state that resulted in the acquittal. It has bothered me. I want you to understand that."

"I do and I don't. If you feel you've been party to a terrible fraud, what the kids call a 'fix,' why not admit it?"

"You're asking too much. I did not kill Jack Christopher."

"You didn't fire the gun that did. But you condoned it—"

"No, no. I deplored it, I've said as much."

He sounded almost pitiful, looking for forgiveness. I took advantage.

"Then say the *rest* of it. Say that the trial was a cover-up and that the public sentiments about what happened were outrageous."

"I'm sorry." He sounded choked. "I can't."

"Then your apology to me, here in the privacy of this car, doesn't mean much, does it? Go to Dr. Schless and tell him that it was a crime, that the killers have gone scot free and that you are as outraged as—"

"Impossible. You're the only person I've ever told this."

"Not even your wife?"

He shook his head. "She least of all. Marge accepts anything I do. I didn't have to tell her. I had to tell you."

"Please drive me back to the motel. I'll tell Dr. Schless or Tom Finnegan what you've told me. Then we'll let you try to deny it."

"All I've said is that I'm sorry your son and the others died . . . I concurred in a miscarriage of justice. But I didn't acquit the police—"

"Your testimony helped."

"Perhaps. I broke my personal code. I live every minute of my life with that knowledge. I go to bed every night wondering how it might have been different . . ."

"You're still hiding, still making excuses for those cold-blooded lying killers—"

He moved his head from side to side. "No, no, you sound like Schless.

They're ordinary men, family men, decent men. It was a panic-inducing situation, and they failed to meet the test. I grant you that. I also assure you, not one of them wanted your son dead."

"Colonel, there were police experts at the trial who were highly critical of what happened. They stated that trained men, properly led men, do not fire live ammunition into an unarmed crowd. Why didn't you say the same thing?"

"I could not. I had an obligation to them."

"And it canceled the truth?"

"If you choose to think so. Helen . . . I need you to appreciate my position . . ."

The chamber group made their appearance then, ending the exchange. Which was a relief. The trio consisted of a father, his son and daughter. The father, Lazar Kirinski, was a violinist. The son Avram was a pianist, and the daughter Sonya was a cellist.

I'd read about them in the Flagg City newspaper, a feature article by the arts editor. They were Soviet Jews, eager to leave the country where they could no longer play, teach or develop their musical skills. Their mother had died in a so-called mental hospital under suspicious circumstances. Bereaved, persecuted, denied a career, Kirinski had joined a group of Jewish dissidents. He gave concerts clandestinely to raise money for their cause. Finally the visas had been granted during a brief thaw in the cold war. Since then, the Kirinski family had been touring the United States, performing on campuses and in town halls, bringing their talents to receptive audiences. They weren't quite in the big time of the concert circuit (Mr. Kirinski had told the interviewer) but they loved their new lives, taught, studied and were fast becoming enthusiastic Americans. The daughter Sonya—a chubby fair girl—admitted to a taste for Big Macs and young Avram had become a St. Louis Cardinal fan.

He laughed. "You see, Helen, you mustn't take a dim view of this country. We can be generous and openhearted. The Kirinskis understand that."

He was right about that. There were two Americas. Or maybe two sides to the same people?

The music was wonderful. Dan and I used to purchase subscriptions to recitals at the Old Surrey Public Library. They'd been reminders of how good the world can be. But we'd lost interest after Jack died. Dan had the notion people were staring at him, talking about us. How good so many things were before Jack was killed. Dan and I would hold hands, sit attentively on the straight-backed chairs in the dimmed hall and listen to talented young people playing Haydn and Mozart . . .

The Kirinskis opened with a Beethoven concerto. The sound was lush, rich, the burnished tones of the cello, the singing of the violin, the melodic power of the piano. It was more intoxicating than wine. Around us insects hummed and night birds called, almost in tune with the music. Under dimmed lights, the campus was an island of peace and sanity, a microcosm of what is best in our world. It was almost impossible to imagine that five years ago guns had blasted the young people, killing and maiming, and that the world had shrugged, looked away, made excuses. *The system works,* my mooning colonel had told the press.

My eyes misted over. I watched the father and his children performing with all that skill and love that comes from hard work, talent, and I felt a pang of jealousy. How courageous of the man to have encouraged his son and his daughter in that hostile climate. The mother dead, their lives seemingly at an end. And now this rebirth in the new nation that had embraced them.

How I envied Lazar Kirinski. As the music rose to its climax, I recalled scenes of Jack's growing up. Yes, we'd had many good times. We'd shared a lot of modest pleasures. I recalled a summer when Jack was in prep school. He'd gotten a job driving the bus for the school's day camp. He wasn't a good enough athlete to have been hired as a counselor and he was too shy to be effective with children, but Turk Kelly, the football coach, had agreed to let him drive the bus and work in the kitchen. It seemed to me and to Dan that Jack was maturing, taking on responsibilities. He loved the job. He enjoyed parking the rattling green-and-white bus in our driveway, taking girls for a spin after camp had closed.

What a fine summer it was! The house was always crowded with young people, friends, pets. We had two dogs and a mangy cat who gave birth to kittens on Dan's favorite rocker on the screened porch. He didn't mind. He laughed and let Fifi take over his chair. Our house was full of life, of laughter, of endless suppers on the porch—country-fresh corn, watermelon, barbecued chicken.

No, I'm not deceiving myself, painting a false picture. It was a good time, maybe one of the best years of our lives. Watching Beth mature —she was home from her freshman year at college, working at a day care center—and best of all seeing Jack's emergence as a young man. Silly, how the responsibility of driving an old bus filled with noisy campers seemed to endow him with so much maturity. Even Susie, our doleful spaniel, sensed it. With liquid brown eyes she gazed at our son, licked his naked feet, shuffled after him, as if announcing to the family: *Here is my new hero.* Up to then she'd been Beth's dog.

Where did it all go? I don't mean just Jack's death. Even before that. When the house emptied. Beth moving in with her young man, finding it harder to communicate with us, Jack drifting off to a kind of jellied life at Joshua College. Even our pets vaporized—Susie falling victim to a teenager's hot rod, her mongrel companion succumbing to a heart attack, the cats disappearing mysteriously into the maw of the oak forest that surrounded our house . . .

"It's beautiful," Offitt said. "Talented people."

I said nothing. Then, "I think it's time to leave. Please."

He took my hand, kissed the back of it. I shuddered inwardly. "Don't do that. I'll get out and walk if—"

Hoarsely, he said, "I can't help it—"

"This is idiotic, I'm getting out."

"No, please. We have a lot to discuss after the concert. Maybe . . . I can meet you halfway regarding what you want of me . . ."

I glanced at him. Not a dissembler or a faker. It must have been hard for him to lie, to accept lies, to defend liars, to play along with schemers. Perhaps I could get him closer to our side. I also began to sense a touch of pity for him. Sooner or later, Dan says, I feel sorry for everyone.

The audience was giving the Kirinski trio a standing ovation. From the black metal fortress of the car we joined the applause. Not only was I cheering the music, but I was full of admiration for the loving cohesion of father, son and daughter. Had I shown Jack enough love? I'm not very demonstrative.

"It's marvelous," Offitt said. "How they have stayed together, shown such courage. They're lucky."

So few people, he said, realized the potential of family relations . . . then almost in passing he mentioned that he'd had an infant son more than forty years ago, a frail child who died at sixteen months of a respiratory ailment.

"I'm sorry . . ."

"Marge was with him when he did. I was in England, training my unit for D day. She was back at Fort Bragg. I got compassion leave and flew back home. There wasn't much to be said. I always felt guilty at not being able to share Marge's grief, not being there when it happened."

"It wasn't your fault," I said, and then I thought, here I am consoling *him*. Had he tricked me into this odd reversal of roles? The parallel between us, the death of our children was obvious—too obvious?

"Maybe you should come to the vigil tomorrow, at least make an appearance," I said.

"I have nothing against the observance, but I think I'd be tagged a hypocrite. I can express my regret in a simple statement to the press, I've done that already. But I can't be party to this event that Schless is orchestrating."

I said nothing. The concert ended. As we drove off the campus—I was praying no one would spot me—I saw an old, frail man walking with a cane, a white-haired fellow, lost in some reverie.

"Judge Frankendorf," Offitt said. "He never misses a concert."

"Lord, he looks fifteen years older than at the trial."

"It hasn't been easy for the judge."

I said that all of these people who condoned the death of my son, who took part in the whitewash, seemed to be suffering so *terribly*. Judge Frankendorf, the colonel, the trigger-happy troopers. I told him that perhaps I should feel guilty—or my dead son should—for having burdened them with so much sorrow.

"You have a right to be bitter."

I watched Frankendorf walk with an old man's mincing steps to a waiting car. A black man in a white jacket helped him in.

"That's Ernest, the maître d' at the club. He takes a personal interest in the judge, sort of looks after him. The colored around here know the judge as a good friend. He's been very progressive on racial matters."

The *colored*. Oh, colonel . . .

He drove me to the motel. At the door he tried to kiss me, and I called on old high school techniques to bob, duck, feint and avoid his lips, disengage his strong arms. No thank you, most especially not with the man who thought "the system worked."

He laughed. "I apologize again . . . May I see you tomorrow?"

I said it would be a busy day. Press conferences, reports, meetings and the all-night vigil.

I opened the door to the room, turned. "It's not like me to deal in trade-offs, but if you want my respect you'll make a public statement. Something that can help us get the civil suit going."

"You ask me to hang myself. I know Schless wants me in the defendant's chair. And I must say I'm disappointed that you put our relationship on that basis."

I said, "If you're sincere, colonel, you have an opportunity to prove it. Goodnight."

I left him, locked the door, heard his car cough and turn in the parking area.


## Billy Mallory


Doc Schless authorized me to use his telephone credit card, so I spent dinner hour in my motel room trying to track down that sleazebag Pulsifer. I figured there weren't that many people in Alaska, and just by going through the phone book I might find him.

First I called Robin and she told me the postmark on his letter was Fairbanks. He'd scratched out the name of a hotel—the Northland Motor Lodge—on the stationery. I tried them and learned that Mr. Pulsifer had stayed there two weeks ago, left no forwarding address and had moved on to Nome. Driving a rented Datsun jeep, they said. I identified myself as Sergeant Mulqueen of the Petoskey, Michigan, police, and that we were trying to reach Mr. Pulsifer because his aunt had died and his widowed mother wanted him home for the funeral but was too distraught to telephone.

No luck. Pulsifer had either become lunch for a grizzly or slid off a glacier into the Bering Sea. Schless wanted him *taped,* on the record, confessing to having been a police plant, the guy who suckered me into torching the Quonset. Well, they'd have to take our word for it. After my twelfth phone call—a bar in Anchorage where geologists were supposed to hang out and exchange exciting stories about rocks—I began to think: *What frigging difference will it make?* They'll call us liars, rotten kids who deserved to get plugged if for nothing else than using dirty language.

*Paranoid.* That's how I felt. A fashionable word from our era but a useful one. I should have split, flown back to Boston to Robin's warm body, our pad in Cambridge and my job as editor of a natural-foods newsletter. Ever try a soybean soufflé topped with eggplant sauce and plantain chips? Guaranteed to open all your ducts and raise your pulse rate.

It was after eleven by now and I felt the need of a friendly bar and some aimless talk with good fellows. I buttoned my faded blue denim jacket over my bull's-eye shirt and walked out of the motel room.

Couldn't believe my eyes. There was Helen Christopher, surburban beauty, an eyeful at age forty-odd, shaking hands, apparently saying good night to a gray-haired dude in a tweed jacket. Tall guy, specs, trim. They didn't see me. He shook her hand, nodded, left.

*Jack Christopher's mother!* The guy looked familiar. He got into a black car and zoomed off. Looked as if they'd just come back from a date or something. I sort of envied him. Mrs. Christopher was quite a class act. She was *mucha mujer.* I'd gathered that she and her husband, a corporate type, didn't get along very well, at least not since Jack's death.

Funny that I should be thinking of corporate types at that moment. Because into the parking lanes in front of the motel pulled a silver Trans-Am driven by my fellow victim, Keith McCandless. Keith had been sort of out of everything these past few days. Frankly I couldn't imagine what had brought him back to Joshua. He and his ritzy wife Gloria were Buzzy and Muffy types. Midwestern prepoids trying to act as if he'd gone to Yale and made Bones and she'd knocked 'em dead at Vassar. They were actually from downstate. Rich, smug, successful and duller than steamed cauliflower.

But Gloria could yell. And she didn't hold her booze too well. They hit the ground fighting, slamming doors, her high heels clicking on the asphalt, big Keith stumbling and tripping.

"Don't you ever make any more public comments about my family!" Gloria was hollering.

"Ah, honey, all I said was your old man was a cheap fuck."

"That's enough! I won't hear another word!"

She got to the door, couldn't find her key, shouted at him to let her in. Keith—he'd been a half-ass jock, a football sub who couldn't block or tackle but helped flesh out the squad—wasn't well coordinated and had trouble finding the key. He dropped it twice, then got to his knees, cursing.

Gloria joined him. And there they were, the most aristocratic members of our band of brothers, searching for a motel key. Their voices were slurred, thick.

I came over and volunteered to help.

"Beat it, Mallory, we don't need your help."

"You could be civil, Keith," Gloria said.

She had a gleaming blonde bell of hair. And a great ass. All tan and smooth, I imagined. So I got down on my knees and made some lame crack about this being like the first act of *La Bohème,* people looking for a lost key in the dark. This attempt at music appreciation got me nowhere, and I realized they were both more zonked than I'd imagined. I found the key.

"Thanks, Billy," Gloria said. "Keith tends to be all thumbs, and he doesn't see well in the dark. G'night."

"Oh, I'm all thumbs, am I? And you don't like what I said about your old man, huh?"

"That's right, Keith. And you can go to hell. I'm sick of this stupid weekend, and the reporters, and you playing a martyr when all you did was get in the way of a bullet that barely scratched you. Some hero."

"So that's how you feel, Gloria? So that's it? C'mon, Mallory, tell her how I bled for a half hour, how I fainted and couldn't get medical help."

"It's true, Gloria. Keith suffered."

"Hunh." She got to her full height. Really a dish, but the booze, the dumbness and the bad temper would probably do her in.

"Are you coming in or not?" Gloria called out to the night.

"The hell I am. Evening's young. Let's go heist a few, Mallory."

"Oh, no," Mrs. McCandless said. "I'm exhausted. I'm fed up with this whole thing. I'm leaving tomorrow."

"Well, I'm not." McCandless—overweight, klutzy—laid a heavy arm on me. "Me and Billy Mallory. Me and my good buddy. Me and Mallory are going to have a few brews. Right, Billy baby?"

"If you say so, Keith. I always wanted to ask you what the hell reinsurance is, and how you made so much money at it."

We ended up in Gaffney's. I have this thing in me, this need to see how far I can go. The fact is I'm yellow. A coward right down to my L. L. Bean hikers. I go around looking for trouble and hope my Celtic wit and facile tongue will rescue me. This time I had big Keith for my protection and camouflage.

What a pair we made when we walked into Gaffney's . . . me in my torn denims, my ponytail, my boots, and the bull's-eye on my T-shirt. And McCandless in his navy blue Stanley Blacker blazer, a maize button-down shirt and a dark blue tie with pheasants—*fucking pheasants!*—on it. He wore tan slacks and crocodile loafers with little brass dingles on the instep. I could have passed for a pusher, Keith for my customer.

Why Gaffney's? Well, it was where the fuzz hung out—state cops, locals, campus police—and it was the world-class hardhat, blue-collar, ethnic workingman's home away from home.

The regulars knew me. Jack Carr, the bartender, was a cool guy. He was one of these rare members of the lower orders who could keep his feet in both camps. He got along fine with cops (his brother Liam was a local police sergeant) but he also had a sympathetic ear for campus crazies, radicals and freaks. He knew me from my days of glory.

"Billy boy," Jack Carr said, "you look like third and ten."

"Feel like it, Jack." I introduced McCandless. Keith had been a fraternity nerd, the nearest thing that passed for an aristocrat at Joshua, and he hadn't frequented Gaffney's.

"Ah, one of the pigeons," Jack Carr said. "Here for the all-night wake? Jesus, I'd like to have the aspirin and pillow concession. There's gonna be a lot of wet keesters out there."

"Why yes, sir," McCandless mumbled. "Do you have any Southern Comfort?"

His kind of drink. It told me he wasn't really a preppy, just playing at it. Catch anyone at Choate or Groton drinking that cough syrup.

Carr served us—I ordered a Heineken—and then got confidential with me. "Maybe you better go home after a round, Billy. In fact, if you split and take Keith here with you the booze is on the house. Some of the chaps who used you for target practice are in the rear booth."

"Who?"

"Kazinski and Dennis Boyle."

"Goodness. On a Saturday night? Without their wives? How gauche."

"Kazinski hates his wife and Boyle's a bachelor. They've been muttering all night about you guys with lead in your ass."

"Keith, baby, you hear that? Two of the pigs who tried to waste us. And who, unless my memory is fading, succeeded in offing three of our number."

I was bombed. I'd been drinking rum with beer with Bernie Hoch earlier and hadn't realized how much I'd soaked up. The Heineken acted like a reagent. It got all the alcohol circulating again. I was fearless, full of true grit.

"Let's beat it, Billy."

"McCandless, I always heard that you were afraid to stick when you played football for old JC. True?"

"No. I have weak ankles. Everyone knows that."

I entwined my meager arm in his navy blazer and stepped off. "Let us confront the enemy. They won't dare punch out the most famous reinsurance man in the state. Ready, Keith?"

"Gloria'll be pissed at me."

"Gloria will adore you for being so brave."

So off we went to the rear of Gaffney's. I could see Carr drawing a brew, leveling the suds with his spatula and keeping a wary eye on us. We didn't mean doodly to him, but cops were steady business.

"Hello, scumbag."

Trooper Adam Kazinski saw us before we saw him. God, he looked awful. He'd put on weight and his face was the color of rancid tomato paste. His nose glowed like a highway flare. But Denny Boyle looked good—handsome guy with thick copper-colored hair and a lantern jaw. A smart young cop. He'd been ticketed to rise in the ranks, everyone thought. That was before Joshua, of course, and before he became a defendant. There was a woman sitting next to Dennis Boyle. White-blonde frizzy hair, skin the color of Light-'n'-Lively milk, maroon lips. She had huge green eyes but they were half-closed.

All three were well oiled. Boyle showed it the least, half-smiling, frozen in the red vinyl booth and under control. Kazinski was deeply potted. The girl—her name was Verlene—looked as if she were ready for beddy-bye and associated sports.

"Sergeant Kazinski," I said. "What a pleasure. Yes, it is I, William Scumbag Mallory. Whom you shot in the chest with your little air rifle. You remember my fellow victim, Keith McCandless?"

"Hiya," Kazinski said. I could see Kazinski was standoffish with Keith. The aroma of country club, golf, success and a good marriage offended him.

"How you doin', Keith?" Boyle asked pleasantly.

"Great, Dennis. Nice to see you, Sergeant Kazinski."

Kazinski let out a combined shout and belch and invited us to join them. Keith sat next to Kazinski, and I wedged in next to Dennis Boyle. Verlene was squashed against the plastic oak wall of Gaffney's. Another round was quickly ordered. Kazinski insisted that the drinks were on him.

Now all of this will sound idiotic. People will hear this, and say, *bullshit,* nonsense, lies. Do you mean to tell us, Mallory, that two of the policemen who shot you and killed three of your fellow students would sit in a ginmill buying you drinks and being winning? But it's true. This is America. Anything goes, if you wait long enough.

I'm told cops develop a mystical bond with criminals. It's as if they shared dark secrets. It's them against the world. Just the way athletes —let's say two boxers—will respect each other more than they will the screaming mob that's egging them on. So some of us (me especially) had come to feel a kind of mad brotherhood with the cops who tried to murder us. During the trial I can recall Bernie, Lyle and me, the most politically conscious of the group, staring over at the state troopers and wondering, are these guys *really* killers? Even though we knew they were.

I don't mean that "God is so good" routine that Wilma Overstreet peddled, that holy business the newspapers slobbered over, Wilma forgiving everyone publicly, confiding that Jesus loved everyone and although she'd never walk again, it was neat-o with her so long as the Lord loved her and loved the cops who'd paralyzed her. Not that, no. I mean a gut feeling deep down that we were part of the same mess. I'm not even sure I hated Boyle and Kazinski and Markland and the others any longer. In some skewed way I felt a . . . a connection to them. (Of course, the three corpses could not be polled on that issue.)

"So you guys are gonna have your rat-fuck tomorrow, huh, Mallory?" Kazinski asked. "Jane Fonda? Folk singers? All that lefto crap?"

"No, sergeant. A modest down-home affair. Tap dancing and a greased pig contest."

Denny Boyle managed a thin smile. "Billy, you hate us, don't you? You'll never admit it was a rotten accident, a mistake."

"Who hates you?" I asked. "Verlene, do I look like I hate anyone?"

"You look cute. Got a joint?"

"Not in public, Ver," Boyle said. "Peace officers don't smoke pot."

"Leastwise not in the heart of downtown Joshua," I said.

Keith grinned stupidly at Kazinski. "I sure don't hate anyone, Sergeant Kazinski. But if it was a mistake, how'd it happen? I mean, I've read the accounts and so on and I still don't know."

Kazinski gargled a few times. "Tell 'em, Dennis."

"Someone heard shots. There was definitely shooting at us. With all that chanting, screaming, cursing, the tear gas popping, it was hard to tell. But several of us distinctly heard small-arms fire coming at us."

"Oh, so that was it," Keith said.

McCandless had truly cornered the market on *dumb*. The story about gunfire coming from our ranks had been discredited and disproved a dozen times, by the FBI, the local police, even the state police. A dozen tape recordings had been analyzed, films studied, photographs subjected to micro-scrutiny. Nothing. No shots. No one had a gun. Zilch. And still Boyle could peddle this stale bagel.

"Dennis, if I may so address you," I said, "that is pigshit and you know it."

Verlene asked, "What'd he say, Denny?"

"Mallory is being rude, Verlene. When facts fail him, he resorts to crudity. You see, that's what was wrong with his crowd, all those rioters and drug freaks. They couldn't face a fair debate, an honest discussion. So they became vulgar and tried to force issues with violence."

"Not me," Keith said. "I hate violence."

Now I knew why he hated to stick. But it was of small moment to me. Truly, I was enjoying sitting there with two men who had tried to waste me. It was a high, pleasure city, like the first deep drag on a fresh dark joint of *sensasemilla*.

Kazinski drained his beer and leaned across the formica table. His baggy eyes were red-rimmed like the old tree ape in Jack London's forgotten (and terrific) novel *The Abysmal Brute*.

"It was me shot you, Billy," he growled. "How do you like that?"

"If it wasn't for the honor of it, sarge, I'd just as soon you missed."

"I aimed at you, scumbag."

"I knew you did, sarge."

"Hurt much?"

"Only when I inhale."

"Can it, Adam," Boyle said.

"Nah, Mallory's okay. Right, Billy? You and me. I shot you. You called me a motherfucker, right? Fair's fair, right?"

"I called you worse than that, sarge."

Verlene was beginning to wake up. "I got to make wee-wah, Dennis, but this is so innaresting. And scary." She stayed.

"Don't have an accident, hon," Boyle said. He kissed her neck.

God, that woman had white skin. I expected Boyle's mouth to be covered with a layer of plaster dust.

Hell, it was no secret. Kazinski had admitted during the trial—and had told two grand juries—that he aimed at me and shot me. But, he explained, it was self-defense. He was convinced I was hiding a gun in my left hand, which was behind my back. More bullshit. I was using both hands. One to throw rocks and gas canisters, the other to cup around my sweet Irish-American mouth, the better to vocalize my sentiments about policemen's sexual preferences. Alternately, I was giving them the old finger.

"I didn't appreciate it, shitass, when you kept hollering at us, 'Who's screwing your wives?' You and the Christopher kid."

"I apologize. It wasn't polite." I doubted Jack had said anything like that.

Keith said, "Sergeant Kazinski, I never said anything like that. I wasn't even in the crowd. I was trying to get to my class in dramatic arts."

"Not you, Keith," Dennis Boyle said. "You were wounded because of irresponsible people like your buddy Mallory. So was the Terragni girl. The others, well, they—"

"Asked for it," I said. "Like Wilma? Or Hubie Colson?"

Boyle's eyes were like a film of blue ice on a drainage ditch. "They provoked us to the limit. Maybe we shouldn't have fired. But no court, no judge, no jury will ever find against us. Mallory, you must understand that after five years. I'd hoped you were older and wiser now."

Verlene pouted. "Is this all we're going to talk about tonight? For God's sake, that business at the college is finished. You guys, you cops, you hang onto it like it's important or something."

Boyle's voice was frigid. "It isn't us, hon. It's people like Mallory who won't let it alone."

"Yeah, Billy. Button your lip."

Kazinski was nailing me with the threatening comical eyes of a drunk. Menace was there but also a kind of blunted barroom drollery. I've seen this curious mixture on the faces of my ethnic brothers in South Boston—part-funning, part-threatening. It's something you get used to. But the problem is, you never know which way the sot is going to jump. Laugh? Spit? Throw a punch? Shoot?

"Why should you be uptight, sarge?" I asked. "You're home free. Nobody laid a glove on you."

"I get sick to my stomach looking at you pukes," Kazinski said. Now he was grinning. Greenish teeth and pink gums. "It ruins my family life. My kids hate to see me unhappy. The wife says I show signs of instability. Wants me to see a psychiatrist. And for what? For doing my duty?"

"Gee, I'm sorry, Sergeant Kazinski," McCandless said. He was falling asleep in his beer. His square blond head was drooping and his eyes were crossed. A big help.

"Mallory, you little prick," Kazinski muttered. He was on the verge of tears, "Mallory, what was you shouting at me? Something about what I eat?"

"Oh, that."

"I heard the *motherfuckers* and the *cocksuckers* and that crap about my wife, but there was something else. You and Hoch and some others. Right up close. Before we retreated to the porch. Back by the fountain."

"Yes, I seem to remember, sarge." I frowned and passed a pale hand over my brow. "Yes, indeed. What you eat."

"Yeah, that burned my ass. What was it?"

"Adam, can't we talk about something else?" asked Verlene.

"Cops eat shit."

"I never said anything like that," McCandless blurted. "I was going to my dramatic arts class . . ."

I commenced chanting, "*Cops eat shit, cops eat shit . . .*"

Kazinski rose and reached across the booth for my denim lapels. "I'll kill the little fucker—"

Boyle intervened with a long arm. "Cut it out, Adam. After all, we invited Billy here."

"Why'd you say that to me? Why'd you rotten kids insult me like that? What'd I ever do to you? I'm a veteran and a taxpayer. A family man. I never beat up nobody who didn't deserve it. I ran boxing classes for little niggers in Flagg City. So why'd you kids have to say things like that to me?"

"I apologize," McCandless said. "I really do."

"It was truly shitty of us," I said.

"Yeah, fuckin' A." Kazinski wiped his eyes, blew his bulbous nose.

Keith dropped his head to the table again and rested it on his arms. He began to snore.

"That bastard Pulsifer," shouted Kazinski. Apparently his weeping could be turned on and off. He must have been in great demand at funerals. "That pimply faced punk. Your buddy, Mallory. Good thing he isn't there. I'd plug him again, only this time I'd have better aim. Shoot the puke right between the eyes."

"Why?"

Kazinski was smiling. See what I mean about these unpredictable drunks? One minute we were pals. Thirty seconds later he'd have been happy to throttle me. I could see Denny Boyle making cautionary gestures with his right hand, as if to say, *Hold it down, Adam, dummy up.*

"That's for me to know and you to find out," Kazinski said.

Verlene said, "Dennis, I wanna go."

"In a second, hon."

It seemed to me (the soberest person present) that Boyle did not intend to leave Kazinski there with me. The older cop was in a babbling mood.

"Come on, sarge. I'm your blood brother. You shot me on the theory I was concealing a lethal weapon. Why are you so pissed at Lyle Pulsifer?"

"Fuck him. And fuck you, Mallory."

"See if I can guess. Lyle was one of yours, right? The fuzz had the goods on him. A drug bust. So he was turned around. He became a fink. Lyle spilled his gut to me, sarge. He got us to torch the Quonset. And he did it on instructions from someone connected with the law. Was it you, Adam?"

"Mallory, you don't know shit."

"I wanna go to bed," McCandless moaned. "Gloria doesn't even know where I am."

I thought of Gloria, that big-boned, high-rumped blonde airhead, sleeping alone in the motel, sulking at Keithy-poo and I suddenly became terribly horny. But I wouldn't be derailed. "Sarge, you know it's true. That's why Pulsifer isn't here. The yellow bastard ran off to Alaska. Come on, who was he working for, Bates Woffler? The college? The local pigs?"

"Now that is idiotic," Boyle said. "We're troopers, Billy. We don't have anything to do with spies or secret agents. We enforce the law."

"And shoot unarmed kids. And kill them."

"We said we're sorry—"

"Let's get back to Pulsifer," I said. "Who made him stir up the trouble? He helped start the riots. He got us moving to the president's house. He got me and Bernie and a few others to cross the fountain, the line you guys had marked off. Who put him up to it?"

"No one," Boyle said wearily.

"Shoulda killed that Pulsifer," Kazinski wailed.

"And me?"

"Yeah, if there's a next time, I'll let you have it too."

"I said, cut it out, Adam," Boyle said. He got to his feet, nudged me out of the booth and took Verlene's arm. She looked as pale as a bleached dog turd. Sorry, but that was the image that hit me. Her eyes were half-shut, as if glued into position, unblinking. Standing, she seemed almost tubercular. I rather admired Trooper Dennis Boyle for being so attentive to her, for trying to protect her from Kazinski's assaults.

Somehow we managed to rouse McCandless, deep in his dreamland of golfing holes-in-one and reinsurance deals. He stumbled a bit, righted himself, then made sure his button-down shirt was properly blooped and that his pheasants were neatly aligned.

Last out, Kazinski wobbled a bit but was a sound boozer, almost in a class with my old man, Emmett Francis Mallory. I could see that Adam had gotten pretty thick across the gut and rump. I wonder if advancing age and the extra lard had affected his shooting eye.

We never did figure out precisely *whose* bullets pinged *which* students. Any of that information, the match-ups, so to speak, came from the mouths of the cops. What happened was that right after the fusillade there was a confusing exchange of guns, mixing of the weapons, shaking out of the magazines, collecting of shells and spent slugs. The federal prosecutor Kalt claimed that before the weapons could be sequestered some of them had been fired over and over in the woods in back of the state police barracks. No matter. They never denied they shot at us, and Kazinski, bless his heart, was the most forthcoming of all. Admitted—with not much prodding—that he'd aimed at me, aimed at Pulsifer, and had killed Andrea Schless.

We made a distinguished group as we staggered across the sawdust floor to the exit. Jack Carr gave me a wink and a thumbs-up sign, as if to say, *Stay out of trouble, you have witnesses.*

Barflies started at us. Guys with potbellies, sideburns, in T-shirts, "gimme" hats and jackets that said "Polish Falcons Softball," "Spanier's Garage Varsity," "Joshua Volunteer Firemen." Not really bad guys. Back in Worcester I used to horse around with guys like that. Some probably did pot and read Playboy and Penthouse. They weren't really Reverend Falwell's folks. Pro football was their code of rules, outlet. They smiled at us, me lugging Keith, the two cops flanking Verlene, who'd now turned the color of a marble gravestone on a cloudy day. A versatile lady in the color department.

"It's Mallory, Sal," one drinker said.

"Hey, pothead! Been shot lately?"

"Just half-shot, Sal."

"Get him outside and finish him off, Kaz."

"Watch it, Denny. He's probably got his lawyer hiding in a car."

Kazinski snorted. In a way he was proud of us. His victims were still alive and functioning. (After all, we weren't Jack, or Andrea, or Lucy. They had had the bad taste to die. As Brian Dooley said after Judge Frankendorf commented that he could not find that anyone's civil rights had been violated, it was a pretty strange case, and maybe His Honor had a point . . . hell, if you're dead you got no civil rights.)

There was a prizefight flickering on a huge color TV set over the bar. As we exited I heard Sal Nobile—an old union buddy of Joe Terragni's —rapping with Matt Gaffney. Matt doesn't tend bar any more. Works the cash register. He's gotten rich in loansharking and bookmaking but he keeps the saloon going out of sentiment. Matt nodded at me. He asked Adam, "How're they hanging, Kaz?"

A final lovely touch as we exited into the mild night air . . . I heard Sal say to Matt, "I can watch two *white* guys fight and I can watch a *white* guy and a *nigger* fight but I'll be fucked if I can watch two *niggers*. It's so boring . . ."

With that the five of us, four jacks and a jill, found ourselves under the yellow-bright sodium street lights.

"Okay, Mallory," Kazinski burbled, "okay, this is it. Put up your dukes. You 'n' me. I got no gun, no club, and you got no rocks. Me 'n' you, Mallory, man to man."

I am small and thin and not too strong. And I hate fighting. Okay, I'm yellow. But I realized, at that sublime moment, that I could have knocked Adam Kazinski down with a fart. The chowderhead was practically on all fours already.

"If you insist, sarge," I said. I handed Keith—who wasn't much better off than Kazinski—my jacket. There I stood, the bull's-eye on my T-shirt clear for all to see, and assumed a pose in imitation of Sugar Ray Robinson, bounced on sneakered feet, flicked my puny left.

*"Graaagh, graaaagh,"* Kazinski gurgled. "Got the little scumbag where I wan' him." He tried to get his fists up but it was like lifting cement blocks underwater.

"Adam," Boyle said, "this isn't right." With that, young Denny— by God, he'd make a fine lawyer some day—deposited Verlene on the hood of a GMC pickup and put his mothering arms around Kazinski.

Keith McCandless, his beer-heavy brain elsewhere, maybe the dogleg on the fourteenth hole, rested against a lamppost and smiled dopily at us.

I danced around Kazinski a few times, daring him to mix it up, calling him a faggot, an asshole, a pig and a Protestant. He kept trying to disengage from Boyle's arms, flailing and falling, but Denny held him tight.

"The winner and new champeen," I said, "William Francis Mallory of Worcester, the Murdering Mick. Fuck you and your whole family, Kazinski."

*"Graaagh, graaagh,* I'll kill the puke. I shoulda kilt him five years ago."

Then he threw up all over Denny Boyle's blue suede shoes.

"Jesus, Kaz . . ." Boyle dropped Kazinski into a pool of his own barf, grabbed a newspaper from a trash bin and began to clean his boots.

226

Sweetly, Keith McCandless was singing. His clear tenor gave throat to the Joshua alma mater. Good old Keith was bracing himself against Gaffney's window and warbling his head off.

> Dear Joshua, dear Joshua,
> In our young hearts you stay,
> Oh, college fair, oh campus rare,
> We'll never say thee nay . . .
> Sound the trumpet 'round the wall,
> For Jericho must fall,
> Joshua, dear Joshua
> To you we give our all . . .

I put my hand over my heart and sang the second chorus with him. Verlene (I learned later she had taken extension courses in bakery management) joined in. Even Trooper Denny Boyle looked as if he wanted to be part of this nocturnal tribute to Joshua College. But he was too busy cleaning his boots and trying to roll Kazinski out of his own mess.

Then, with that unpredictable change of mood and vigor of which drunks are capable, Kazinski popped into a sitting position and shouted at the world, "Fuckin' Offitt! Fuckin' colonel! Rat bastard West Point hard-on. Stay away from that chickenshit colonel, Mallory, *y'hear?*"

Wearied by his outburst—what did it mean?—he rolled over on his side and passed out.

## Helen Christopher

When the phone rang I was furious. I'd told the desk clerk that I was sick and tired of crank calls—we'd all been getting them—and to accept none until seven in the morning. The last thing I needed was some heavy breather or some patriot telling me to get out of town while I was in one piece.

It was the night clerk telling me he'd screened the call and it was a

227

young woman who said she was my daughter. The red figures of the digital clock radio told me it was one-fifteen in the morning. I turned on a light, sat up in bed, and felt myself trembling.

"Mother?"

"Beth. My God, where are you? In Cambridge?"

"I'm in Old Surrey. Don't panic, everything is under control, everyone's okay."

"Oh, dear. It isn't the baby, is it?"

"No, mother. Laurie's fine. I left her in Cambridge . . . It's dad."

"What . . . what . . . ?" Guilt threatened to drown me. I was not proud of myself. Going to a concert with Offitt, even though I'd told myself there was some method in my madness . . .

"He wrecked the station wagon. He's okay. He's in county hospital. I'm with him. No broken bones. Just a lot of nasty bruises and bumps. Dr. Aaronson is with him right now."

"Can I talk to him?"

"Talk? His face is a purple lump and he can't move his jaw. His head hit the windshield."

"Oh, God. It's my fault—"

"Mother, will you stop acting like a twit? He's okay. No internal bleeding, not a bone broken. The god of drunken husbands protected him."

She sounded so cold. So unfeeling. But I understood. She'd never cared much for her father. He was not affectionate with her. He'd craved a son, didn't hide his disappointment in Beth, a gangly shy girl. It had been left to me to try to boost Beth's confidence, encourage her, tell her how pretty she was, how bright. (She was . . . she won the French Prize, the European History Prize and the Emil Pletske American Legion Post Citizenship Medal at graduation . . .)

"Tell me exactly what happened. Why were you in Old Surrey? Are you sure he's all right?"

Well, she conceded, he was in pain, and there was a chance there were some hairline fractures in his left leg, but all his vital signs were good. He was heavily sedated and not in too much pain. Dr. Aaronson said he could probably be sent home in two or three days.

As for her being in Old Surrey, she told me that Dan had called her that morning. He was quite drunk, carrying on about how I'd deserted him, how I'd never get over Jack's death and that it was a shadow over our lives and that all he'd tried to do with that letter was to warn other kids and their parents. In a way, he told Beth, he was doing it for me, writing that letter, trying to explain that it was Jack's fault, not ours.

I said nothing. The horror of his reaction to Jack's murder was something I'd tried to ignore. Made believe to myself that someone else had written the letter. Made excuses for it. Our friends and neighbors and relatives—except for Beth—never talked about it.

"He sounded worse and worse, said he didn't want to live any more, that he needed you and you'd run out on him. And then he begged me to come down and stay with him. His friends were all playing golf or tennis or sailing, and besides none of them understood him, how he'd been hurt. He started to bawl and he kept saying, if only Jack had been tougher, smarter, if only he hadn't let others influence him and drag him around. Then he said maybe he'd kill himself. He couldn't handle living with this."

"Oh God . . . poor Dan—"

"Poor Dan, yes," Beth said. "I guess I was elected. I didn't want to involve Peter in this so I told him to look after the baby and I drove down from Boston."

She'd reached Old Surrey in late afternoon and found her father in his bathrobe and pajamas, unshaven, rummaging through photograph albums, clippings. Mostly stuff relating to Jack. Jack's Boy Scout merit badges. Newspaper articles about his troop. A photo of Jack the day he won an award for installing the trail markers at the Old Surrey Nature Center. Faded photos of Jack at Little League tryouts. Jack and Dan fishing on the sound the summer we rented a house in Watch Hill.

According to Beth, he kept repeating, *Why'd he do it? Why'd he do it?*

"I explained to him after a pot of black coffee that maybe he'd better concern himself with what *others* did to Jack, the police and the city and the judge. He didn't understand. He blames Jack and the students who led the riot. He kept saying, 'You ask for it, you'll get it.' "

"And the accident?" I drew a robe around me, shivered, sat upright on the edge of the bed.

"I hung around. Made him dinner, which he refused to eat. I even told him it wasn't too late to get on a plane, fly to Flagg City and meet you in Joshua. I said maybe it would do him good to spend a night on the campus holding a candle in his son's memory. But you know dad.

That Christopher mind was on automatic pilot. I should know. I have some of that in me. Jack was more like you, mother. A softie."

"How did he wreck the car?"

Around eleven-fifteen, halfway through the TV news, he'd gotten dressed and left the house. She'd gone to sleep upstairs and didn't hear him leave. The next thing she knew, she was on the phone with the local police. (In fact, it was a man she'd gone to high school with, Patrolman Henry Ribnik.) Mr. Christopher, Ribnik reported, had run his Ford station wagon into the long stone wall on Muskrat Drive. He'd made a wide turn while speeding north on Trumbull Road, skidded, tried to straighten out and had plowed into the wall surrounding the Ambleton estate. The car was "totalled." Dan was a mess but he was alive.

"So I woke up Dr. Aaronson. He and his wife both came to the hospital. Blanche Aaronson is terrific. She asked about you, said if I couldn't stay they'd look after dad, and in fact she's waiting for me in the hospital lobby."

"I'm coming home," I said.

"No. Don't you dare."

"Beth, don't argue with me. I know how you feel about your father, but he needs me. I'm getting the first flight out, I'll be back home tomorrow."

"You do, mother, and I'll never talk to you again."

"Your father is hurt. I never should have left him—"

"Mother, you have to look at yourself in the mirror someday and admit that you can't go on being a doormat for him, always excusing and explaining him. I suppose he was good to you years ago. But he's not exactly reciprocated. He's said outrageous things. And now he ruins this trip you've made to honor your son's memory by damn near killing himself. It's his revenge on you!"

"Beth, I'm ashamed of you. You sound as heartless as he once did. As if the accident were his fault . . . Can't you be at all sympathetic?"

"I'm daddy's little girl. No pity. No mercy. No forgiveness. Mother, you *stay* in Joshua."

"I . . . I'll be home this afternoon. I think there's a ten A.M. flight to La Guardia."

"Mother, listen to me. If you come back, if you betray Jack, if you run out on this memorial to your son for that . . . that . . . heartless man, I'll never talk to you again."

"Beth—"

"I mean it. You lost a son, a *son.* All right, it was a terrible accident, a dreadful mistake. But you know what the worst of it was? It was your husband making excuses for the police, writing that horrid letter, exposing his self-righteous law-and-order crap in the newspapers. *That's* the shame. Not any stupid thing that Jack did. God Almighty, you owe him nothing, not a bloody thing. He'll be home in a few days, sipping from the bottle again, stewing in his own juice. Now I want you to stay in Joshua and pay your respects to Jack and those other students. I mean it, mother."

"I don't know what to say. I'm exhausted. I'm confused—"

"Take a Valium and go to sleep. Dad'll survive. If you want, I'll meet you at the airport on Monday. He'll still be in the hospital then. Fair enough?"

By all that seemed fair and decent and proper, I should have flown back to Connecticut. Jack was dead. Our vigil, the guitar-playing and prayers, the speeches and workshop couldn't bring him back to life. If anything, the observances renewed the pain. I was not Dave Schless, determined to keep the issue alive, forever feeding on outrage.

And Dan. I knew what he had tried to do driving that car in the middle of the night. He wanted out. He wanted to end it or at least punish himself. My heart ached for him.

Beth repeated she'd never speak to me again if I came home. So I made no decision, mumbled excuses, weighed options, and finally told her to give my love to Dan, and to tell him I'd be home very soon.

"Mother, make your stand now. I'll have more to say to you tomorrow."

It's odd . . . Beth seeks out other-worldly guidance but is very much of this world in most matters . . . tough, even unyielding, and often materially inclined. I once heard her and her husband arguing over whether they should visit his aging grandfather in Vermont. Peter was against it. He disliked the cranky old man. But Beth prevailed. "Look," she said, "do you want to ruin any chance of inheriting what little money he has left?" They went to Vermont.

Self-interest rules the day. Those who give with no strings attached are rare indeed. And I thought of Jack. I grant you, he was a good if not saintly boy (he did spend a summer working with inner-city children in Hartford), but he was undemanding, had few needs, did not whine about allowances, fancy clothes, a car, all the things his peers craved. He was quiet, accepting, not yet really formed, matured . . . Which made his early death doubly hard for me to bear. I would have liked him to have had the chance to mature to the point where he adored a girl, yearned to buy her gifts, worked hard for whatever it was he came to value . . .

No, Jack was no saint, God knows I'm not, and Dan . . . well, in a way Dan evoked my admiration. Dr. Aaronson had told Beth that when the paramedics pried him out of the wrecked car he kept joking about the Ambletons' stone wall. "Damn thing was moving at me at about fifty miles an hour," he said. And when he was offered oxygen, he said, no thanks, I'd prefer a double Glenfiddich. Brand names to the end for my Dan . . .

## Karl August Frankendorf

The concert was magnificent, exhilarating. I had my usual seat of honor in the front row, next to President and Mrs. Cudlipp, the mayor, District Attorney George Dempsey and some of the Eversons. The younger Eversons all know me and like me, and joke about my old friendship with their grandfather. (The one who used to call me Sister Mary and Four Eyes. He's long dead, a victim of a stroke. I can't say I wept at the news.)

I thought the calming effect of the music would help me sleep, but I'm wide awake now, thinking about Colonel Offitt and what Winnington and Dempsey told me about "suppressed information."

It's all nonsense after the fact. I conducted the case fairly. Nobody's rights were violated. I made that clear. When you join a murderous mob you forfeit your rights. We shoot looters, don't we?

But I could not get Colonel Offitt out of my mind. I had at first rather liked the men. A splendid witness for the defense. But later I found him a trifle standoffish. Perhaps too handsome and youthful for a man his age.

Yet Winnington and Dempsey sounded worried. But why should they be? We all did what was expected of us. Justice prevailed. I *believe* that. I'm sorry about those dead people, but no one should bear any guilt except perhaps the agitators who incited the youths . . .

My hands are trembling. I am convinced it's nothing more than advancing age. Anyone who tries to tell me I'm going downhill because of "guilt feelings" or "second thoughts" about my conduct of the trial would be assuming too much. I reject such a notion out of hand.

## Dr. David Schless

Less and less reporters are showing up for our press briefings. Still, it's Sunday, a bright sunny spring morning, so who can blame them?

Luckily, one network TV crew is here, and so is Ed Hodges, the Associated Press man from the state capital. The one I got to know during the trial. Best of all, Arnold Shreck, the famous syndicated columnist, ambled into press headquarters in the basement of Dexter Hall and took a seat at the back of the room.

God, I was delighted to see him. He treated me a bit tentatively, taking notes, chewing on his pencil, futzing with those huge cheaters he wore, and avoiding my eyes. (When he yawned, I noticed that he had severe malocclusion on the left side of his jaw. I could have fixed it for him, for a hell of a lot less than he'd have to pay in New York.)

On our side there was me, Mallory, Alvord Jensen, Tom Finnegan and a new recruit to our cause—Peggy Sharpless, the state assembly-woman. Jensen and Finnegan had convinced her the past few days and she was determined to get our case before the legislature as soon as it reconvened. It would be a long wait, but I was patient. I'd wait forever to get a crack at these bastards.

"What's the good word, Dave?" the AP man Hodges asked.

We sat on cheap orange stacking chairs that universities seem to favor. I was at the head of a long orange plastic table. Coffee containers, cigarette butts, stacks of handouts littered the room.

"Couple of new items," I said. "Al, is it okay if I start without a prayer?"

Jensen laughed. "It's Sunday, Dave. I imagine all those who desire prayer have done their praying."

I addressed myself to Arnold Shreck. He had a column in this Sunday's paper, not about us but about evidence that communist agents were behind the food stamp program! Shreck was a stuck whistle, one long shrill bleat. And yet (I was informed) he'd once been a bright, even liberal type, full of detente, *angst* over migrant workers, a partisan of equal rights and low-cost housing. Somewhere along the line he'd been bitten by the right-wing bug. It was his insurance policy against *Der Tag.* He'd be a good Jew who believed in the death penalty, school prayer and big defense spending, and hated abortion, gun control and quotas. Shreck had counted the house, was frightened by what he saw and had changed his script between acts.

"Mr. Shreck," I asked, "who is Miles Pendragon?"

"What?"

"Miles Pendragon. Do you know him?"

"Yes, but I don't see what this—"

"Was he the source of your column to the effect that this memorial observance of the Joshua massacre is being secretly manipulated by the Soviet Union?"

Shreck hunched forward, grinned with all his teeth and took off his black cheaters.

"How about it, Arnold?" I asked. "Did you get your information from a man named Miles Pendragon?"

"I did. But that is no secret, Dr. Schless. Mr. Pendragon runs a reliable news service. He is a highly regarded source for matters concerning the communist conspiracy."

"How is he on secular humanists?" I asked. I get these wild hairs up my nose every now and then.

Shreck nibbled the templepiece of his specs. "I am not aware he's taken any position. Mr. Pendragon is an expert on Soviet infiltration of the media, the universities and the clergy."

"He is also, according to the FBI," I said—there was no point in wasting time with Shreck—"a perjurer, a liar, a confidence man. This information was furnished by the Bureau itself. They have warned journalists to steer clear of Pendragon. So much for your expert source who furnished you with the revelation that our observance was a creation of the KGB. Care to comment?"

Hodges, the AP guy, was scribbling away. "This for real, Dave? You got an imperial gallon of libel there if anyone prints it."

"Call your Washington bureau, Ed. They'll be happy to confirm what I just told you. It's no secret about Pendragon. It's all on the record. To date he hasn't sued anyone. Arnie, we look forward to a retraction."

Shreck looked as if someone had rammed an icicle into his *kishkas*. Poor guy. He'd learn about getting down in the dirt with those professional commie hunters, that mob of ex-reds, twisted philosophers, lunatic phony patriots. Not that I'm in favor of communists. You think I don't know who wants to wipe out Israel? You think I want to see all those trees I paid for in the Negev turned to ashes by some camelfucker armed with Russian bombs? No way. It's just that you don't go around hollering communist at anyone you disagree with. You could look up and down our group, examine the backgrounds of the students involved, the parents and faculty and clergy, and you'd be hard put to smoke out a party member or even a dupe.

Which brought me to Billy Mallory. He was sitting at the other end of the table, holding his head in his hands and looking like a rainy morning in Scranton. He hadn't shaved and his eyes were rimmed with mauve smudges.

"I have one more item of interest for the press. Billy Mallory, the man cited as the radical leader of the riot, our legendary flag waver and rock thrower, has something to say."

So Billy did his number. The letter from Lyle Pulsifer about being a police agent, how the cops told him to instigate the riot and specifically to enlist the help of Billy and some bikers to torch the Quonset hut.

"Anyone checked it out with the police?" the TV reporter asked.

"It's a helluva charge, Dave," Hodges said. "We've had rumors about this but they've never stuck. Where's Pulsifer?"

Billy and I took turns giving explanations about Lyle being in Alaska and how he didn't reveal in his letter who precisely awarded him his graduate degree in arson.

Local cops? the reporters wanted to know. State police? Guys in civvies? Campus fuzz? Neither Mallory nor I knew. We realized we didn't have much of a case. Still, someone might print it. It wasn't libelous and it would make a nice item. I'd learned to play their game, and I had no shame.

Hodges wanted to know if we had heard about a counterdemonstration being organized by families of the police, the Young Americans for Freedom (whose?), the Right-to-Life party (in support of shooting students?) and the United Gun Clubs of Flagg County.

Jensen said he respected the rights of others to disagree with us, and after all, we weren't holding the vigil to point the finger at anyone (not exactly true). We welcomed an open discussion with the authorities. As a matter of fact, they'd been invited to the weekend workshops, everyone from the governor down to the police dispatcher, but none had seen fit to participate.

When the conference ended—I admit the reaction to Pulsifer's story and Shreck's source was less than earthshaking—I noticed that Helen had come into the room and was standing in the back. Lovely as ever, in tan linen and low heels. Why do I always recall how she looked, what she wore? Maybe because she at least seemed the essence of calm, an island of decorum and civility in the midst of our *sturm und drang*.

"Did I miss anything?" she asked.

People were leaving, the TV crew packing up, Hodges asking Billy to get him a photostat of Pulsifer's letter and to see if he could locate Lyle and have him confirm the story personally with Ed. Also the names of the cops who had manipulated him.

"Not much." She was wearing dark glasses, and looked pale. "You okay, Helen?"

"I had some . . . news last night."

"Oh?"

"My husband was in an automobile accident. He's in the hospital."

The booze. Handsome Dan, with his white hair and rugged face. An intelligent friendly guy. Except he wanted to absolve the people who killed his son. "Serious?" I asked.

"My daughter says no. He's badly bruised and may have a leg fracture. I'm thinking of going home."

"I can understand that. We won't feel let down if you go, Helen. But we'll miss you."

"I . . . I can't make my mind up. I have the feeling I'm responsible, he didn't want me to go to Joshua. I hope what we're doing is going to prove worthwhile."

236

We were standing in the doorway of the barren room. Mallory was calling Alaska. On such frail reeds did we base our hopes. Did it truly matter whether he and Pulsifer were set up by the cops? Did that change anything? Would it change the minds of the people who whispered, gleefully, that Andrea's body was syphilitic? Or that Lucy Terragni was pregnant with a "nigger baby"? Or that Jack Christopher had a gun on him when he was killed? I held back my own doubts.

"If I didn't think so, Helen, I wouldn't be devoting my life to it. Believe me, Rita and I could be thinking of retiring to Palm Beach in five years. But I won't quit. Of course, not everyone's as hardheaded as I am. Comes from a lifetime of staring at bicuspids."

She laughed. "No it doesn't, Dave. You've also got a good heart."

We walked upstairs and into the lobby then out to the campus. Rita was sleeping late. She'd been having nightmares again. Dreams about Andrea coming back. Covered with blood, asking if she could use the car, arguing with us about her new boyfriend, planning a trip to France. Does the pain ever leave?

"Has anyone learned anything more about Colonel Offitt?" Helen asked.

"Such as?"

"Oh, that he hasn't told everything. Didn't you mention that? Wasn't Harriet Blochman hinting at that?"

"Yeah, we we can't nail anything. Brian Dooley says he's tried to talk to Offitt a half dozen times, and the guy says he's had his say. Nothing to add."

She paused and tilted her head. The morning sun fringed the edge of her light brown hair with gold. "I was with him last night."

Funny. I wasn't especially surprised. I'd seen the way Ironpants had been surveying her. "He's got good taste—"

"He took me to the concert."

"Rita and I were there. Didn't see you."

"I thought it would be wise for us to remain in his car. Believe me, it was uncomfortable. But I tried to get some information out of him. He was almost acting as if he wanted to tell me some things—"

"Opinions or facts?"

"I said that if he showed up at one of our meetings, or spoke at the vigil it would show his sincerity about his regreats. But he seemed to be a step beyond that . . . not just a *mea culpa* or a statement of regret or a promise that the police wouldn't fire at unarmed students again.

It was, I felt, that he was *hiding* information. That he had important things to say but couldn't bring himself to do it . . . Dave, and please don't repeat this, he made a pass at me. I almost got ill."

Across the campus they were setting up the iron piping and the wooden boards for the platform. Signs were going up. Nylon ropes strung on metal rods to mark off the area of the vigil. People sang and laughed as they worked. The campus was alive with greenery and early flowers. And Offitt had made a pass at our Helen!

"What did you do?"

"I sent him home."

"Helen, you've got a problem. You say Dan isn't too badly hurt?"

"He's upset, but not badly hurt . . . I'll call him in a little while."

"Then I wish you'd stay. Tell the colonel you'll see him again—please, hear me out. You can work on his sensitivities. You're hurt, your marriage is in trouble, husband in traction, daughter hysterical. But you're staying in Joshua because you owe it to Jack. And by God, *he* owes something to Jack. If he knows anything, tell him he must for his honor come clean. I know it's asking a lot of you . . . that it's distasteful. But it could be very important. Forgive my bluntness."

I saw Finnegan motioning to me. We had a meeting with President Cudlipp to review ground rules for the vigil.

She was less shocked than I'd expected.

"Let me think about it. I've never been too good at decisions."

"Helen, it's up to you, of course." Our Mata Hari! If anyone could get Offitt to talk—if the guy had anything to reveal—our Helen could. Love (and lust) makes men do strange things. Maybe the colonel was far enough gone to oblige us. And maybe we'd all underestimated the stuff in Helen Christopher.

Something made me feel like going to mass this morning. Normally I go about eight times a year—Easter, Christmas, a few other days. Since Lucy died I find I don't have much desire to go. I consider myself a good Catholic. But Joey never was much on church. And when Lucy died and Father O'Mara made a speech about violence leading to more violence and the need to respect authority, no matter where it came from, I soured on it too.

But it was so beautiful this morning. Hot sun, clear sky, the air fresh and sweet. Up in Flagg City the factories have turned the air smoky.

After breakfast, Joey and I walked to Holy Family Church, took seats at the back and enjoyed the singing and the service. I took communion from a nice black priest I'd never seen before, and Joey stayed quietly in his pew. He looked exhausted. He was thinking of Lucy, I'm sure, and how the nuns always praised her, and wrote nice things in her yearbook, and said she'd make a marvelous teacher. He keeps it locked inside. Don't believe what you read about Italians letting all their emotions out.

Father Schmidt helped celebrate mass. He's one of the reasons I can get Joey into a church now and then. He was kind to us, even though nearly everyone in Joshua sided with the cops and hated the students. But he listened to our side and helped us form our committee. It almost cost him his parish and there was talk at one time of the bishop transferring him to Texas. Then a new bishop took over, and said he'd support Father Schmidt down the line. They teach that there's only one true church, and one set of rules. So how is it that one bishop can say shut up about your dead daughter, the troopers were right, and another bishop can say this is an outrage, this was a crime, and we want justice?

Father Schmidt is a short gray man. He never says much and he's supposed to have had a drinking problem years ago but licked it. He's generally well liked, even though a lot of people are sore at him for siding with us.

So I stared at him during the service and he smiled back at me, and when it was over he walked to the front to greet the people.

"You okay, Joey?" I asked.

"Sure. Little of the old religion can't hurt."

"You were thinking about Lucy." I'd seen him wiping his eyes.

"How can I help it? The nuns loved her."

"Who didn't?"

On the steps of the church I saw Father Schmidt and the young black priest—Father Turner, his name was—chatting with some women. Funny how women outnumber men more than three to one in most churches. And yet I keep hearing the women are the ones who want to change a lot of things—divorce, birth control, lady priests, and so on. Me, I try to be a good wife and mother, and don't bother myself with such radical things. Though come to think of it, why shouldn't a woman be allowed to be a priest? We all pray to the Blessed Virgin and she sure was a woman.

There was a woman standing on the bottom step talking to Father Schmidt. I asked Joey if he recognized her, because she looked familiar. She was short and sort of shapeless. A pug-nosed face, teased black hair (it was dyed because nobody had hair that black) and dressed in a green suit that sagged a little.

"Angie Trippi," Joe said. "Lou Trippi's wife."

"Oh, one of them. She's gotten fat."

State Trooper Louis Trippi had been one of the defendants. One of the six who fired their guns into the students. It never came out whether he hit anyone, although the prosecutor seemed to think his bullet hit Hubie Colson. But the guns were so mixed up and even fired *afterwards* to confuse the whole thing, so that it was never established. Anyway, Trippi had gone on trial and like all the others had been acquitted.

Joey knew some of his relatives slightly in Flagg City. Factory workers like Joey. Angela, I think her maiden name was Randazzo, came from the same background, Italian-Americans like us, working people whose great-grandparents came west to build the railroads and stayed on.

"I got an urge to talk to her," Joey said.

"Why?"

"I dunno. I never hated Trippi. The guy seemed sorry. Not like Kazinski."

Angie Trippi had waddled down the steps to a blue Pontiac and was fiddling with the keys. The car was dirty and had rust spots on the doors, a big dent on the fender and a parking light missing. We greeted Father Schmidt and followed Mrs. Trippi.

"Angie," Joe said. "Wait up."

She turned and shaded her eyes from the morning sun. "Who? Oh. Didn't recognize you."

"Joe Terragni. You remember my wife Sally? We used to be neighbors of your sister-in-law in Flagg. How you doin'?"

She looked scared. Oh, she knew who we were. You don't forget so easily. The parents of a child your husband may have killed? But it wasn't her fault. She was kind of a dumb woman.

"How's Lou?" Joe asked. "Still with the troop?"

"Whaddya wanna know for?"

"Just curious."

She drew away. "Then why all that garbage this weekend? Raking it all up in the newspapers and on television? Don't you think we have feelings? Don't you think cops have families and it hurts to have all these lousy things said over and over about that business?"

"Look, Angie," Joe said, "no one's sore at you. At least your kids are alive and well. We lost a daughter—"

"I'm sorry for you. So was Lou. He never knew what happened. He was scared he'd be killed that day."

Joey tugged at the brim of his golf hat. "Maybe I could talk to Lou. He at home?"

"You ain't heard?"

I asked her what she meant.

"Him and me broke up. He run out on me. He lives in Delray Beach, Florida."

"Gee, I'm sorry, Angie," I said. "When did it happen?"

"A year ago. Look, I got a Sunday dinner to prepare for my kids."

"Hold it, Angie," Joe said. "It must be tough. Funny your in-laws never mentioned he left you."

"They ain't proud of it. Lou was a hero to them. To a lot of people. They blame me and I never was anything but a good wife, took care of his kids, stuck up for him."

I was sure all of that was true. But she sulked a lot. One of those women who made a career out of being a nag.

Something was brewing in Joey's mind. Maybe some bar gossip he'd heard. Rumors in the shop, at the bowling lanes. You see, Joey was one of them. Me too. People like Helen Christopher and Dr. Schless and Dr. Bernie Hoch and Reverend Jensen and Professor Finnegan—

they're different. They don't really know about us. They don't understand us. They don't know about the troopers and their families, or about assembly-line guys like Joey. It's two different worlds.

"You got a job?" Joey asked. "You know, I have contacts in Flagg City. The union, the Italian–American Society."

"I'm a checker at Safeway."

Joey pursed his lips. "Maybe we could do better for you. I'm back with the union headquarters. I was reinstated. We might find a spot for you at the tile factory or maybe B&R Bearings."

"What do you wanna help *me* for? We were enemies during the trial. Your daughter got killed. My Louie was marked for life, and Jesus, do I have to explain to you it helped wreck our marriage?"

"How?" I asked. "What'd we have to do with it?"

"Oh, not you and your husband. Not even that dentist or those other people. It was just Lou was never the same. Sure, you'll say, our daughter's dead, well, I'm sorry, but lemme tell you both, there's sometimes worse things than being dead." She began to sniffle, buried her pug nose in a handkerchief.

"We'll try to give you a hand, Angie," Joe said. Then he asked, "Who was the woman?"

"Ethel Hofheimer. I thought the whole world knew."

"Ethel Hofheimer?" I asked.

"Hofheimer?" Joey repeated. "The policeman's sister?"

"His *wife*. Stub Hofheimer's *wife*. One of Lou's buddies. A guy he went through the police academy with. They worked fires and riots together, they rode in the same patrol car, they bowled together. And that skinny blonde who used to look down her nose at us and called us wops, she takes away my Louie."

"What about Stub?" Joey asked. "How'd he take it?"

"He was so humiliated he resigned from the troop. Didn't even get his twenty years. But they gave him a good reference and he moved. They had one kid, a daughter, she's about twenty, and she went with Ethel and Lou to Florida. I don't know why I'm tellin' you this, except it's no secret."

"Where's Stub Hofheimer?" Joey asked.

"Somewhere in Arizona. He's a city policeman. He hits spics on the head when he's sober enough."

There was some kind of dark shadow on Joey's face. Like the day we got the telephone call that Lucy was dead. Joey did not break down or scream or curse. But his face turned dark, in some frightening way, his eyes looked like stones, and I could see the lines growing deep, cutting into his cheeks and his forehead. My Joey's a handsome man —rugged face, lined from hard work, and he was always a good-time guy, full of jokes and games, especially with the children. But he changed that afternoon when we heard that Lucy had been killed. And that look on his face. I saw it again the day they threw him out of the American Legion post (they took him back a year later) and the day the union council decided he was "un-American" because he circulated a petition asking for a grand jury investigation. A dark look. Not just anger. More scary.

"*Stub,*" Joey said. "That chunky guy with fat cheeks. He was once the heavyweight wrestling champ at Jefferson High, right?"

"Mary Our Mother. He was such an old friend of Lou's. And a friend of mine. We all went to Mary Our Mother. I'm not mad at him. I'm mad at that bitch of a wife. Stub, he's the kind you feel sorry for."

It was getting warm in the sun. Angie Trippi said she had to go home but Joey convinced her to have a beer with us. There was a tavern on the corner just opening—The Copper Kettle—and we went into the dark beer-smelling place. I ordered a Tab and Joey and Angie drank Michelob. Joey began telling her how brave she was, and how it must be tough for a woman all alone with children, and did Lou pay her alimony?

Suddenly he asked her, "How come they called Hofheimer Stub? His name was Francis, right?"

"He hated Francis. Said it sounded like a girl. They used to call him Butch in high school. The Stub stuff started after he joined the force. You know, the way men kid each other, especially cops. Locker-room stuff. Always kidding. They used to call Lou Big Wop or Godfather. That kind of thing."

"What'd Stub mean? He was a pretty hefty guy."

Angie Trippi turned her head and grinned in a funny way. I have to say, it's not like women like Angie and me to talk dirty or tell off-color jokes or anything like that. It isn't allowed. My father washed my mouth out with soap for saying *hell.* Our men don't cheat on us (usually) and they never use bad language in front of women. Joey once knocked down a steelworker who made the mistake of telling me to f---

off when I objected to how loud he was playing the jukebox at the Veterans Bowling Lanes.

"I thought everyone knew," Angie said.

"Knew what?"

"About Stub."

"I didn't know," Joey said.

"Maybe I'd better not say it with Sally listening. I don't owe those Hofheimers anything, but it's sort of sick. Something maybe Sally don't want to hear."

"I'll spend a penny." I got up, hoping I didn't look as down-at-the-heel overweight as Angie Trippi, and went to the ladies' room. The odor of Lysol almost made me faint.

When I got back Joey was on his second beer and Angie was ready to leave to make dinner for her kids. They were two boys, fourteen and nineteen, and I gathered they'd been hurt by their father's taking off. One had been arrested for smoking pot, and the other was on probation for stealing school supplies from Mary Our Mother.

"Remember," Joey said, "if we can help with a job we'll be glad to. And try to find Hofheimer's phone number for me. At least where he's working in Arizona."

"Okay. And thanks. Nice seein' ya both."

The sunlight in the doorway turned her into, what do you call it, a silhouette, and she was so dumpy and plain that my heart went out to her. It was odd, too, that I felt really sorry for the way she'd been made to suffer through no fault of her own, for what happened to her husband after the shooting. I heard they got poison pen letters and obscene phone calls and threats. And then grand jury hearings, the trial, and maybe the civil suit that Dr. Schless kept talking about. And on top of that her husband running off with his buddy's wife. I had no recollection of Ethel Hofheimer. I barely remembered her ex-husband.

"What about that nickname Stub?" I asked.

"Small penis."

"*What?* That's disgusting."

"Police humor. That's the story Angie gave me. Hofheimer took a lot of razzing. Ethel went around blabbing that her husband, Trooper Francis Hofheimer, the former wrestling champ, had been short-changed below. Not only that, he didn't do much with what little he had. Didn't get mileage."

"Joey!"

"I'm just repeating what the lady told me."

"I've never heard of such a thing in my life."

He winked at me. "That's 'cause you've been lucky in love, Sally. Let's go. I got to talk to Doc Schless and Finnegan."

Driving back to the motel, Joey kept repeating—*Stub, Stub.* Then he said: "It must have burned his butt. Those guys. All *macho,* guns, fists. And his good buddies ranking him about the size of his peepee."

"Ugh."

"Angie said it drove Hofheimer nuts. He once smashed the water cooler at the barracks after they played a dirty trick on him."

"What kind?"

"Not for your ears."

"I've heard plenty just now."

"Okay. They pasted half a peanut shell to a rubber band and hung it on a hook in his locker."

"What's so terrible about that?"

"Trippi and Kazinski attached a sign to it. *Stub's Jock Strap.*"

"Oh, that's *terrible.*" But I couldn't help laughing.

"Angie says it was no secret that Ethel Hofheimer had a roving eye. And it roved right over to Lou."

Joey was frowning, chewing on some idea, trying to arrange things in his head. He's only got a high school education—the union paid for a year of courses at the state university in labor relations—but he's always had a sharp mind, always scored high on intelligence tests.

He swung the car down Washington Street. There were a few posters in store windows and on telephone poles inviting people to our vigil.

"Wonder how long her eye had been on Trippi," Joey said. "How long they'd been cheating on Hofheimer. I wish Mrs. Trippi had hung around longer. If she doesn't call me with Hofheimer's new town, I'll get back to her."

"Sherlock Terragni," I said. "Perry Mason. What are you looking for?"

"I'm not sure."

Joey swung the car through the open campus gate. I tried to ignore the happy memories of Lucy, the times we'd spent with her here. When I saw that wooden platform that had been erected, the roped-off areas, the P.A. system, I got a sinking feeling in my stomach. Maybe it's not what I wanted. Not the way I wanted to remember her. Maybe it's better doing these things alone.

## Helen Christopher

Dave and Rita wanted me to meet with Peggy Sharpless and other members of the committee. Peggy, the young state assemblywoman— I must say I admired her courage and her intelligence—had gotten some legal opinions on the chances of a state law allowing us to sue. Dave wanted to arrange a conference phone call with Brian Dooley and see how best to proceed.

"Things are looking better," Dave had said to me after the press briefing. "Peggy—God, she's a find—says that her head count in the legislature is just about a push. If we can come up with a blockbuster we might swing enough votes."

We were standing outside the columns of Dexter Hall enjoying the sun (as much as I could enjoy anything at that moment) and I said I'd have to run off and call my husband.

"Give Dan my best," Dave Schless said.

"Mine too," Rita added.

"And look, Helen. I was mostly kidding about Colonel Offitt. I shouldn't burden you with spy jobs when you've got this new problem." Dave looked guilty. "In fact, maybe you should head back to Connecticut. We'll miss you but we'll manage. I know you'll be with us in spirit."

"At the moment I'm not sure that to do, Dave. I'm going to phone Dan right now." I left them.

Some students had hung a bedsheet out of a dorm window. It was some foolish message—Greek letters and a proclamation of their athletic prowess, intramural softball champions, something like that. It made me think of Jack and his eagerness to join a fraternity. Neither Dan nor I approved. Joshua was not a "frat" school. But Jack, I suspect, needed the camaraderie, the sense of prestige he felt that being a Phi Gam or a Beta Theta Pi would give him. All that silly hazing, the rituals. I wished he hadn't. It filled me with pity that he felt he needed that prop.

I remembered the first summer he was home, working at the Gavin Paper Company with Harlan Weinberg, a neighbor's son. Harlan was a scholarship soccer star at Brown, an A-student, a multi-talented boy. He was also a bit cocky. Rather cruelly, I thought, he'd made fun of Jack's talk about frats and beer busts, pointing out that at Brown and other Ivy League schools fraternity students were considered "nerds," "weewahs" and "doodahs." The brightest kids, the best athletes, the ones who would win Fulbrights and fellowships and make All-American teams tended to stay independent and were proud of it. It seemed to rock Jack. He never did pledge a fraternity.

I suppose the fact that he grew up to be overweight, and didn't attract many friends and very few girls, upset him. I wanted so badly for him to be happy and . . . well, motivated. Maybe that's why he joined that mob. At last he could belong to something. And putting himself in the front ranks, taunting the police, facing those gunbarrels. Did it make sense? Maybe not, except to Jack . . .

I called from my motel room.

Dan sounded as if his voice were being filtered through cotton.

"This is Helen, Dan. How are you?"

"How do I sound?"

"Not too good."

"Percodan, I'm loaded with it. Gives me that nice fuzzy feeling but dulls everything. Why'd you wait so long to call?"

"Beth said you weren't in any condition to receive calls and I thought you might be sleeping late—sedated. Are you in pain?"

"Not much, so long as I'm doped up."

"No bones broken?"

"No. What they thought was a hairline fracture wasn't. My head hurts like hell. Slammed into the windshield, I've got some great purple bruises on my chest. Other than that I'm beautiful. I'm being discharged in a couple of days. I guess you'll grab the first plane out?"

"I . . . I . . ."

He ignored my hesitation. "Frankly, Beth is a pain in the neck. I don't want her lecturing me. I asked her to sneak me a fifth of vodka, something to make these godawful hospital lunches palatable, so she brought me some honey yogurt."

"Dan?"

"Yeah. Obviously I can't meet you at the airport, but let's splurge. I'll tell Beth to call the limo service."

". . . I'm not coming home today. I'll come home late tomorrow. I'm staying for the vigil—"

"Vigil, Jesus. A bunch of half-zonked kids and some pinko professors. I don't want my son remembered by them."

"Whom would you prefer? The police who killed him?"

"That's a pretty low blow. Helen, I'm in pain, I can't think too well. I've got a totalled station wagon in Ferrara's Garage. I need you to tie up the loose ends, get after the insurance company, hospital bills. I'm sorry I did what I did. But I'm under strain too. I haven't told you this but last week the board rejected my plan for marketing the new valve kits."

"I'm sorry."

"It means no raise. Maybe no bonus. It's getting to be a young man's business. All those smart kids with MBA's from Columbia and Penn. Look, I don't mean to cry on your shoulder. We'll manage, but I want you here."

"A day's difference won't matter, if I come to see you tonight or tomorrow afternoon . . . Dan, I wish you were out here to help me honor our son."

"With candles?" He paused, perhaps sensing he was hurting me. "You okay? You feel all right?"

"Of course."

"Well, all you'll get is heartache . . ."

His voice was choking, muffled. He seemed to be struggling not to show his real feelings . . . still deceiving himself because they were too painful.

"We'll never agree on this," he said. "Maybe it should be off limits, something we don't talk about anymore."

"If that's what you want."

"That, and a lot of other things. I'm getting the feeling that fifty-one is old . . . screwing up my marriage, my job. Even my golf game is going downhill. I can't wait to see you, Helen. Believe it or not, I still love you."

I had to say it . . . was it true? . . . "I love you too, Dan. And please try to understand why I'm staying."

248

"Sure. Well, don't catch cold tonight. Take care of yourself . . ."

And we said our good-byes again. I felt . . . empty. Love? Hate? Too strong. Much worse, God help me, I pitied him.

A musical group—guitars, drums, a singer—had taken over the platform and the P.A. system. I heard the lyrics of one of the old Vietnam protest songs. How antiquated it seemed. No one seemed to know the words.

*Dan.* I wished I could help him, but I didn't know how. Did I ever? We weren't really rich or powerful or famous, but by most standards we were at least *secure.* Jobs, vacations, a fine home, a crime-free town, cars, a boat, the club . . . It seemed impossible that it had fallen apart so suddenly, so devastatingly.

At least Dan had struck out, even if in a way I thought was all wrong, had shown some of his agony. Had I shown too little? Me and my Anglo-Saxon restraint . . . Would it have helped Dan, and me, if I had cried more, agonized, let it, as the kids say, all hang out?

## Colonel Gregory Offitt

My recollection is that I used the tape recorder twice during my pretrial meetings with Woffler. I confess there was something about the young fellow—young enough to be my son—that held me. Much of what he said I agreed with. Discipline, order, hierarchies. It was his way of approaching these matters that disturbed me.

Now I find myself trying to recall what was said at those heated sessions in his office. Jays and finches are chattering around the bird feeder; they help me reconstruct in my mind how the conversations went.

Slumped in his high leather chair, Woffler had the look of congenital illness on his smooth face. He usually began his meetings with me with the rather unsubtle reminder that "We're all together on this one." He was taking a major role in the pretrial proceedings, even though it was a federal case, and he had no official role except to furnish evidence and data to both the defense of the troopers and the government. Still, his was the kind of sharp intelligence one could not easily dismiss.

I said he could count on me.

Woffler smiled. He looked like a skull enjoying a joke. He seemed to be getting more frail every time I saw him. Bony projections of cheekbones, gray stains under his soft brown eyes.

He said there was no question that the whole "event"—the riot, the burnings and killings—had been orchestrated by the extreme left. Agents from New York and Chicago, whose names would be made known, had actively sought fatalities and had gotten them. They were increasingly frustrated that their protests and marches and demonstrations had gotten sparser and less effective. What we confronted, Bates said quietly—his voice seemed weaker each time we met—was a vast conspiracy. Radical agents had penetrated the "highest levels of government" and that was why the justice department was prosecuting my policemen. There was no question about it, he said.

I reminded him that the riot at Joshua College at least seemed nonpolitical. It had started as a "spring bust" and had grown into something more violent when a group protesting the increase in tuition tried to hold a rally.

He answered that was exactly why it was so useful to the radical left. The events were camouflaged, had no evident political aspects, and so the deaths could be made to look especially brutal.

But was it possible, I asked, that there was a bad miscalculation, a failure of communication? That no one provoked it, no one wanted it, and that the deaths were accidental?

Woffler would not accept that. He said that as far as he was concerned the Joshua Massacre was the beginning of Armageddon for our country. He related it to the civil rights movement, the ERA and those who had a grand design for taking over the republic. He was not afraid to stand on the front lines and turn them back. (All of this talk in his low, resonant, persuasive voice.)

Did I disagree with President Cudlipp's call for state police? he asked.

I said I did not. I was a state official and I obeyed orders.

Woffler smiled and said I had evaded his question.

So I stated more precisely that I agreed with it.

We spent a good deal of time reviewing the ground rules for the demonstration—the line across the main campus running through the fountain, midway between Dexter Hall and the administration building, the localizing of rallies, and so forth.

We agreed that it was unfortunate that Captain Durham, wounded by a rock, had to leave the portico and that Lieutenant Mrak was with the communications truck, some distance away. Woffler seemed to imply that I had been derelict in my duties in going inside the building at the height of the rioting. There was almost an implication that I had been tricked into leaving the scene by some unnamed conspirator. We agreed that it was unfortunate that poor Kazinski was left in charge when I left the scene.

My mind kept going back to Helen and I found myself unable to recall other parts of the conversation. So I got out the tiny tape recorder and played one of the reels.

At first there were street noises, phones ringing. I could clearly recall Woffler's high-ceilinged room, the flag, the photographs of J. Edgar Hoover and John Wayne.

My voice was first. I asked about the photographs.

*They are irrelevant. They'll never get into court.*

*I'm told the federal prosecutor had subpoenaed every single photograph that was taken.*

*Kalt, yes. He's part of the conspiracy too.*

*Kalt? He's a Republican—*

*They can be subverted too. He won't get far with them. Almost all those photos are fakes.*

*That isn't what I have heard—*

*You have heard incorrectly. The defense will prove them to be forgeries. I am working with Winnington to establish the fraudulence of the photographs.*

*What if you can't?*

*It doesn't matter. No one will believe them.*

*But the police labs, the FBI, independent experts have vouched for their authenticity . . .*

*I'll decide what is authentic and what isn't. Don't trouble yourself over it, Colonel Offitt.*

At this point I opened my briefcase and extracted a set of schematic diagrams showing the positioning of the police and the students prior to and during the shooting. I recall placing them on his desk.

Woffler asked, *What are these?*

*Schematics, Bates. I had our people draw them, based on the photographs.*

He started to cough painfully. *Get rid of them. If the photos are fakes, then it follows that these schematics, as you call them, are also fakes.*

*Look at this one,* I said. *The lab people coordinated over sixty photos and came up with this. You can see that the mob is almost a football field's length away from the portico. There's a handful of students here, a larger group here. But there isn't any mob, and the troopers don't appear to be surrounded. Note the position of my men—Kazinski here, then Case, Trippi and Markland on the right—*

*What are these crosses?*

*The dead.*

*And these?*

*The wounded.*

There was a pause. *Interesting stuff, colonel, but hardly conclusive. Still, we'll see to it that they don't get into court.*

*Too late. Kalt has copies of these. He subpoenaed all of our files a week ago.*

Another pause, longer. *These drawings are lies. Everyone knows the mob was surrounding your men, forming a tight ring around them, pressing in.*

*I don't think—*

*No, no, no. Let me finish. These have no validity. In court I'll expect you to state that they were based on erroneous information. You and your laboratory expert will testify that the schematics are incorrect in every detail. That should be simple enough.*

*But I was there. The only ones up front were a handful tossing gas canisters back. Mallory, Pulsifer, Christopher, a few others.*

*Colonel, I must impress on you that issues that transcend the death of three misguided students confronts us. That's why I not only have no interest in these drawings or the fake pictures they are based on. I must ask you to reject them and tell the jury that you have restudied them and find them inaccurate and misleading.*

*How—?*

*Colonel, we're engaged in a life-and-death struggle here. You may not like some of my methods, but I know whereof I speak. We cannot let these left-wing atheists steal our birthrights. They do not play by the rules, therefore we will not. I do not think I'm an unreasonable man. Nor are you.*

*. . . You have raised some serious questions, Bates, but—*

*Indeed I have. Have you and your troopers agreed on a version?*

*Version?*

*Of what happened. The mob. The threats. The cursing. The missiles. The snipers. The return fire.*

*I, it wasn't quite—*

*It will be. Colonel, you are a brave man with a brilliant record, a man of honor, respected by his peers. What I ask you to do is nothing less than put that honor on the line.*

I couldn't listen to any more.

It got worse, and worse. What a retreat for Colonel Gregory Offitt, holder of Silver Stars, Purple Hearts, one of the Long Gray Line.

For a while I studied scrawled notes I'd made after this meeting with young Woffler. He's dead now. I recalled the way he kept patting his lips, the fine rim of sweat on his forehead, the hollows under his mournful eyes. How effortlessly he made his case . . . Did I fear him? No. But he was something new for me, a sort I had never met up with.

Three times I have wanted to call Helen and three times I drew my hand away. Instead, I phoned Marge in Tucson and was relieved to hear that she was happy to be with our daughter and grandchildren. I said I would leave on Monday, since the weekend appeared to be coming to a peaceful, uneventful close.

## Dr. David Schless

We were working through lunch in the press room, running off our mimeograph newsletter. It was Tom Finnegan's idea. The college wouldn't let us have access to a Xerox machine—can you believe that? —so Tom had borrowed an old-fashioned mimeo job from the sociology department, and there we were, cutting stencils and duplicating this little poop sheet.

Tom and Bernie Hoch were the editors. They led with Mallory's story on Pulsifer. Also featured was my information on Pendragon, the character who said we were KGB dupes. Peg Sharpless bylined a piece for us on her campaign to introduce a bill in the legislature that would give us the right to bring a civil suit. And Hubie Colson did a where-are-they-today article. He disclosed, among other things, that his Poland China hogs had twice won prizes at the county fair, and that Dr. Bernie Hoch was being awarded a fellowship for postgraduate work in skin diseases of children. Hot stuff.

But it pained me to read it. If it hadn't been for those police hotheads Andrea would probably be married by now, or in a doctoral program, or traveling in Italy, the one place she wanted to go more than anywhere in the world. And the Christopher boy—working, dating girls. And Lucy, probably in Flagg City, teaching school . . .

I was brooding over this when Joe Terragni, looking grim, walked in. I like the guy. He knew several of the troopers personally. He had been a cop-lover. Hell, I have nothing against cops. Where'd we be without them? I can even understand how they got rattled, frightened. But not what they did. It hardly reflected well on their leadership or training. And the cover-up, closing ranks against us, determined to wipe out the truth. Rita says someday I may have to choose between our marriage and the Joshua Massacre. Maybe she's right . . .

Terragni wanted to talk to me and Finnegan. We sent one of the undergraduates out for coffee and sat down in a small office adjacent to the press room. There was a view of the campus from the window. It looked green and fresh.

Joe got to the point. At church he and Sally had run into the ex-wife of Trooper Louis Trippi. Woman named Angela. They knew her slightly. She was divorced from Lou, she told them, and she also told them a story about how Trooper Francis "Stub" Hofheimer's wife, Ethel, whom she described as "that blonde bitch," had stolen her Lou and they'd split for Florida. Hofheimer, she said, had also quit the force and was working in Arizona.

Terragni told the story haltingly, with pauses for sips of coffee. If I didn't know better, I'd wonder if he'd had too many postmass beers.

Finnegan yanked at his curly beard and asked him, "So what has this all got to do with five years ago?"

"I'm not sure, Tom. But Angie Trippi told me—not in front of my missus—why they called Hofheimer Stub."

Finnegan frowned at me and I frowned back.

"We give up, Joe," I said. "Why?"

Terragni's oversized dark features sort of screwed themselves together. He was trying to sort things out, to reach conclusions.

Finnegan tried to rescue him. "He was clumsy? Stubbed his toes a lot?"

"Maybe he'd worked as a movie usher," I tried. "You know, may I see your stub, sir?"

"He had a tiny cock."

All I could think of to say was, "How tiny?"

"Angie Trippi never measured it, but it was a joke all over the barracks. *Stub* meant his penis, what there was of it. The guys, especially Trippi and Kazinski, were always playing jokes on him."

Finnegan and I just sat there. In a way it was a relief from the tensions, the hatreds, the lies. A mean (though pleasant) thought crossed my mind. Those trigger-happy cops, those confident lawbreakers weren't all so superior in the *putz* department after all. I've heard that's often the case with men who love guns, killing animals and bashing heads.

One day, Terragni said, Kazinski taped a rubber finger-cot to Hofheimer's locker. He'd filled it with Edge shaving gel and put a sign under it: *Stub's Scumbag.*

Apparently this was considered high humor at Troop B. But I still couldn't see where this had any bearing on us.

Joe was studying us—two well-educated fumblers, the dentist and the professor—as if we were backward children. And at the moment he had a point. Joe Terragni was one of them. He was much closer to the policemen who killed his daughter and my daughter than Professor Thomas Finnegan and I could ever be. So we listened.

"No man worth a plugged nickel would take that kind of razzing," Joe said. "It must have burned Hofheimer's ass. I think he had a couple of fights over it. With Kazinski once and maybe with Kevin Case. Any guy who puts up with that and don't hit back is in for trouble the rest of his life. It's as bad as a guy using dirty language in front of another man's wife. I once hit a guy so hard I broke two knuckles and he lost four teeth. He said *cocksucker* in front of Sally. But Hofheimer must have been a candy-ass. He took all that crap from his buddies and didn't do much. You see, doc, it wasn't just his dingus was so small, he wasn't good in the kip altogether."

"Sad," I said. "We could use part of our fund to get him sex therapy. Supervised Surrogate Program. Dial-a-Sex. Maybe he's queer for grasshoppers or can't do it unless he's wearing a bathing cap."

"Don't you guys see what I'm getting at?"

We didn't. Finnegan looked bemused. His scholarly journals, his research papers, his studies of working-class patterns downstate did not cover the tragic case of Francis Hofheimer's *schlong*.

"His wife Ethel must have played around. Then she ran off with Trippi. Good family man, Catholic, honest cop. She must have wanted it real bad, and it must have killed Hofheimer."

"But what has this got to do with the shootings?"

"I think Hofheimer fired first."

Finnegan's green eyes were glinting. "Wait a minute. I'm getting a clue."

"He fired first. The others got scared and also fired. I'm gonna prove it."

Maybe I'm still an innocent. Nice Jewish boy, does his homework, doesn't drink, dates high school sweetheart, marries her eight years later, doesn't play around, loves his wife, etc.

Terragni leaned forward. "Remember what those kids were yelling just before the shooting started?"

I said, "They yelled a lot of things."

"Yeah, but the guys up front. Billy, and the Christopher kid and Pulsifer and some of the girls."

"Pigs," I said. "MF. Lots of things."

"They were yelling, 'Who's fucking your wives?' "

Finnegan nodded. "It's on tape. And the first shot comes a few seconds after that. The mystery shot that nobody ever traced. Then the guns opened up. The famous twenty-second barrage."

Now it was dawning on me. But I didn't buy it. Not at that moment, anyway. Too simple. Too pat.

Terragni said, "That's all a yo-yo like Hofheimer had to hear, That's all he needed after a long hot morning, no sleep, the riot helmet and gas mask suffocating him. He sees a bunch of these foul-mouthed kids. He's got no kids of his own. What do they mean to him? And listen to what they're shouting at him. 'Who's fucking your wives?' By God, he knows who. It's his buddy Trippi, on the line with him. Ethel Hofheimer has a reputation. A dame who had to go outside for her sex.

256

Stud hears the kids taunting them. He figures they know something. They mean it for *him*. Well, goddammit, he'll show them who's screwing his wife. He'll blast their punk heads off. Maybe he didn't even realize what he was going to do. But the magazines were jammed home. Rounds in the chamber. The guns were off safety. The kids were in the cross-hairs. Nobody was going to shame him in public. *Me, me,* that's who they're yelling at. Forget the MF's and the other names they called them. There was one insult Hofheimer wouldn't take. So he hit back. He'd show them he was a real man."

"That gun was an extension of his cock," Finnegan said, getting with it.

"And what about the others who fired?" I asked.

"Panic. Fear. Those guys were choking in the masks. Rocks bouncing off their helmets. Sticks, waterbags. It was more than they could handle. Case and Doyle were hyperventilating, almost fainting. Mallory says one of the canisters he threw back hit Markland in the face. All they needed was to hear that first shot. And *wham!* Five other guys start firing. The C.O., Offitt, he's inside arguing with Cudlipp. Captain Durham's out of business with a bloody bump on his head. That leaves meathead Kazinski in charge. So they start shooting. By the time Offitt gets there and sees what's happened and starts grabbing guys by the throat and knocking down gun barrels, there's three dead and six wounded. All because Hofheimer went batty for a few seconds."

Finnegan sighed. "Nice theory, Joe. But we'll never prove it."

I agreed.

Terragni persisted. "Those guys on the portico knew who fired the first shot. And they probably knew why. But they rehearsed their lines. They stuck to their story."

"But not their guns," I added.

"Right. Changed guns around," Joe daid. "Destroyed bullets. Fired them afterward. Then that crap about snipers. A gun on the Christopher kid, a throw-down, the oldest police trick in the world. And Kazinski saying Mallory was hiding a pistol behind his back. That pothead wouldn't know which end of a piece to fire. He was too busy giving them the finger. I feel it in my bones, doc, Tom, I know how far you can go in abusing guys like that, and what they'll do."

"You may be right, Joe," I said. "But I agree with Tom. We not only can't prove it, it'll never stand up in court. So long as the police knew a united front and keep repeating they were afraid they'd be overwhelmed, we'll be in trouble."

"So how can we ever expect to win a new trial?" Joe asked.

Tom threw his hands up. "A different jury. A different judge. Someone who'll let the photographs be studied in court, who'll let our lawyers cross-examine the police on what the pictures show."

"You know," Joe said, "I used to be a hip-hip-hooray guy, believed in the system. Now . . . didn't I hear that writer Shreck, whatever his name is—that egghead from New York, didn't I hear him bragging that bad as the killings were, they had a healthy effect? That students mind their own business now? Aren't in any hurry to charge police lines or burn buildings?"

Finnegan said, "But times do change, Joe. People can wake up. Look, fifteen years ago blacks got beaten or turned away when they tried to register or vote. Today it's not a problem. Not only does the law protect them but most whites *accept* it. In southern states they elect black officials. People learn, they change . . ."

"Then let 'em change and swallow the truth about our kids getting murdered," Joe said.

"Agreed," Finnegan said. "So what do we do with your friend Stub?"

"I'm gonna call him in Arizona. I'm gonna ask him to come clean. To talk. To admit that he panicked and fired that HK–91. That he lost his head and killed and wounded people."

I got up, stretched. "Good luck, Joe. You might get him to admit he blew his cool and pulled the trigger. But no guy like Stub will admit it was because he was ashamed of his small weewee. Or that he couldn't get it up for Ethel."

Joe got up. "I'm gonna track down Hofheimer and try to get him to talk. Not about his cock but that he panicked and shot first. Was afraid he'd be overrun . . . I've got to try. I may even fly out west and see him."

"He may be right," I said, after Joe left.

Finnegan shook his head. "If he thinks he can nail that one down, get Hofheimer to talk, he's crazy. Poor Joe . . . under other circumstances it could have been him up there on the portico."

"I don't think he'd have invented a story, or planted a rusty gun on a kid or lied about a sniper . . ."

No answer from Helen's motel room. I tried the press center at the committee office in Dexter Hall. She wasn't there. I didn't want to identify myself to the young woman, probably a student volunteer, who answered. She didn't know when Helen would be back.

So I poured myself a gin on the rocks and started playing the tape again. Woffler's strong voice, my own a bit wary as the realization came on me what he wanted and what he was doing to me. Not like me. I've always had a good parade-ground bellow, although in normal conversation I'm low-keyed and weigh my words. But I sounded different on the tape. I was ashamed of what I was hearing in the cool loneliness of my screened porch.

One's mind plays tricks. I discovered—to my surprise—that I'd also taped a conversation with Woffler *before* he went before the state grand jury. How could I not have remembered?

The tiny reel was in a separate unmarked envelope. Had I forgotten about it because I wanted to forget?

My voice was clear, firm. At this early stage in the legal proceedings, I thought I saw my duty clearly and knew where we had to go.

*The men tell me they deeply regret what happened. They admit they fired in fear. Couldn't we say they suffered a temporary lapse? Fright, anxiety . . . that would be a legitimate defense.*

*Colonel, they need no defense. It's the mob and the crowd behind it I intend to send to prison.*

*Yes, I see . . . but I'm advised that the federal government will move under the Civil Rights Act. A federal jury may view the Joshua matter differently—*

*Civil rights? What rights? The right to kill, burn, loot, maim and overthrow the established order? Oh, no, colonel. An old army man should know better. No judge, state or federal, will ever let that happen. Rights? A mob forfeits its rights.*

*I was just thinking we should be prepared in case the fed—*

*You may be indicted.*

*Me?*

*Why not? You were the commandant. Your men pulled the triggers.*

*I tell you, Colonel Offitt, when those radicals in Washington, those bureaucratic liberals, smell blood they'll go for your jugular as well as the necks of your innocent men.*

*I'll face that if it happens.*

*Yes, I suspect you will. Therefore, it is necessary that you assist me in every way in presenting my case to the state jury.*

*I have already said I will.*

*Good.*

*In that regard I have told Sergeant Kazinski to withdraw his story about the pistol he found on the Christopher lad. And the men now agree that it's doubtful that there was sniper fire. Of course, they may have imagined that during the height of the confrontation.*

*My belief is that there was a sniper.*

*The FBI says—*

*I don't trust them. Not since Hoover died. They may very well be infiltrated too. We'll find witnesses who will swear they saw snipers.*

*There does appear to have been one shot fired a moment before the fusillade, but the lab says it sounds like one of our own rifles.*

*No, no, we'll prove it was a sniper. No one issued an order to the men to fire, did they? You? Kazinski?*

*No one.*

*Which proves it was a sniper.*

*I'm not so sure—*

*Of course you're sure. If ever there was a clear case of self-defense, of legitimate use of force against an armed rabble, this is it. I have never been so confident of winning a case in my life.*

*The photographs—*

*I don't intend to show them to the jury. They will be filed and forgotten. They have no bearing on this case.*

*But the parents—*

*What makes you think I am not sympathetic to them? Except for that dentist. He's a bad one, colonel.*

*Dr. Schless?*

*We have discovered some interesting things about Dr. David Schless. He and his wife contributed to the Urban League and the American Civil Liberties Union.*

*Those are not exactly radical groups.*

*They're worse. Schless also signed a petition urging arms talks with the Soviet Union.*

*So have millions of people.*

*I am discussing a total picture. When a doctor makes a diagnosis, colonel, he takes into account more than one symptom. The overall picture on Schless is that he is dangerously tilted toward the left.*

*He's also a tough man, Bates. He faced down an armed mob in front of the hospital where his daughter lay dead. Not one of them would take him on.*

*I do not really care for any testimonials to Dr. Schless. I have a full dossier on him and I'll introduce it at the proper time.*

*The other parents?*

*I find nothing compromising in the backgrounds of the Terragnis or the Christophers, although the Christopher woman appears to have had a curious interest in the Council on Foreign Relations. She went to a meeting—*

*So did I.*

*You should have known better, colonel.*

*Bates, I must ask you not to talk to me in that manner. I am old enough to be your father. I want to know how many wars you fought in, how many times you were wounded for your country. I don't need to defend my patriotism to you. You are, I'm told, a brilliant legal mind, a respected law enforcement officer and possibly a future governor of our state. None of that gives you the right to lecture me or to cast aspersions on my background or—*

*Don't be oversensitive, colonel. Once again, we're talking about the overall picture . . . seminars at Columbia and MIT, meetings of the Council on Foreign Relations, a distinct hue begins to emerge, colonel. Not too attractive for someone in your line of work, with such an honorable reputation . . .*

There was a long hiatus on the tape. I recalled myself seething, enraged, not really able to score a point with this sleek, sick, maddening and locquacious young man.

Finally he said, *So we're agreed . . . The men were being overrun. The mob surrounded them on all sides. They were hurling lethal missiles. Your police had no choice but to fire back—*

*I can't agree to that. They may have felt threatened, but there are all kinds of threats in riot situations. One doesn't lightly shoot live ammunition into a crowd.*

*We will prove, and I'm sure you'll agree, that under certain circumstances it not only is justified but mandatory.*

*The men may have been panicked but—*

*But, nothing, colonel. We have a provable case against the students and their instigators. I ask for your cooperation. How shall I put it? We want you on the team, colonel. You're getting ready to retire, aren't you? Surely you don't want to leave office under a cloud . . .*

I switched it off. Worse was to come. I put the recorder and the reel of tape back in the envelope along with the transcript and my notes.

Sundays Marge and I usually did chores around the house, worked in the garden, took it easy. I'd given up golf but sometimes I played tennis late afternoons with some older men at the country club. Golf was never my game. Too slow. My tennis used to be pretty good. I was a finalist in the officers' singles in Seoul many years ago.

Today was a fine day but I had no desire to play. At times like this I wish I had a son—he'd be a grown man by now—whom I would have taught to put topspin on his forehand, come to net, develop a slicing second serve. We'd be playing a set right now.

I once had a brother officer, George Kaplan, whose younger boy, an indifferent student (Kaplan was a Phi Beta Kappa and had a graduate degree in electrical engineering) became a tennis pro. Not good enough for the big tournaments but a tremendous club player, a star in college and in their home town on Long Island. The boy gave George a great deal of honest joy. They made a championship father-and-son doubles team and traded tennis lore, tennis books, clippings from the newspapers, tennis talk. I met the boy once—can't recall his name—and envied George this father-son communion.

Oh, I love our daughter and my grandchildren, but I should have had a son . . . Odd how this gap in my life makes me think of Helen, who lost a son.

I phoned her motel room. She didn't seem eager to talk to me, sounded distracted, weary. I badly wanted to cheer her up.

She told me she'd had a difficult conversation with her husband. Apparently he'd totalled their station wagon. He wasn't severely injured, his self-confidence more bruised than his body, but he was in the hospital for observation.

"So you're leaving?" I asked—unable to conceal the disappointment in my voice.

"As of the moment, no."

"I'm sorry he's injured, but I'm glad you're staying. I'd like to see you. I feel I owe you more than that apology, expressions of regret."

What had happened to my old parade-ground command presence? My crisp, authoritative, peremptory tone? I was pleading, begging. Damnit, I knew what I wanted. I wanted Helen Christopher.

She paused. "I'll think about it."


## Helen Christopher


Dave Schless listened, watched, as I spoke to the colonel, hung up.

"Go," he said. "He knows something. You can get it out of him."

"I *can't.*"

"Yes, you can. And you know why."

We were in my room. It was late afternoon. For some reason the air-conditioning was uncontrollable and it was too cold. I wanted to open a door, but Dave insisted on security arrangements.

"It's not right . . . not this calculated . . ."

"Helen, nobody's asking you to compromise yourself, for God's sake."

"Then what *are* you asking?"

"To get him to talk, produce evidence. Dooley and the others are convinced that man has hidden valuable notes, papers, material that never got to court, that Woffler suppressed or made him suppress. There've been hints all along that Offitt was never too keen on the whitewash."

"So I'm supposed to be your secret agent? I'm not exactly right for the role."

Dave drew the shades. "Yes, you are, Helen. I saw the look in our colonel's eye. So did you. You told me about that walk in the park this morning, what he said . . ."

"Dave, this makes me feel smarmy," I said.

"How did you feel when Jack was killed? Just call Ironpants back and tell him you'll see him this evening. He can bring the champagne and roses."

"That isn't funny."

"I know. It's our ballgame. And yours."

I felt chilly, fiddled with the air-conditioning. It was one of those old paint-encrusted things in a long case under the window. Finally I was able to turn it off altogether, and suddenly I was too damn warm.

"Helen," Dave said, seeing my resistance, "if we can break this guy open, Peggy Sharpless says it may just swing enough votes in the legislature. They'll pass the bill and we can get all of them into court again. Wouldn't you love to see that crowd squirming on the witness stand one more time? And this time the judge won't throw out the photographs or do defense counsel's work or cut off cross-examination. Helen, call him . . ."

I took the plunge, picked up the phone. To be honest, along with my reluctance was an excitement about the challenge, about what depended on me.

At long last I was being put to a test, forced to play by rules that were banned in the Potter family. I was being sent into combat, no holds barred. So to speak.

## Sally Terragni

In late afternoon while we were resting in the room Angela Trippi called. She'd located Stub Hofheimer's town but had no telephone number. It wasn't Arizona. He was in Vista, New Mexico.

Joey called information and asked for the city police department. Yes, they had a member of the force named Francis Hofheimer. The sergeant Joe spoke to didn't call him "Stub." He was Patrolman Hof-heimer or Frank.

Unfortunately it was his day off and he couldn't be located. Nor was it, they said, the department's policy to give out home phone numbers. So Joe left a message for Stub to call him when he came on duty. He tried information again, but there were no Hofheimers listed in Vista or the surrounding country.

"Unlisted," Joey said.

We held each other, half-dressed, and dozed. I was sorry that I let myself get heavier and sort of messy. Before Lucy died I was careful about my appearance. Tried to keep my weight down (Joey was kind, said he liked me on the plump side) took care of my skin, used the right makeup, always had my hair in curlers so I'd look good at night. And I always had good features—a high forehead, straight nose, full lips and dark brown eyes. Like Lucy. I can remember Joey staring at my com-munion picture, with me holding the tiny white book and a bouquet, all in white, and he said, "I love you so much, Sal, because you look just like Lucy. The two of you. Mother and daughter could be the same kid."

I cried then and hugged him. In a way it wasn't fair to our other four children. They never got the love we gave Lucy. It's wrong of me to think this. Sometimes I wonder if God punished us for being so proud of her—no, that doesn't make sense, does it? Why would God pick on *her*? She was the best person I ever knew.

Late afternoon the phone rang. Joey jumped out of bed. He thought it was Hofheimer. It wasn't. It was Trooper Dennis Boyle. Joey couldn't believe he was talking to him. There'd been a rule among the six men (in fact all policemen who'd been called out that day) to say nothing. A lot of the men who weren't indicted, who'd never fired their guns, were witnesses at the trial. They too never breathed a word to anyone. Even the colonel and the captain. "It's finished," they'd all say. "Over."

"Joe Terragni? Dennis Boyle."

"Yeah—?"

"Can I talk to you?"

"Where?"

Boyle mentioned a corner of the campus behind the physics lab. There was a sort of enclosure there with benches and it was so out of the way that on Sunday there'd be no students, teachers or townspeople.

It was half past four, a breezy sunny afternoon. We got to the little circle of benches in back of the lab building and saw Dennis Boyle and an older man.

"Markland," Joey said.

"One of the six."

"Yeah. Funny kind of guy. Part Indian. He was up for sergeant but after the tiral, they put him on hold. A good cop."

"He may have killed Lucy."

"We'll never know, Sally."

The two men were in civilian clothes. No state policeman had come on campus in uniform for five years. Orders from the governor. Boyle was wearing a tan nylon jacket. Markland had on a dark blue sweater. He looked like a high school coach, maybe a teacher. Neither of them looked like killers, men who would deliberately shoot into a crowd of unarmed young people.

I don't think they expected me—but they got up, shook hands with Joey and me.

I sat at the far end of the green bench. Joey, half-turned, faced Boyle and Markland.

"What's up?" Joey asked. He knew both of them, Boyle fairly well, Markland by name and face.

"We thought you might want to know a few things," Boyle said. "First off, would it make a difference if we said we're sorry? I mean, really sorry?"

"Sorry?"

Markland coughed. He was an olive-skinned, horse-faced man. Coal-black hair, a kind of solemn way of talking. "More than sorry. We feel terrible about it. It was a mistake. No one knows what happened. We still don't. And we got to live with it all our lives—"

I couldn't keep quiet. "How about what me and Joey have to live with? Or the Schlesses, or the Christophers?"

"We know," Dennis Boyle said. "We know it's much worse for you. But we have feelings, we've got families. Joe. You have to believe me that we have nightmares over this. We aren't nuts or sadists who like to shoot people. Some of the guys acted and said things that weren't right. But all the guys, especially me and Wally and Kevin Case, we're haunted by this. That's the word, isn't it, Wally?"

"Right, it sure is . . . I got kids of my own. Boy in college. He asks me about it all the time. It isn't easy for a man to have his kid suspect he was a murderer."

Boyle took it up. "If we could, Joe, we'd bring those students back to live. They weren't our enemies. I've prayed I could put all those bullets back in the magazines, bring the guns to port arms—"

"Then why did you do it?" I asked.

He shook his head. There was a rim of gold from the setting sun on his coppery hair. Joey told me he was the smartest of the six, a young man who'd get his law degree and go places. "I honestly don't know, Mrs. Terragni. I just don't know."

Markland said, "I don't either."

"So?" Joey asked. "What do you guys want? I should forgive you? Write a letter to the paper like Jack Christopher's father did, saying he'd shake your hand?"

Markland shook his head. "Just that you'd try to understand. We didn't want it that way. If we could do anything . . . I'm a father too . . ."

Markland said he wasn't as bright as Denny. He was middle-aged, set in his trooper's job. No law school for him. Not a bad life. But tough to live under a cloud . . .

Boyle then asked, "Is it true Schless and the others are trying to get us into court again?"

"The others include Sally and me," Joey said.

"But," Markland said, "we didn't mean to hurt anyone. We heard shots. Those gas masks were choking us, a hot day, no sleep . . ."

I believed they didn't want to kill our child. But she was dead. I couldn't feel sorry for them . . . I'm no saint.

"You mentioned Kevin Case feels the way you guys do. What about Kazinski?"

"Same way," Boyle said. "But you know the sarge. Has to act like a hardhead. He doesn't like to talk about it. But he knows it shouldn't have happened."

Usually I let Joey do the talking. That's the way it is with us. Joey has the say and makes the decisions. But I had to say something.

"Dennis, why haven't any of you said this to the newspapers? Why couldn't at least one of you come out and said what you're saying now?"

Boyle hesitated. He looked away, shaking his head. "I don't know. I guess . . . our lawyers . . . you know . . ."

"Didn't want any of you guys to talk? To give the idea maybe you were wrong?" Joey said.

Boyle didn't say anything.

"Who told you guys to load up?" Joey asked.

Boyle squinted into the sun. "We aren't sure. No one remembers. Someone put a magazine in and some other guys did the same."

"Come on," Joe said, "I've read the drill for riot situations. An officer has to give the order. *Load and lock.* That means yanking the clip out of your ammo belt, ramming it home. Then if you're gonna shoot you take the piece off safety."

"That can happen very fast when things get confused," Boyle said. "Those new HK–91s . . . seconds, is all."

"Six guys?"

"It was more," Boyle said. "It was only six of us fired. Maybe ten guys loaded. We were scared, Joe, really scared."

"Trained policemen like you?" I said. "Why?"

His eyes were almost wet. "I don't know. Honest, I don't know."

*"You don't know,"* Joe repeated. "But what does it matter. You guys are alive and free and my daughter's dead."

"I'm sorry. I *said* so. All the guys are. Markland, Kazinski, Case . . ."

"Than, damn it, at least say so in public."

"Hard to, Joe."

I drew my breath in. "I can see why you won't. People might get the idea you were wrong. I can tell you, Dennis Boyle, at first I wasn't too much for Dr. Schless's civil suit, but I surely am now. We're going to back him down the line and get you people into court. And make you pay for what you did."

"Why keep it going?" Boyle asked. "You won't win, you can't. We did our job, we protected the town, the college. People understand that."

Joe nodded at me and we got up.

"Why'd you guys call Hofheimer 'Stub'?" Joe suddenly asked him.

268

There was a second when a smile began to form on Boyle's face. "Stub? Beats me. Chunky guy."

"You sure?"

"Yeah, I guess so. I was never close to him."

"Why'd he leave Joshua?"

"Couldn't take the heat. It wasn't easy for any of the guys. You should see the ugly letters, listen to the obscene phone calls. Most of us have unlisted numbers now. Calling us fascist pigs, worse things that I can't mention in front of your wife. Some of the guys couldn't handle it. Hofheimer was one."

"And Trippi?"

"Him too. Resigned, went out of state."

Joey said, "I heard Trippi ran off with Hofheimer's wife."

"Could be. I was never buddy-buddy with either guy. Lou put up with the same dirty phone calls and letters. Who could blame him?"

Boyle too got up. "Look, I'm only talking for myself, Joe. But supposed I talked to the other guys. I'd get in touch with Trippi and Hofheimer. I'd talk to Colonel Offitt and Captain Durham. And suppose we put out a letter of . . . regret. Something like that. Say how sorry we were. That we didn't mean to hurt anyone, that it was a mixed-up, confused situation and we . . . well, you know what I mean."

"You do what you want," Joe said.

We walked away.

Joey took my arm. "He's scared. They're all scared."

## Helen Christopher

A little after five that afternoon he picked me up outside the coffee shop. The vigil was due to start at nine. I wasn't exactly looking forward to it. My mind was a jumble—guilt over Dan's injuries and my not flying home, guilt or at least an unease about my new career as a spy leading Offitt on, guilt over my lack of enthusiasm for a night on the cold campus nursing a candle . . .

Offitt got out of the black Chevrolet. Gray tweed jacket, darker gray slacks. He could have been a retired stockbroker in Old Surrey, a man with an Ivy League background and long years of service in a Wall Street bond house.

"Helen. Good evening."

"Hello . . . Greg."

"First time you called me by my name."

Oh, God . . . we got in the car and drove off.

"How is your husband?"

"He'll be home tomorrow." We were silent for a while, and when we turned down a narrow tree-shaded street of pleasant frame houses he looked at me in a way that made me turn away. What a role Dave Schless had invented for me. Was there ever a woman less suited to be a secret agent?

The colonel's home was modest yet attractive, yellow frame Williamsburg colonial set back from the street, with a steeply graded lawn and beds of azaleas, forsythia and weigela. A flag descended from a pristine white pole, and he told me it was the flag given him at his last command at Fort Dix, New Jersey, when he retired from the army. He proudly showed me the flower beds and the vegetable garden at the rear of the house, some distance from an old-fashioned screened porch.

"The earth here is excellent," he said. "Rocky but full of minerals. I spent the first year we lived here digging and hauling rocks and stones so we could build the gardens. I used them to create that retaining wall."

"It's attractive."

"The neighbors thought I was something of an eccentric. Commandant of the state police working like a day laborer? But I've never been afraid of work. As a boy I did the same thing on the family farm in southern Vermont. It was a pleasant way of returning to a world I'd lost. My father's farm was auctioned off during the Depression and dad went to work in a lumber mill . . ."

We walked around the garden and into a miniature orchard—four different kinds of apples, he told me. He seemed to know a great deal about caring for them, how to improve production, fight pests. He even liked to bake pies, put up applesauce and apple butter. He said his wife used to be good at it but had lost interest these past few years.

"Let's go inside, I'll make something cool to drink," he said.

The house was cluttered but attractive—needlepoint, old photographs, chintz, antique maple furniture, flowered wallpaper. The colors were subdued, restful. Most everything in the rooms had, I sensed, some association with the Offitts' past.

I pointed to a curious old chest on four raised legs and asked him what it was.

"Grain bin. Eighteenth century, maybe seventeen sixties. It was in my mother's family from way back. It's about all I ever salvaged from the old farm in Vermont. My brothers and I used to keep our athletic equipment in it—gloves, bats, ice skates, fishing tackle."

We sat in the musty living room. It had that clean yet slightly damp odor of a very old house. I noticed a photograph of him as a young lieutenant, evidently just out of West Point. (There were no medals on his tunic.) He looked lean, with hard features, a faint smile.

"Jack once brought me a birthday present when he was twelve years old," I said abruptly, nervously. "I'd started a small tutoring service to supplement our income and I was keeping a little office in the corner of the sewing room. He knew I loved stationery so he made up a kit for me—envelopes, mailing labels, pads, pencils. It couldn't have cost him much but he packaged it himself in an old candy box, wrapped it with gold paper and scotch tape. I cried when he gave it to me. The gesture, you see, was so pure, so innocent."

He watched me from across the room. I was sitting on a sagging gray sofa. He was sitting, back straight, legs crossed, on a lavender wing chair.

"Well," I said, "That moment won't ever return."

"You're a sensitive woman," he said. "Believe me, if I could bring your son back to life, if some magic power were given to me, I'd do it . . . Helen . . . I know you don't want to hear this, but I need to say it anyway . . . I see in you what I've missed most of my married life —no, please hear me out. You . . . you . . . you're so alive, vibrant, a woman of love and understanding. That story you told about your son's bringing you the gift . . . how you haven't forgotten it . . . my past was always filled with regrets. I think women have an advantage . . ."

"Because we're not afraid to show our feelings? When Jack was killed Dan hardly ever cried in front of me, but I could hear him alone, locked in the bathroom or in his basement workshop. His bravado made it worse. I wish that my husband had been able to express some of David Schless's outrage. He will never be the same."

"Will you?"

"Of course not. The memories are harder to stand each day."

"Yes . . . well, then this weekend must be a double effort for you. All the reminders—"

"I think I have the strength for it."

"I'm sure you do."

I, of course, wasn't so sure . . . including my ability to carry off this mission Dave Schless had sent me on.

He made drinks, vodka-and-tonics, and while he busied himself at a small bar built into an old kitchen cupboard—another colonial relic, he said—I looked at more photographs on the wall. Gregory Offitt climbing the ladder—cadet, lieutenant, captain, major, colonel. Offitt on the beach at Normandy, crouching behind a burning tank; entering a French village, back against a brick wall; watching a file of German prisoners parade by, disarmed, dirty, beaten; at the wheel of a jeep stuck in the snows of the Huertgen forest. And having a medal pinned on his breast by a general. I also looked at his wedding picture. He was lean and sparkling in one of those dress uniforms with double rows of brass buttons. His bride was wispy and frail, as if in soft focus.

And suddenly I felt unclean, dishonest about this effort to ferret out information from Offitt. Even though I didn't trust him, and his behavior at the trial had offended me. He was, after all, one of *them.* For all his protestations about his remorse and sorrow, his feelings about my son's death, he'd helped rationalize and justify what happened. Still, it made me uncomfortable. It wasn't my style to lead anyone on . . .

After he'd brought drinks he abruptly pulled me up from the couch and locked his hands around my waist. I tried to pry them loose and duck away from him at the same time.

"I want to make love to you . . ."

It was ridiculous and sad and humiliating all at the same time.

"No, let me go—" Damn Dave Schless, I thought. And me too, for letting myself in for this.

"Do you hate me?" he was saying.

"No, I almost feel sorry for you. You at least have to live with the fraud you helped perpetrate. You knew the truth about what happened and you did nothing—"

"I said the truth."

"I've heard otherwise."

"What have you heard?"

Thank God he was finally giving me my opening. "That you're hiding evidence."

". . . Who says that?"

"Dr. Schless. Our lawyers. They say you have access to material that could change things around for us . . ."

He said nothing, drained his drink, went back to the bar. As he poured himself a second—straight vodka this time—he said, "And that's why you came here, isn't it?"

"Yes. I'm not very good at dissembling."

"Nor am I."

Now I felt defensive. "I'm not too proud of myself."

"I know I've been targeted by Schless and the others. The weak link. The strange thing is my men—my former troopers—think of me in the same way. If I may say so, it's the penalty I pay for having such a reputation for honesty. Yes, they know that a legal fraud was perpetrated. They can only deceive themselves so far. But as said, their concern was survival . . . and who can blame them? They've survived, beaten a jail sentence and they intend to keep it that way."

I could not believe my ears. "You're saying the trial was a fraud?"

"Yes."

I held my breath, waiting for more.

"I can't lie to you. Not anymore. I've been coming to this anyway. Yes, the trial was tilted from the start. A united front to acquit the police."

"Will you say this in public?"

"No."

"Can I repeat it to the committee?"

"If you want to destroy me, yes."

So there it was. He'd put the burden on me. Actually I didn't want to ruin him. But I also wanted the truth to be known . . . for Jack, for all of them . . .

"Even if I do tell," I said, "and repeat it to the press, you can deny it again, say I invented the story. Your telling is the only proof . . ."

"I had no choice but to defend my men, part of my code . . ." He seemed to be talking to himself.

"Maybe you were twisting the code?"

"Maybe. It would have been simpler if I'd been somewhere else. At the police command post. But I was *there* . . . I had to say what I did, even under oath."

"*Had* to?"

"Yes."

"And now you regret it? To what end?"—Don't stop now, I ordered myself—"To bed me down?"

"I admit it. I would like to make love to you, but what I most want is your respect, maybe even understanding. That sounds terrible, doesn't it? Stiff, formal, part of an exercise. But I am sincere. And let me say, it's your loss that intensifies my feelings about you. Knowing about what you suffered. And that however inadvertently I helped wound you. But I must tell you that even if I had testified in a different way, even if I'd failed my men and satisfied you and the others, the trial would not have gone differently."

"There may be a second trial."

"I know. And that's why you're here. You want something from me . . . Who told you to accept my invitation? Finnegan? Schless?"

"Does it matter? The point is, people think you're hiding something."

"And if I give to you something that will be proof . . ."

"I'll give it to the committee's lawyers."

"And I gain—"

"Your honor."

"Not enough." His voice sounded muffled, hoarse. But he smiled. I forced myself to smile back.

He nodded abruptly, as though making a decision, said he had to get some "things."

I wandered the half-dark room again and noticed on the wall what seemed a handcrafted metal plaque mounted on burnished wood.

It read:

### "No Bug Outs"

To Major Gregory Offitt, Battalion's Last Hero.
To the Yalu and Back.
The Naktong Line, the Chonson River and the Chosin Reservoir.
From his officers and noncoms, with affection and anger. For the

old man who walked when we did, and froze when we did, and fought when we did.

I almost felt ashamed. *This is a good man, a brave man,* I had to silently acknowledge. And what was I . . . ?

He came back before I could face up to that troubling question. He was carrying a dark red envelope bound with string, and a tiny tape recorder, no bigger than a cigarette case. He set them on the marble coffee table, a grim smile on his face.

"Am I being recorded?" I asked.

"Oh, no. Our personal conversations are for no one's ears except ours."

"It's a pity we stand on opposite sides of the river, colonel . . ."

"Maybe not, maybe not."

He explained that the tiny recording maching was a police surveillance mechanism. He had borrowed it from the state police headquarters five years ago during the investigation. It took a specially made narrow tape, and the entire apparatus could be strapped to one's chest or hidden in a pocket.

"I was, as they say, wired during most of my meetings with the late Bates Woffler."

"The state prosecutor."

"Interesting fellow. I'm sure you recall him."

"I never saw him. He's the one who indicted the students and teachers."

"He told me he'd indict the dead if the law would let him. When the federal government moved in he kept a low profile. I suppose one shouldn't speak ill of the dead. No doubt he's now enforcing Saint Peter's laws, keeping order in Heaven."

"What did you record?" I couldn't believe this was actually happening.

"Three days of talks with him, on and off. His preliminary investigation just before he convened the state grand jury. My testimony was considered crucial. Then I met with him several times after Judge Althouse ordered the burning of the jury's findings, and the federal government said it would move to indict my six men."

"So you met with him prior to both of the legal proceedings?" Good Lord, I was sounding more like Dave Schless or Brian Dooley.

"Yes. You see, I was—and I hope I still am—respected in the state. My combat record counts for a good deal here. Woffler understood that. He talked tough but he'd never been under fire, never put his life on the line for his country. Interesting . . . there were three photographs on the wall behind him. J. Edgar Hoover, General Patton and John Wayne."

"Not the president?"

"Bates had his own heroes." The colonel smiled. "Strange, the things you remember. I told Woffler I understood Hoover and Patton—in fact I knew the general personally and liked him—but what was a movie actor doing on the wall? It didn't faze him. He said that John Wayne was a great force for good in this country. He had come down hard on commies, freaks, radicals, criminals and minority agitators. I reminded Bates that Wayne was an actor, surely a decent fellow, but he'd never worn his country's uniform, never served in combat. As far as I knew, he'd never been a law enforcement officer, tracked down a communist or a criminal or even given anyone a parking ticket. I wondered when was the last time Wayne had, off-screen, walked point for his platoon or jumped on a Japanese tank and dropped a grenade down the hatch. Bates didn't take kindly to my needling."

I stared at the tape, as if asking him to roll it, to let me hear what he had kept hidden.

"I've made transcripts of the earlier parts of the tape," he said. "They lead up to the last day's interview."

With that he gave me a thick manila envelope, a bit larger than letter size. It had been stuffed inside the big blood-red envelope. "These are for you. Read them and do what you want with them. Now I'd like you to listen to the last session I had with Woffler. He never knew I was recording him. This was several weeks before the start of the trial presided over by Judge Frankendorf. By now the federal grand jury had heard testimony. It was that grand jury that indicted my guardsmen. After you have listened to this I will let you decide if you want it. We can have copies made for me, and then you can put the original in a safe or give it to that angry dentist who seems determined to hound me to my grave."

"And what do I do in return?"

"Nothing. I'll make no demands. If you choose to show your

gratitude in some manner, I'll be pleased. If not, I will understand."

Too good to be true?

## Dr. David Schless

So far, so good.

At dusk the crowd started to gather. Lots of kids, damn near the whole student body, and a majority of the faculty, according to Harriet. Apparently word had gotten around via the college newspaper that the administration intends to build that humongous computer complex on the site of the massacre. The students, as I've said, tended to be non-political, but the news angered them. Besides, it was spring and the juices were flowing.

Very few of the kids were political, most of them looking eager and fresh-faced, couples holding hands, finding seats on the grass, smooching, kidding around, tossing Frisbees, sipping soft drinks. It was hard not to like them, even the Young Americans for Freedom, who had draped a banner from a frat house reading LAW AND ORDER FIRST, PROTESTS SECOND. The promised counterdemonstration of super-patriots showed no signs of developing.

Rita and I walked through the crowd. Few people knew us. Assemblywoman Peggy Sharpless gave us a thumbs-up sign. She said that President Cudlipp, impressed with the peaceful tone of the observance, might in defiance of the trustees put in an appearance. Father Schmidt was definitely going to be there, and of course Al Jensen, and a young rabbi from Flagg City, Joshua having no synagogue of its own. So we'd have God on our side, or at least some of God's reps.

We also made sure that American flags and bunting bedecked the wooden platform and iron piping. I'd insisted on it. I have often wondered why right-wing people think they own the flag. Who says so? I am a liberal, and I love the flag. I also love the Bill of Rights, *and* I believe in God. So we'd rented every flag we could in the county, and in addition to the Stars and Stripes we had the college banner—a trumpet and a wall—and the state flag, and several I couldn't identify. It looked fine. No one could accuse us of being commies, not even Arnold Shreck.

"Hey, doc! Want a joint?"

Billy Mallory, bandylegged and undernourished, sidled up to me.

"Louder, Billy. Make sure the campus cops hear it. I warned you. No grass, no *nothing*. I catch you handing out free samples I'll burn your Irish keester."

"I'm kidding, I'm kidding. I swear, I'm clean."

Two ghastly-looking girls in long frizzy hair, granny glasses and bib overalls tailed our charming Billy. God knows where he'd found them. They hung on his every word, said nothing.

"Any news?" Rita asked him.

He tried to look wise, succeeded in suggesting a drunken jockey. "I found Pulsifer. Well, not exactly, but I learned what's happened to him."

"Go on," I said.

"He got busted in Juneau."

"For what?"

"Phony Social Security card. I spoke to the Alaskan fuzz, and they said they were advising him to leave the state right away. In fact, they helped him sell some possessions to get him on the next flight to Seattle."

"But you didn't talk to him again?"

"Left word with the cops. Identified myself as Professor Horace Dermody of the Joshua College department of geology and asked that Mr. Pulsifer contact me as soon as he reached Seattle. I had some old term papers of his that might be worth publishing. He'll get the message."

"Every little bit helps, Billy."

"Yeah, hope so."

Bernie and Sandra Hoch joined us as we walked toward the platform. Finnegan was testing the loudspeaker. Bernie Hoch was carrying the baby in one of those face-to-face slings. Sandra was holding hands with him. I felt as if they were my own kids, and I sensed that warmth, that good family feeling we all had; Hubie and Billy and Keith . . . And Joe Terragni, whose world had come apart, whose notions of right and

278

wrong had gone down the tubes after Lucy died. And Helen, off on her spy mission. I wondered how she was doing . . .

Well, we'd do some good . . . we'd show the country we hadn't forgotten, by God, we *never* would. And maybe, just maybe, we'd get some kind of justice before we were finished. And based on Francis Stub Hofheimer's having fired the first angry shot, followed by more bullets and terrible deaths, over an insult to his potency? Well, whoever said tragedy didn't have its absurd side too . . .

In fact, wasn't that at the basis of wars, riots, barroom fistfights . . . *mine's bigger 'n yours, hah-hah-hah?* Aren't we and the Russkies involved in the same kind of cockfight?

The crowd kept growing. I could see Harriet and Tom handing out the candles for the vigil. They wouldn't last the night, but we had an ample supply, donated by a committee of local shop owners led by the Feins and Karlinskys, who called them "candles of peace."

"How are you, big bear?"

I kissed Rita's cheek. "Surviving." And still hoping. No one fought in the streets anymore. But we still had the courts. Maybe we'd have our innings after all.

## Billy Mallory

My last public appearance, folks. I dressed for the occasion. Frazzled suede jacket with cowboy fringes, Indian headband, cutoffs, sandals. My T-shirt read: MACROBIOTIC MEALS, INC., an advertisement for Robin's earlier restaurant, which went bust when the cops discovered we were growing mushrooms illegally in the basement.

I felt pretty good. Just seeing all those undergraduates out there laughing and milling and tossing Frisbees, eager to get their candles for the all-night tribute to us, made me a little less pessimistic than I usually am these days. The two foxes from Idiot House trailed me like trained spaniels. One carried blankets, since it was our intention to spend the night on the lawn, and the other had a hamper filled with a thermos of hot herbal tea, seven-grain bread sandwiches and raw carrots. What else could life possibly offer me?

Looking a bit out of place, Keith and Gloria McCandless ambled by. No, they would not stay all night but they would listen to the speeches, although Gloria thought the whole thing was a drag. As for my drinking buddy of last night, Keith claimed he had no recollection of our musical interlude on the sidewalk outside of Gaffney's. All he would own up to was that "Bill and I had a few beers, hon." He was wearing a double-breasted blazer with an embroidered crest on the breast pocket, and Gloria informed me it signified their "club." What? I asked. Aqua Velva After-Shave Club? The Mystery Book Club? For this I got a short nose turned even higher up, a toss of her mane of golden hair, and a tilt to that great tan WASP rump that I would never see.

All in all things were looking up. Among the speakers would be Tom Finnegan, Assemblywoman Sharpless, President Cudlipp (a last-minute entry) and a consumer advocate leader from Chicago. Not exactly an all-star cast, but maybe it was just as well that Jane Fonda, Joan Baez and Dr. Spock couldn't make it. They tend to get the other side aroused, and the last thing we wanted was any more ill feeling. You see what I mean when I say I'm a burned-out case?

Near the platform I saw Joe Terragni and his wife Sally talking animatedly with some parents of current Joshua students, the kids hanging back shyly, the mothers and fathers, in earnest polyester, fat, crew-cut nice plain people, listening respectfully to Joe. A missionary to the gentiles. They seemed genuinely interested, nodded their heads, and as I walked by a big red-headed guy with a beer belly and sideburns and the look of a used-car dealer or a smelter foreman was shaking his head and saying, "No, they shouldna killed anyone, no way."

Yes, we progress slowly. I have to hope so . . . We got the crap kicked out of us, and we left damn little to show. Pot. Rock. Bells. But on the body politic, minor lasting effect. Just look at the Supreme Court . . . damn few faded denims under the robes, no tendency to blow grass inside the chambers, not much sympathy for wretches who run afoul of the law . . . Doc Schless is right. The right things get done for the wrong reasons. And you can't confront the powers head-on. You got to talk it out, work con jobs, convince people it's for their own good. How, I'm not sure, but maybe we're getting there. Maybe . . .

Hubie Colson nudged me. He was carrying a big cooler full of Coors and decided that he would truly get tanked tonight. Tomorrow it was back to his prize-winning hogs and the wife who wouldn't let him get zonked. He had his reasons for being at Joshua, and I had mine, and doc had his. I still wonder if it mattered any more. But it had to. You don't quit. Not even a yellowbelly like Billy Mallory.

## Colonel Gregory Offitt

I've decided I will be a gentleman. What will happen will happen. Or won't. I would not lay my hands on her. I wanted her respect. I wanted her to understand me. Dammit, I also wanted to make love to her . . .

"So," she was saying, "these were recorded in the prosecutor's office?"

"Yes."

"When?"

I checked the date on the label on the tape. It was some time after the federal grand jury had indicted my men. My recollection was that the government trial of my troopers began a month or so later. Again, I had been a crucial witness for the defense.

"And these?" She held up the envelope I had given her.

"Related conversations. Before the federal grand jury hearings, some of them before the state grand jury."

"You certainly seem to have been one of Mr. Woffler's favorites."

"I told you I was a vital part of the proceedings. I also told you why . . . a holder of the Silver Star, the Bronze Star, and five Oak Leaf Clusters and three Purple Hearts merits some respect. Even if not as much as John Wayne."

"I gather you made sure you kept that respect."

I sensed her wariness of me, the implied criticism. She crossed her legs. Was she smiling? Yes. Apparently in control, a sense of balance. *Balance.* I had lost it. Somewhere between that terrible day on the portico of the president's office and the trials and hearings that followed, the rug had been yanked out from under me.

"I did what was expected of me. You will now be able to judge for yourself. You have these tapes."

"I promise nothing—"

"I understand."

But my display of grace under pressure—I had been under pressure for a long time—was largely show. Inside I felt some strange unravelling. As if part of me were disintegrating. I recalled a biography of Kipling, where he first sensed that he was seriously ill. A dissecting aneurysm, I believe, was the eventual cause of his death. *Something within me has come apart,* he said. I'd loved Kipling. *The Mark of the Beast. Soldiers Three. Barrack Room Ballads.* Through my mind ran the old rhythms, strong as drumbeats . . .

> They are hangin' Danny Deever,
> You must mark him in his place,
> For he shot a comrade sleepin'
> You must look 'im in the face,
> Nine hundred of his county
> And the regiment's disgrace . . .

"All right," I said. "This was one of my last meetings with Woffler. Before he finished preparing this material for the defense lawyers. You see, he was in an odd position. He'd been rebuffed on the indictments he'd returned, shamed by Judge Althouse's ruling. Now that the federal government had taken over and reversed the case—my policemen as defendants, not the students—he was determined to give Merritt Winnington every advantage in his defense efforts. And since he had interviewed me over and over and knew my feelings well, he was given me as his special assignment. Winnington must have appreciated that."

I depressed the button, raised the volume. For a miniaturized machine, the sound was remarkably loud, the words astonishingly clear.

# Helen Christopher

I leaned forward. Colonel Offitt poured himself another straight vodka and sat on a piano bench (there was no piano in the room) and gazed out the picture window to the darkening garden.

"That's Woffler's voice," he said. "Notice how low, soft. He enunciated very clearly, spoke slowly. A very persuasive man . . ."

*Nice to see you again, colonel.*

*Nice seeing you, Bates.*

*I guess we're clear on your testimony. Things are falling into place nicely. Frankendorf will be an impartial judge. Merritt is pleased.*

*I hear he is a good judge.*

*Oh, he is. Oddly, he has been liberal on many issues. But we won't hold that against him . . . Colonel, we have had some minor disputes here, so I thought it would be good to review where we stand.*

Colonel Offitt turned the recorder off. "When you and Dr. Schless look at the notes I made you'll see that Woffler and I had some arguments over the events."

"And this last meeting was to resolve your differences?"

"Yes."

He depressed the button again. Woffler was speaking, with that strange, resonant quality . . .

*Colonel, you've read my analysis? The one I gave to the defense counsel?*

*Yes.*

*And you're in accord?*

*Not entirely.*

*I beg your pardon?*

*I'm considering changing some of my testimony.*

*Details, I suppose.*

*No, the substance of it.*

*You must be joking. You can't.*

*I've spent hours, days reviewing the photographs and the recordings. I even looked at some film shot by the local station and by some students. And I had the lab draw up some new schematics—*

*I thought we already covered that ground.*

*There's no harm in reviewing it.*

*But there is, Gregory. May I call you Gregory?*

*Of course.*

*You were saying?*

*Bates, I have come to two inescapable conclusions.*

*Two?*

There was a long pause on the tape. Shufflings, movings. Colonel Offitt got up, folded his arms, stood in a shadow near the old grain bin. He lowered his head. Then the voices again . . .

*Please listen to me, Bates, hear me out.*

*I am, colonel.*

*First, my men had no right to fire the weapons. It was contradictory to any riot control situation. They had no right to load up and fire.*

*Your second conclusion?*

*Their lives were never in danger. Not for a moment.*

*Nonsense. There were injuries. Men hyperventilating. Under siege.*

*Yes, they were hit by rocks, and they were miserable and perhaps frightened. But it was not a life-threatening situation.*

*What else?*

*Men armed with the destructive power of those automatic weapons have no right to fire them at unarmed civilians a football field away.*

*Some were closer.*

*A handful, at most a dozen, maybe fifteen. Not an armed mob about to overrun their ranks. No one was ever killed by a stone or a stick or a gas canister—*

*You have already sworn under oath that their lives were endangered.*

*I'll change my . . . view of the event.*

*Did I hear you correctly?*

*You did. I'll be called as a witness at the trial and I'll base my changed attitude on careful studies of the evidence.*

*This . . . is . . . serious, Gregory. You are taking your stand with the enemies of decent society. How can you possibly do that?*

*I'm not a radical or a rebel or a bleeding-heart liberal, Bates. But I repeat—those troopers should not have fired their guns and they were not endangered.*

*You will have to do lot of explaining regarding your earlier testimony.*

*I'm prepared to.*

*You may be charged with perjury.*

*I'll take my chances.*

*How will it look, Gregory? I mean, at this stage in your life, charged with lying? Admitting you lied?*

*I did not lie. I've changed my perception of events.*

*No one will believe you.*

*Perhaps. I will readily agree that my men were threatened, abused, in danger of sustaining injuries, insulted, baited. The students behaved abominably and should have been disciplined. But I can't condone blasting away with live ammunition.*

*How many times were you congratulated for standing up for your men? How many times have you heard that the police should have shot them all?*

*More often than I care to think of.*

*You will hear it again. What has gotten into you, Gregory?*

*The facts.*

*Do you disagree with my point that society was threatened? At least that a violent, destructive mob was on the loose?*

*Mobs can be controlled without bullets.*

*Then that was your failing.*

*It may have been. I thought my men were well trained. I will accept any blame for a breakdown of procedures.*

*Don't put this on so modest a level. Breakdown, indeed. Your men stood between civilization and a destructive rabble. I must tell you, you cannot go in front of Frankendorf's jury and reverse yourself. You will only succeed in shaming yourself and very possibly getting your loyal men convicted.*

*Maybe they should be.*

*Then you should be convicted with them.*

*Maybe I should. Actually I suspect that even if I change my testimony they will be acquitted. This will be a local jury, people from here back our troopers right or wrong . . .*

*Now at least you are making some sense. And keep in your mind that your men feared for their lives, that they were right to shoot back.*

*Back?*

*Yes. To return fire. To answer the lethal barrage of stones, concrete, canisters. But never mind that for the moment . . . How do you intend to make known your . . . change of heart?*

*I'm talking to Kalt tomorrow.*

*Then I will make certain you are indicted for perjury.*

*I'll take that risk.*

Another pause. Chairs moving, a phone ringing. The reel hummed, giving off a faint noise. Colonel Offitt was still standing in the shadows. He seemed to be half-smiling.

And then I heard the soft, insinuating voice of prosecutor Bates Woffler again.

*You realize you will ruin your career, your reputation, Gregory.*

*I've thought of that.*

*You will violate the code.*

*Code? If I give testimony I don't really believe in, then I will violate the code.*

*Colonel, what is the foremost duty of a commanding officer? What is the very foundation of his command?*

*Leadership.*

*And what does that imply?*

*A concern for his men, among other things.*

*Absolutely. A commanding officer stands by his men, first, last and always. Your men are not criminals. They did not wantonly shoot those students down. If you choose, look upon it as an accident, a miscalculation. So be it. But they are not guilty. Mistaken, perhaps, guilty of bad judgment. But not of any crime. I repeat, a commanding officer stands by his men. If you let these innocent men down, if they are convicted and serve time, or are discharged dishonorably with loss of pension, it will be on your shoulders . . . Well?*

*You raise an important point.*

*I certainly do. I'm pleased finally to be getting through to you. You know better than I or anyone your obligation to your men. If you wish, express remorse, regret, pain over the deaths. Very natural and laudable. But you must not desert your men. Your loyal men whose lives, whose families depend on you. I for one would not want your conscience if you did.*

*I wish to God there were a different way . . . but it's true . . . I don't want to hurt them . . . I must not . . .*

The tape spun to a silent end.

The colonel said he had one more reel, but that he and Woffler kept covering the same ground. Why the men fired, whether they were justified, what was at stake . . .

"What about the federal prosecutor?" I asked. "You didn't go."

286

"No . . . I did not."

"And you didn't make any further statements about the shootings?"

"None."

"Except that you were glad that 'the system works.' "

"Please, don't remind me. Woffler raised what seemed the crucial, unanswerable point. My men depended on me, I couldn't abandon them. And I was weak . . . I didn't want to be considered a traitor to my people, couldn't face the censure I knew I would get from them, from the public. The colonel was no hero this time. Still . . . I'm not sure it would have made a difference. The defense counsel, Winnington, told me later that even if I'd taken the stand and changed my story the jury would have acquitted the police. Apparently there was no way any jury anywhere would convict."

"And why do you tell me all this now?"

He leaned back, held a hand to his forehead as if in pain. "Because I want your respect, Helen."

"What about your own?"

"That too, I suppose."

He turned off the tape recorder, put it in a small leather case and held it out to me. "Give it to Dr. Schless. Ask him to have it copied on quarter-inch tape and then arrange to get the original and the machine back to me."

"Are you sure?"

"I've never been surer of anything."

"No quid pro quo?"

He stood up and took a step toward me. "I've already answered that. You know how I feel, what I want. And that I won't pursue it. It would demean both of us."

"Thank you. I admire you for doing this, giving up these tapes and notes. I want you to know that."

He nodded, smiled. "I'll drive you back to the college."

How easy it had been—and how miserable it made me feel.

At the car, as he opened the door, he said, "Thank you, the memories will be good."

I thought of that first meeting in the restaurant, how I'd recoiled from him. How I felt now as I tucked the tape recorder into my purse. "This should help right the record," I said. "What more can I say except thank you." I kissed his cheek.

"A splendid reward," he said. "Not quite what I'd hoped for, but one

I'll treasure. Now I'll get you off to the vigil. You'll understand if I don't take part. Too old to be holding candles in the night air."

## Dr. David Schless

Outside, they were singing. "We Shall Overcome." "We Shall Not Be Moved." "This Land is Your Land . . ." And the one that always made Rita cry, "Teach Your Children."

It was dark now and the candles were flickering on the lawn in front of the platform. A group was playing the melody and some kids from the Joshua College Glee Club were leading the singing.

We'd had a few introductory speeches—benedictions from Jensen, Father Schmidt and the rabbi, and some brief words of welcome from Cudlipp, who fielded some *boos* but was good-natured about it.

Some students raised signs reading NO COMPUTER CENTER and WHO WAS GUILTY? but the crowd was orderly. I'd had my outriders, Colson and Dr. Hoch, looking for the patriotic counterdemonstration but it was not to be seen. There was stock-car racing at the Flagg City Speedway, and that had drawn a nice crowd of our usual opponents.

So I could hear the singing drifting in as we sat in plastic chairs around the table in the conference room off our press center. It was then that Helen gave me the midget tape recorder.

She also gave me a bulging manila envelope, the kind you send your tax returns in. Finnegan, Harriet Blochman and Rita were there too. I assured Helen we'd keep the stuff in a safe at the motel that night. I'd have it all photocopied and transferred tomorrow and send the originals back to Offitt, as she'd asked us to do.

Helen said she felt sorry for him. "This will ruin him."

"I doubt it," Finnegan said. "He's untouchable. He can say he changed his mind, studied the evidence again."

"Wait till you hear what he says. And wait till you read his notes."

The wheels spun. So did my head. Ironpants Offitt had just switched polarity. What we heard was Offitt and Woffler arguing, ever so politely. What they said was enough to curl my teeth.

Finnegan was grinning like he'd been chosen chairman of the Saint Patrick's Day parade. Harriet kept blinking, taking notes, saying we had to guard the reel of tapes with our lives. I told her I'd sleep with it strapped to my chest if necessary.

What an earful the colonel had given us! And all thanks to Helen Christopher. I guess stranger things have happened, but I couldn't imagine when . . . For a moment I had fantasies of local vigilantes coming at us again, trying to steal the precious tapes, under orders to seize and burn them.

We played the second reel—the one Helen had not yet heard. If the first one curled my teeth, this one straightened them again.

On it, Woffler was cleverly bending Offitt to his will, making the honorable old combat veteran toe the line. His line . . .

*I can't do it, Bates.*

*But you must. Not just for your men. Your country demands it of you. It is entitled. It has supported you all your career. You know that.*

*And I know what's proper riot procedure and what is not—*

*I will have to make certain that you do not alter your testimony, Greg. I'm not afraid of you.*

*Does that apply to your conscience, colonel? Your men need you. They depend on you. As does this community, and nation.*

*Don't preach to me, Bates. And dammit, stop lecturing me about my country and what I owe it. My career has been in its service.*

*My point exactly. But you will cancel out the fine things you have done, all that service. You must not let yourself be misled—*

*By what? Facts? Photographs? Recordings? Films? Eyewitnesses?*

*They can mislead, bear false witness. You have already testified truthfully. You have told me the truth many times, colonel. Don't change now.*

*Dammit, are you accusing me of lying?*

*I am not. Only of temporarily losing perspective. And if you for one moment think that that Schless and the others will let you breathe, even if you do change your view of events, you are mistaken. They want your blood, they will pursue you to the grave. Take your stand with your people, your conscience. You will not regret it . . .*

And in the end, Offitt did. He could not face up to betraying his own troops, even if he knew they, and he, were wrong.

But now, finally . . . I wanted to let out a war whoop, but Rita restrained me.

Later, when there was a break in the ceremonies—the lines were forming for the parade around the campus, each person bearing a candle—Peggy Sharpless joined us.

The singing was louder as the slow-moving marchers strolled by. We let Peggy listen to some of Offitt's dialogue with Bates Woffler. Her face turned several shades whiter, and then she clapped her hands to her cheeks.

"This will do it," she said. "But what made him change his mind?"

"We don't really know," I said, not looking at Helen. And for once I restrained myself and didn't press her about what had happened between her and Offitt. Later Rita said she was proud of me for that, and that she would have killed me if I had. She also said she was sure nothing had happened.

Helen volunteered nothing. No question, a real lady.

## Karl August Frankendorf

Oh dear, what appalling news.

Merritt Winnington called me this morning, as I was sitting up in bed, reading some Longfellow to calm my mind.

Colonel Offitt is dead.

He took his own life. I can hardly believe it. That fine, honorable, brave man, who was such an effective witness, who stood by his men, who defended them—and the college and society—from the mob.

Merritt was as upset as I was. Normally in such control, he sounded unnerved. After all, Colonel Offitt had been a tower of strength for Winnington's side. (I was going to say *our* side; as in a sense it was, the side of order and peace.)

"Blew his brains out," Merritt said. "A real mess, Gus. Up in the attic. He kept a brand new automatic rifle there, an HK–91, standard police issue. Seems he took it with him when he retired, and had a supply of rounds. One was all that was needed."

"Did he leave any note?"

"Just to say he loved his wife, his daughter and his grandchild, and hoped they would forgive him."

"Anything about . . . ah . . . the trial? The hearings?"

"Nothing. I don't think that had anything to do with it. No one does. Greg was on our team. Hell, he was protecting his men, and why not? Bit of a stiff-ass, but I liked him. He told it like it was. I'll never forget the way the jury perked up and paid attention when he gave his version of the events and explained why his men had to shoot back."

"Shoot back, yes." As I agreed with Merritt, I suppose I really was a bit confused. *Shoot back?* I don't recall. Was anyone shooting at the police? Was that ever established? My mind isn't what it was.

"Governor was on the phone extending his condolences," Winnington went on. "And some veterans from Offitt's division are arranging for a burial in Arlington. He was a hero to a lot of guys. A good soldier."

"I'm sure of it, Merritt."

There was a pause, then Winnington said, "They telephoned Mrs. Offitt and she's on her way back. Took it like a soldier. An army wife, lots of courage." He dropped his voice. "Offitt had this footlocker, an old army box, and I asked the cops to impound the material in it— papers, photographs, that sort of thing. Dempsey and I gave them a quick look, and they seem okay . . . harmless. His campaigns, letters, decorations—Jesus, he was a brave guy—but nothing that related to Joshua College. I guess everything he had to say on that is on record anyway."

"Ah. Yes, of course."

"You know Gus, there were these rumors aboard that he withheld something, that he told Woffler things that never got into court. But we couldn't find anything . . ."

"Was it legal for you to go through this material?" I asked it without thinking.

"Looking for a suicide note," George said. "Perfectly appropriate. Oh, we had a warrant but it really wasn't necessary. If he *was* hiding anything about the shootings he must have put it somewhere else . . . or else there isn't anything. Which is most likely. So that's no worry. It's just that son of a bitch Schless and his crowd. They had that candlelight parade last night, the lefties and freaks singing and praying. Who knows . . . maybe it helped push poor Offitt off the edge."

"Was he threatened?"

"No. But it may well have revived a lot of feelings . . . Why in hell he had lunch with some of them I'll never know. Anyway, they still think they have a civil suit to look forward to. I'll bet against it."

"Can I help? That poor Mrs. Offitt. And the colonel was such a fine gentleman. What a pity that a creature like Schless, that boor and ruffian, had to hound him. I hope it rests heavily on his conscience."

I had a fainting spell after Merritt hung up. I called Ernest at the club to see if his brother Claude could come over and spend the day with me. Claude is a retired Pullman porter, a decent man in his seventies who is happy to be my part-time "gentleman's gentleman."

Claude brought me the morning paper from the mailbox—I was still in my paisley robe and pajamas—and brewed me some Earl Grey tea. I have trained him to serve it English style, "hotting" the pot, letting the water come to a rolling boil, steeping the leaves (never, *never* a teabag) and adding a touch of milk to heighten the flavor.

As I sipped tea and sat with my feet on an ottoman listening to Ravel, an item in the *Clarion-Ledger* caught my eye.

There was a corruption case before federal court in Michigan, and to my utter astonishment *a state judge had been subpoenaed and called as a witness for the defense.* I was stunned. I had never heard of such a thing. Anyone can be subpoenaed, of course, but invariably—so far as I can recall—the presiding judge will not permit a fellow jurist to take the witness stand. But it had happened in Michigan. Could it happen to me? And why are standards so low these days in the judiciary?

Idly, I mused on Colonel Offitt's tragic death. The man was in excellent health, enjoying his retirement. I can only conclude that people like that vile dentist and the others, notably the radical element like Finnegan and revolutionaries like the Mallory excrescence, drove him to it. May they reap everlasting scorn and guilt for destroying so valorous a man.

# Dr. David Schless

It's going well. The state legislature passed our special bill. Can you believe it?

Only four months after we staged our memorial observance and poor Gregory Offitt took the barrel of that black weapon in his mouth. I kind of liked the guy. I confess I liked him better after he gave Helen his tapes.

We fed them, a little at a time—to draw out the suspense—to the press. As I said, I'd gotten to know AP and UPI people as well as some key people at the networks. They were pleased to help out. No opinions, just facts—Offitt's voice, Woffler's voice.

Three weeks after I'd made sure that the tapes—and the transcripts of other meetings—had made their way to the seven o'clock news and the front pages, the legislature voted, narrowly to be sure, to let us sue anyone we wanted as individuals, but not as employees of the state. We have a list. Not just the six troopers who were acquitted, but seven others who fired weapons, as well as several public officials and President Cudlipp. Believe it or not, I was against hitting him with a civil suit, but Brian Dooley said hit 'em all. It would reinforce our case.

We're asking for $40 million. Yes, that's right, forty million dollars. I don't care if I don't get a nickel. I want them all in court and I want them to admit what they did, killed people deliberately and that it was inexcusable. But most of all I want all the official people to own up that they *lied, covered up, faked it, invoked the law* while they made a shambles of it.

Rita says she thinks the forty million is a mistake, that it sounds like blood money, that we want to get rich off our children's deaths. I tell her it's the only language these people understand.

I'm sorry about Offitt. I am. He was the best of that lot, far and away, and deserved better. Hell of a way for a brave man to go. Does it prove anything?

Dooley and his team are preparing the case carefully. No trial date has been set. Winnington and a new team are going to represent the troopers again, and I can see what's coming. I think a lot will depend on the judge. We'll see.

Does it make the pain easier? No. The day doesn't go by that I don't sit in Andrea's shaded room and look at the photographs and feel the hurt, the anger, the loss. Does it help? It's all we have left, the memories.

I'm glad I took her to ball games and told her about DiMaggio, and that Rita gave her ballet lessons and told her about Balanchine, and that we tried to make her happy . . .

## Helen Christopher

We tried, oh Lord, we tried.

Dan tried to cut down on his drinking, but it was a lost cause. I don't think it did anything for him anymore. But the smell of alcohol, the rituals, the banter, the awful jokes apparently kept him at the bottle.

We slept together fitfully. He'd get tired, try to get it over with, fail, fall away sweating and angry, and somehow manage to blame it on me.

I never told him about Colonel Offitt's interest in me, or that I was the one who got the tapes that changed things around for the lawsuit. I must say Dave and the others on the committee were good at keeping the matter quiet and not pressing me. All they told the press was that the colonel's tapes and notes were given "willingly" to them; that he had wanted the parents of the dead students to have them. That was fine with me.

"What kind of a guy was he?" Dan would ask.

"Intelligent. Unhappy."

"Hunh. Who isn't unhappy?"

I was offered a full-time teaching job in a private school in Surrey Heights, the next town over, and I accepted. It paid less than the public high school I'd taught in, but it was good, rewarding work. Dan and I saw less and less of each other. When I went to visit Beth in Boston he begged off. Too tiring. He couldn't stand the incense they burned, all the guru talk, the Indian pictures on the wall. So I went alone. Beth told me again to leave him.

To my surprise, neighbors told me he was having an affair with a waitress at the country club, that he'd been seen in bars with her and that she'd been in our house while I was in Boston. Don't ask me how they knew. I didn't ask.

I suppose I should have been angry, hurt, but I wasn't. Poor, confused man. Maybe I wasn't the world's most inventive and enthusiastic lover anymore, but I think I did deserve some respect. I tried to give it. He might have been more discreet about his affair with Wanda Glowacki, age twenty-six. I was entitled, I thought, to that.

In any case, I filed for divorce and it was all very amicable and polite, the way things are done in Old Surrey. I've gotten a small apartment in Surrey Heights, near the school, and I can truly say a burden has been lifted from my back. I'll miss Dan. I loved him once. I pitied him when he refused to face up to the truth about our son's death. But I'm content to let someone else put up with his neuroses, his drunkenness, his self-destructiveness. And the pity of it is that beneath the surface there is a decent man.

So here I am in a neat, modular, new two-bedroom apartment. My settlement and my income will just about let me keep the place, but of course there'll be no more country clubs and Caribbean vacations. Which somehow don't matter. Did they ever?

I might add that several widowed and divorced gentlemen from Old Surrey have left their calling cards. Will it sound peculiar if I say that none of them measure up to Colonel Gregory Offitt? It was horrible when he took his life. In a way I felt responsible. That I'd given him nothing, taken the evidence and run.

The man was troubled, I know that. And I don't think I'm looking for the luxury of guilt. But I can't help looking back at that last meeting, wondering if I'd been kinder . . . But there's no good in such thoughts. Not for him, not for me.

I've decided I won't go back to Joshua for the civil trial. Enough. I've done the best I could for my son. No more candlelight parades, no more schemes to get information from the other side. Finnegan and Schless seem to respect my decision. I'm grateful to them. We'll leave it at that.

## Billy Mallory

Robin's been trying to restore Lyle's muscle tone with tofu, alfalfa sprouts and rhubarb yogurt. Of course she'll make him pay. No free rides in Robin's health food restaurant.

So there we sit, Pulsifer and me, two charred embers, while Robin sifts whole wheat flour, hollers at the waitresses and makes me change the sitar records, or haul out the garbage, or run out to the Syrian bakery for more pita pockets. Ah, the active life of a retired radical. Tabouli is running out of my ears.

Lyle is still gaunt, pockmarked, a pale anteater under a mop of bushy yellow hair. Alaska did him no good, but he survived. I figured the grizzlies took one look at him and upchucked.

I filled him in on how I heard tell that Doc Schless put up Jack Christopher's mother—a classy good-looking head, although Lyle did not remember her—to somehow make off with those tapes, and how it got us the ruling to file for a civil suit against the fuzz and other upholders of the law.

"Nobody will ever find against the cops."

I guess he had a right to feel that way. The police had used him, gotten their money's worth out of him, taught him that it was a loser's game. For college kids anyway. Bad mothers can get away with it, as can wheeler-dealers and even some corporations. But breaking the law is not a good idea for callow youths on campuses, black or white. It didn't help the four white kids they shot at Kent State, or the black kids who were killed at Jackson State.

Healthy, invigorating American sport, right? It sort of echoes and reechoes in my mind . . . *they should have killed three hundred . . . four hundred . . .*

Fuck 'em.

The trial is next week. Joey and I will attend as many sessions as possible. I'll be there every day, and if Joey can switch some of his vacation, he'll come too. Yes, I've said it all along. We owe it to Lucy.

And we don't care about the money. We just want the truth to come out. I can't stand the lies any more.

My other children think we're neglecting them, that we always favored Lucy, and that even with her dead and gone we still favor her over them. The worst thing is, maybe it's true.

Dr. Schless thinks we have a chance of winning if we get a sympathetic judge. One who lets our lawyers use the photographs and the diagrams and the FBI reports and the tapes. No one knows for sure at the moment. We can only hope.

Things are much better in Flagg City for us. Ever since the news came out about the things Colonel Offitt said on the tapes, the ones Helen Christopher got for us, they think better of us. Like now they say, yes, the police were in the wrong. They had a reason, maybe, to shoot, but it was wrong. Up to now they never said that. They backed them and they were sorry more weren't killed. But you don't hear much of that anymore.

Anyway, we don't go to Joshua, especially the college. We'll be back for the trial and that will be it. Except once. That was two days ago, when the college started to break ground for the new computer center.

Professor Blochman called us and said that they were organizing a demonstration against the groundbreaking. The college was going to put up the huge building right on the spot where the three students were killed. To sort of destroy the lawn, the whole area, so that no one would remember. Harriet Blochman said they probably couldn't stop them, but they wanted the country to know that this was an awful thing to do, an insult.

So Joey and I drove in from Flagg City. It was the end of July, very hot and muggy, and I was wearing a yellow print dress that didn't do much for my figure. I put on weight easily and I'm tired all the time. I can't stay young and thin like Helen Christopher or Rita Schless.

We parked outside the main gates and walked across the campus to the long lawn between Dexter Hall and the president's office, where our daughter died.

There were about thirty students and faculty standing around behind a police barricade. Not much of a crowd. There were signs being waved.

NO COMPUTERS
HONOR THE DEAD

MACHINES CAN KILL
PEOPLE DESERVE BETTER

CHRISTOPHER
TERRAGNI
SCHLESS

"Same thing all over," Joey said. "Let's go home, Sal."

"No. I'll go join them if you don't want to."

A huge yellow payloader was squatting to one side on the edge of the parking lot, waiting to dig out chunks of grass and earth. I could see the new provost nervously conferring with some campus policemen. There were no state troopers around.

The crowd was orderly. They chanted a bit. But no dirty words, no threats. No one threw a rock or a stick or anything else. I saw Professor Blochman and Professor Finnegan and a few others but I didn't recognize any of the students. None of the wounded students had come back for this sad protest.

I said hello to Harriet Blochman and Tom Finnegan.

"What now?" Joey asked them. "You can't stop it."

"I know," Finnegan said, "but we should let them know we sure don't like the idea."

Joey coughed and said they'd do anything they want to. Three times we'd tried to get a memorial statue or a plaque put up to remember the dead and three times the trustees had refused. They preferred their computer center. It meant government contracts, tuition, and who were we to say that it wasn't worthwhile and would help young people get jobs and prepare for life?

Harriet said that was true but that the building should go somewhere else.

While we talked the driver turned the engine over and the giant yellow machine, with its huge scoop lowered, began to leave the parking lot and rumble across the lawn toward where the hole would be dug.

Joey said, "I know the guy driving it. Al Morano. His daughter went to dancing school with Lucy."

"He's not personally responsible," I said. "It's a job."

The protesters began to chant *No, no, no* and some were crying. Finnegan ran over to the provost and started to plead with him. It was all peaceful and sad and weak and you could see no one would pay any attention to us.

There were some photographers there and some TV people with cameras from the local stations. I don't know what got into me but I walked up to one of them.

There I was, an overweight Italian-American lady with two years of high school, a good Catholic, and all I ever did was go to church and raise children and work in a plastics factory, and I said, "Want a good picture?"

They looked at me as if I was crazy but followed me.

As the payloader came rumbling and crunching toward the lawn I ran in front of it and I got to my knees and lay down flat on my back in front of the big yellow scoop with the huge steel teeth.

Joey screamed at me and ran to me. The driver stopped the payloader about a yard from my head. The grass felt cool and moist and I lay there staring at the cloudy sky.

"Sal, are you crazy? Get up."

"No," I said, "You lie down with me."

And he did. And so did a dozen other people, right in the path of the payloader, with me closest to the big teeth and the giant scoop.

"It's the least I can do for her," I said, not fighting the tears.

"I know," Joey said. "We tried everything else."

Everything stopped. The driver cut the motor and waited.

Joey put his arm around me and we stayed on the wet grass, looking into each other's eyes. I could barely hear the campus cops begging us to please get up, to let the work go on.

Of course I knew we'd have to and that maybe we'd be charged with something and people might start calling us radicals and troublemakers all over again.

But I didn't care. I wanted everyone to know how I felt and how I would always feel and that I wasn't finished fighting.